110654890

The Birds of
Lincolnshire and South Humberside

by
Stephen Lorand and Keith Atkin

Leading Edge
press and publishing

First published 1989 by Leading Edge Press and Publishing, The Old Chapel, Burtersett, Hawes, North Yorkshire, DL8 3PB   Tel (096 97) 566

© Stephen Lorand and Keith Atkin, 1989

This book is copyright under the Berne convention. All rights are reserved. Apart from any fair dealing for research, private study or review as permitted under the Copyright Act, 1956, no part of this publication may be reproduced, stored in a retrieval system, or transmitted in any form or by any means electronic, mechanical, photocopying, recording or otherwise, without the permission of the copyright holder.

British Library Cataloguing-in-Publication Data

Lorand, Stephen
    The Birds of Lincolnshire and South Humberside
    1. Lincolnshire. Birds
    I. Title. II. Atkin, Keith 1938-
    598.29425'3

    ISBN 0-948135-11-5

Editing and design: Barbara Allen
Photographs: Keith Atkin. All taken in Lincolnshire and South Humberside mostly using
    Canon SLR and 600mm Novoflex telephoto lens
Maps and diagrams: Keith Atkin and Ruth Abbott
Type: Maureen Edwards for Leading Edge using Apple Macintosh™ and Aldus PageMaker™
Printing: Impression, Leeds; Tyneside Free Press, Newcastle upon Tyne

LINCOLNSHIRE
LIBRARY SERVICE   -47

L·598·2

Front cover: top left, Willow Warbler; top right, Short-eared Owl; bottom left, Ruff; bottom right, Sabine's Gull; centre, Great-crested Grebes.

Preface

The publishers would like to stress that this book is an avifauna — that is, a list of all species to be found in the county — *not* a manual with which to recognise different birds. For those interested in this however, the authors would suggest *The Shell Guide to the Birds of Britain and Ireland*, published by Michael Joseph, as a companion guide.

We also take the opportunity to thank Anne Goodall, Honorary Secretary of the Lincolnshire Bird Club, for all her help and advice, and to express our gratitude to the following organisations whose support and commitment helped guarantee the publication of this superbly realised work by Stephen Lorand and Keith Atkin: the Lincolnshire Bird Club, Lincolnshire and South Humberside Trust for Nature Conservation, Lincolnshire Naturalists' Union and the county councils of Lincolnshire and Humberside.

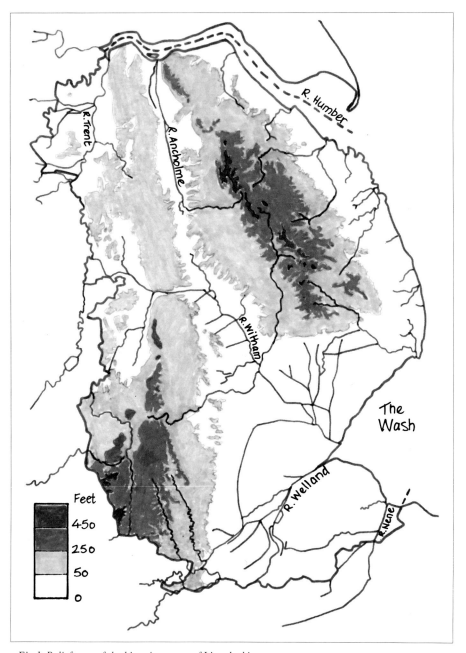

Fig 1. Relief map of the historic county of Lincolnshire

Contents

Photographs

Photographs by Keith Atkin — all taken in Lincolnshire and South Humberside

Text figures and maps

Foreword

by A.E. Smith, OBE, MA
Co-author of *The Birds of Lincolnshire*

When the late Dick Cornwallis and I compiled our account of Lincolnshire birds in 1955 a new impetus was already lifting Lincolnshire ornithology out of the comparative neglect which it had suffered for several decades. We conceived the List and the background chapters of our book primarily as a basis for further study and investigation, and it is therefore a particular pleasure to me to write a foreword for this new work by two of Lincolnshire's leading ornithologists, Keith Atkin and Stephen Lorand.

Our knowledge of the birds of the historic county of Lincolnshire has been transformed in the last 40 years by widespread and intensive observation and by study of their numbers, distribution and movements. The results are evident in the detailed and comprehensive List which forms the major part of this book. For all the main species we are given an account not only of present-day status and distribution, but also of changes which have taken place in the past. The List is a model of its kind, the product of meticulous and skilful research. It will be an indispensable point of reference for all future studies of Lincolnshire birds.

The book has still more to offer. Part One contains an extensive account of bird habitats in the historic county and descriptions of many sites of special ornithological interest. It provides an essential basis for an understanding of the distribution of birds throughout the area. Part Two consists of a fascinating account of the history of birds and of ornithology in Lincolnshire. With the aid of carefully chosen quotations and references it recounts the decline through fen drainage, downland reclamation and other largely agricultural causes of one of the richest avifaunas of any English county. Loss and impoverishment of habitat has continued in the agricultural revolution of the last 50 years, but the List that follows shows how much bird life there is still to be enjoyed, to be studied and to be cared for by timely measures of conservation of the kind which find frequent mention in this book.

I congratulate the authors on a fine achievement and I warmly commend their work to the reader.

A. E. Smith

Introduction

There have been many advances in our knowledge of the county's avifauna since the publication of *The Birds of Lincolnshire* by A.E. Smith and R.K. Cornwallis over 30 years ago. Much new information on the status of many species has necessitated a complete re-assessment of their numbers, migrations and distribution. Several species formerly considered as being rare and irregular vagrants are now recorded much more frequently, while new additions continue to be admitted to the county List at a fairly steady rate. For many years, records have been summarized in the annual reports published by the Lincolnshire Naturalists' Union, and more recently by the Lincolnshire Bird Club.

In 1974, the new county of Humberside was formed and this included the northern fringe of the historic county of Lincolnshire. However, natural history recording has continued to be based on the old boundaries. For convenience in this work, both Lincolnshire and South Humberside are usually referred to as Lincolnshire.

Increased leisure hours, greater mobility and a wealth of bird identification guides have all contributed significantly to the growing interest in ornithology. In 1949, the Bird Observatory and Field Research Station was established at Gibraltar Point, and this provided the fundamental incentive to many contemporary ornithologists and the basis for the various aspects of their studies. The rewards from regular and systematic recording in defined areas were better realised and more observers and ringers have paid close attention to localities where the ornithological potential was previously unknown. Many areas, both inland and on the coast, are now covered on a regular basis and it is encouraging to note an increase in observations from the south of the county, much of which has been neglected in the past.

The development of improved catching techniques has brought an enormous increase in the scale of bird-ringing undertaken in the county. Information amounting from this activity has been of utmost importance and has greatly added to our understanding of populations, movements and so on. Much of this success is the outcome of studies made by individual workers whose notable achievements often match the well-organized efforts of the several ringing groups which operate in Lincolnshire.

In the past, there have been several surveys, both on a regional and national scale, attempting to determine the distribution and breeding populations of certain selected species. More recently, the British Trust for Ornithology launched its successful Atlas project, a national survey aimed at plotting the breeding distribution of all species during 1968-72. This was the most advanced investigation ever attempted, and hundreds of ornithologists contributed. The information relating to Lincolnshire was of considerable assistance when we were assessing breeding status and distribution, particularly in the remoter areas and in the light of the significant changes which have affected the county's habitats in modern times.

The agricultural scene which is so dominant in Lincolnshire has altered considerably in recent years. Many hundreds of miles of hedgerows have now disappeared, although some recompense is evident by the re-afforestation of several areas by the Forestry Commission. Clay and gravel workings, the construction of new reservoirs, the continuing spread of urbanisation, reclamation of marshes and wetlands and many other schemes all comprise an ever-changing landscape, often to the detriment of wildlife, but sometimes to its benefit. Fortunately, a broad variety of habitats is now preserved as nature reserves under the auspices of the Lincolnshire and South Humberside Trust for Nature Conservation, formerly the Lincolnshire Naturalists' Trust. But for the Trust, some of these habitats would have been irretrievably lost. Other bodies making a major contribution to the conservation of valuable habitats include the Nature Conservancy Council, the Royal Society for the Protection of Birds and the Woodland Trust. Anglian Water has recently undertaken a detailed survey of the flora and fauna on all its rivers, in order that they may be managed in the most sympathetic way for wildlife.

Acknowledgements

Our warm thanks go to those people who gave us help and information in a number of ways. In particular we are grateful to the staff of the British Museum (Natural History) at Tring and South Kensington, and also to the staff of Cambridge University Library, Lincoln Central Library and Lincolnshire Archives; the curator of Louth Museum for much time and valuable assistance; the editors of *British Birds* for permission to quote certain notes; E.J. Redshaw for permission to extract information from the minute books of the Spalding Gentlemen's Society; Len and Betty Watkinson for generous assistance, encouragement and hospitality, and to Val Lorand for typing the manuscript.

We are also grateful to the following for access to unpublished material and help in other ways: Alan Ball, county recorder, and the Lincolnshire Bird Club for making available the unpublished 1988 records, G.K. Brown, G.P. Catley, M. Davies, P. Davis, A.L. Goodall, R. Lambert, J. Ostler, C.L.Ottaway, A.G. Parker, R.E.M. Pilcher, D.N. Robinson, A.E. Smith, R. Taylor and A.E. Vine.

Part One:
Regional distribution of the main ornithological sites

The historic county of Lincolnshire lies on the east coast between Yorkshire and Norfolk. Of the English counties, it is second only in size to historic Yorkshire, covering an area of nearly 2,800 square miles, with maximum distances of 75 miles from north to south and 47 miles from east to west *(fig 1)*. Two extensive ranges of hills, one of limestone and the other of chalk, rise to a little over 500 feet and add variety to a landscape that is otherwise mainly flat and very low-lying.

The area is intensively farmed — few counties in England have seen their landscapes change so drastically in the interests of agriculture. The major changes took place between 150 and 200 years ago when huge areas of fenland were drained and large areas of heath, common and wold were enclosed and destroyed. Since then, the process has continued at a reduced rate, with ever-increasing pressure on those birds which need specialised habitats such as marsh and heath.

Woodland is scarce in the county, covering only about three per cent of the area, compared with a national average of eight per cent. The acquisition of thousands of acres in the last 50 years by the Forestry Commission has meant a change from deciduous woodland to conifers in many areas and the afforestation of large areas of heathland.

Efficient drainage by artificially banked rivers and dykes and an average rainfall of only 24 inches means that the chance of natural flooding is fairly remote over most of the county and flood meadows have been almost eliminated. On the credit side, the extraction of gravel and building of reservoirs has created many new wetland areas, providing habitat for a great variety of aquatic bird-life.

Details of the flora and descriptions of the main habitats in the county can be found in *The Flora of Lincolnshire* by E.J. Gibbons (1975). Useful chapters are Geology and Scenery by D.N. Robinson and Weather and Climate by F.A. Barnes.

A system of 13 natural regions based on geological features and surface deposits was proposed by J.W. Blackwood (1972) for use in ecological surveys. In the following regional description of the county and sites of ornithological interest, we have broadly followed this, but have incorporated some of the smaller, rather scattered regions into larger ones. The result is a system of nine continuous geographical regions, all with fairly well-defined boundaries *(fig 2)*.

1. The Isle of Axholme

This is the smallest region, covering 80 square miles in the extreme north-west, and is the only part of the county lying west of the River Trent. Bordered by Yorkshire in the

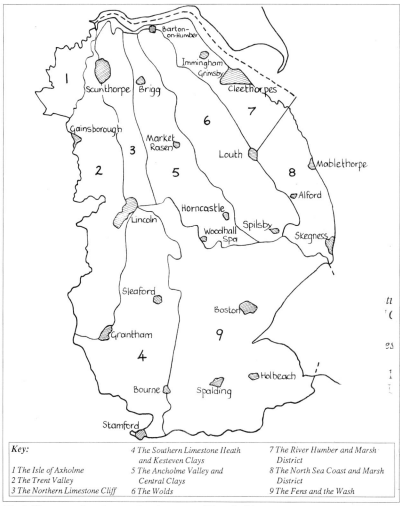

Key:

	4 The Southern Limestone Heath and Kesteven Clays	7 The River Humber and Marsh District
1 The Isle of Axholme	5 The Ancholme Valley and Central Clays	8 The North Sea Coast and Marsh District
2 The Trent Valley		
3 The Northern Limestone Cliff	6 The Wolds	9 The Fens and the Wash

Fig 2. The natural regions and main towns of Lincolnshire

north and west and by Nottinghamshire in the south, the area is somewhat remote to most of the county's ornithologists, since the only direct access is at Keadby Bridge. However, the Lincolnshire & South Humberside Trust for Nature Conservation has established several nature reserves in the Isle and the management of these has generated much local interest.

Most of the villages are sited on a central ridge of low hills, rising above 100 feet in only a few places. These are surrounded by a flat area, barely above sea level, which was once part of a large region of moors, peat bogs and fens. Drainage was commenced by Vermuyden in the seventeenth century and initially met with not inconsiderable

11

opposition from local people, who attempted to sabotage the work. Unfortunately for the naturalist this did not succeed and, by the middle of the nineteenth century, much of the land had been improved. This was accomplished by the use of warping drains to deposit silt from the Trent on the fields.

Unlike most other areas of lowland Lincolnshire, some parts of the Isle have defied cultivation, and Curlews and Snipe breed in a few rough fields. Long-eared Owls breed in most of the small, scattered woods as well as in several thorn thickets and the Whinchat has its county stronghold here. For many years, the villagers retained the right to extract peat from raised bogs which remained as the rest of the land was drained and used for agriculture. Several of these turbaries survive as fragments of the former habitat and the most important ones are Trust reserves.

The 24 acre turbary at the Haxey reserve is dominated by birch woodlands, though interesting breeding species have included Green Woodpeckers and Long-eared Owls. The more extensive reserve at Epworth Turbary, covering 82 acres, has a more representative series of habitats including areas of bog and wet heath. A variety of birds breed here, including Woodcock, Snipe, Whinchats and Tree Pipits.

One of the most important reserves in the county is at Crowle Waste, covering 300 acres. Deep extraction of peat has created extensive open bogs attracting breeding Teal, Snipe and Water Rails. The drier areas are dominated by birch scrub, heather and bracken and breeding species include Woodcock, Nightjars, Whinchats and good numbers of warblers. In winter, Merlins and Hen Harriers are regular visitors and Rough-legged Buzzards have occasionally been seen. The reserve is a continuation of the similar, though larger, Thorne Waste in Yorkshire (Limbert et al 1986). The term 'Waste' is rather unfortunate as planners have regarded the area as suitable for dumping fly ash or even for building an airport. Such a fate would be a tragedy as few similar wild areas exist in lowland England and the area should surely one day become a national nature reserve.

Two small woodlands at Langholme and Bird's Wood, near Haxey Turbary, are also Trust reserves. Both are fairly similar, being mainly birch and oak on sand. They contain a variety of woodland species including many tits and warblers, as well as Green and Great Spotted Woodpeckers and Long-eared Owls. A small area of disused sand pits adjacent to Bird's Wood attracts a few wildfowl, waders and Sand Martins.

Another series of sand pits close to Crowle appears to be rarely visited by bird-watchers, but contains a good selection of breeding species and might repay regular watching. Recently, however, more intensive use for water sports has reduced the value for wildfowl of the largest area of open water.

2. The Trent Valley

A mainly lowland region of clays and gravels extends along the western side of the county, between the limestone ridge and the River Trent, with an area of 380 square miles. Apart from the Trent, there are several other river systems and quite large areas of grassland still remain. Low hills of boulder clay rising to less than 100 feet hold little of interest, but there are several areas of sandy heathland. As in similar areas elsewhere in the county these have been heavily afforested, but some interesting birds still occur.

Extraction of gravel has resulted in several new wetland habitats west of Lincoln and these contain a great variety of bird life.

In the north of the region a wood and scrub-covered cliff of 200 feet at Burton Stather overlooks the Trent and there are a few pits with Reed Warbler colonies. The area would make an interesting site for the study of migration along the Trent, but only a few records have been received from there.

South and west of Scunthorpe, are a few small areas of woodland, pits and fragments of heathland. Both Arctic Redpoll and Serin were caught and ringed on Brumby Common in 1976 and an immature Crane wintered in rough fields near the River Eau in 1978/9.

The once extensive heaths at Scotton and Laughton Commons have been dominated by pine plantations for many years. However, a few areas of open, sandy birch and pine heath and several boggy ponds still remain and species such as Curlew, Nightjar and Tree Pipit can still be found. The Trust maintains a fragment of the old habitat on its 36 acres Scotton Common Reserve. Long-eared Owls breed in some of the mature plantations and Black-headed Gulls on a few of the ponds.

Mature deciduous woodland and parkland in the Gainsborough area is rarely visited by ornithologists, except during counts of the Herons at Wharton Wood. Nuthatches have bred occasionally and Hawfinches are sometimes seen, though both could be as a result of birds wandering from established populations in the Clumber Park area of Nottinghamshire. South of Gainsborough, along the River Trent, Lea Marsh has long been a good site for breeding waders including Curlew and Redshank, and wintering wildfowl. It has proved to be one of the most regular areas in the county for Bewick's Swans.

Until the late 1960s, a few undrained remnants of the old Fens were still to be found bordering the River Till and south of the Fossdyke Canal between Lincoln and Saxilby. Breeding species included Snipe, Redshank and Shoveler and there was a Black-headed Gull colony in the most extensive area at Pyewipe Marsh, just west of Lincoln. Sadly, however, this area has now been almost completely destroyed by drainage.

An old lake at Fillingham and the railway ballast pit at Lincoln have long histories of breeding Great Crested Grebes, wildfowl and the occurrence of interesting migrants, but the former does not receive much attention at present. More interest has been generated by the numerous gravel pits that have been excavated west of Lincoln. Those at Burton are now completely worked-out and make an attractive Trust reserve with additional woodland and scrub. There is a wealth of birdlife at all times of the year. In the breeding season, the pits are important for grebes, Tufted Ducks and Pochard, and wintering wildfowl usually include a flock of Wigeon. Waders occur when the water levels are low and all three species of woodpeckers are seen regularly. Vagrants have included Hoopoe, Little Bittern and a Great Reed Warbler in song for several weeks in the summer of 1979.

Another extensive series of gravel pits on the south-western edge of Lincoln at Hartsholme, North Hykeham, Thorpe and Whisby has produced a number of interesting records. Breeding birds include Little Ringed Plovers and Common Terns, sometimes even within the city boundary. A large winter gull roost usually forms at Apex Pit, North Hykeham, and many wildfowl winter at Whisby, where there is an excellent variety of

A pine plantation at Laughton Common

Burton gravel pits attract a wide variety of breeding birds

breeding species. The latter has been a Trust reserve for several years and has now become a Nature Park, with general public access. There are interesting areas of scrub and woodland in Hartsholme Park, with many warblers and a regular flock of wintering Siskins on the alders. Siskins also frequently occur in Boultham Park, Lincoln.

Fine areas of mature, mixed woodland dominate the landscape around Doddington and Skellingthorpe. Apart from the usual woodland breeding species, there are large finch roosts in some areas and an old-established heronry at Doddington.

Another gravel pit at North Scarle has a large Black-headed Gull colony and sometimes ten or more pairs of Common Terns amongst them. A smaller pit has recently been excavated near Swinderby airfield, where both Ringed and Little Ringed Plovers have nested.

Extensive heaths at Norton Disney and Stapleford have been planted with conifers, although open areas still leave habitat for heathland species and the area is one of the county's strongholds for Nightjars. Crossbills have been seen in some years and may occasionally breed, and Nightingales used to be common in rhododendrons bordering the conifer plantations.

Marshy areas near the Rivers Brant and Witham have now all been drained, though a few Bewick's or Whooper Swans sometimes winter. Areas of grassland have regular flocks of wintering Golden Plovers, and Curlews and Redshanks may still breed at one or two localities.

Up to about 1970, the large Grantham sewage farm near the village of Marston was an excellent place for waders. In addition to the usual settling ponds, some large, grassy fields were flooded, creating excellent wetland habitat. The number and variety of birds were large, including all the usual species and a few vagrants as well. Amongst the latter were Spotted Crake and White-winged Black Tern. A Black-winged Stilt wintered in 1968/9, despite a period of heavy snow. Sadly, modernisation of the plant has largely destroyed what was one of the county's most popular bird-watching areas. Only a few small settling ponds remain, but some grassland is still occasionally flooded.

3. The Northern Limestone Cliff

Running north from Lincoln to the Humber, the narrow range of limestone hills has a steep western escarpment, barely rising above 200 feet, and a gentle eastern dip slope covering an area of 160 square miles. Much of the area is rather dry, with only small hedges and there are few areas of interest to the birdwatcher. The exception is in the Scunthorpe area, where cover sands have resulted in large areas of sandy warrens, open heath and woodlands. Much of the original habitat has been destroyed by extensive ironstone mining and the development of Scunthorpe, although the new habitats created have proved interesting for birds.

North of Scunthorpe, Risby Warren is the only extensive area of sandy heath that remains. Raptors are fairly frequent visitors and it is one of the few areas in the county where Wheatears might still occasionally nest. The many ironstone quarries have produced several interesting wetland habitats suitable for wildfowl and waders. These have been readily exploited by nesting Ringed and Little Ringed Plovers and, in 1979, a pair of Common Sandpipers bred in one area for the first time in the county, although they were suspected of doing so in the same quarry in the previous two years. An industrial lake at Ashbyville produces some interesting wildfowl and wader records, and Black Redstarts have nested in the steelworks complex on several occasions.

The extensive woodlands at Broughton hold a great variety of birds. Although there are large areas of conifers, there are still some mature deciduous and mixed woodlands, with small areas of open heathland. Crossbills have bred occasionally and Wood Warblers could still do so, as a few sing in the area some years in spring and early summer. At Twigmoor, Lesser Spotted Woodpeckers are seen fairly often and Siskins are regular winter visitors. The once massive Black-headed Gull colony has long since been deserted, but the ponds still attract some interesting wildfowl. Large areas of heathland still exist here and have most of the usual birds associated with that habitat.

Much of Manton Warren has been cultivated, but extraction of sand has created some interesting new wetland habitats at Messingham sand quarries where there is a thriving colony of Black-headed Gulls. The pits are now a Trust reserve and attract many wildfowl and waders. Two birds new to the county list occurred there in 1979 — a Ring-necked Duck from America and a Great White Egret from eastern Europe.

North of Kirton Lindsey, quarries associated with the cement works, including a large flooded area, are also good for wildfowl and waders. The area had the distinction of providing the first British record of Houbara Bustard, when one was shot there in 1847.

Regular ringing at a Swallow roost in reed beds at Norton Place Lake has produced some interesting recoveries. Another lake in Riseholme Park has breeding Canada Geese and occasionally attracts other interesting waterfowl and scarce visitors such as the Osprey.

The cliff stops abruptly at the Witham gap in Lincoln and is dominated by Lincoln Cathedral. Few birdwatchers would think of looking here, but Kestrels breed occasionally on the towers and Hobby and Black Redstart have been recorded. Tawny Owls are regular in trees around the nearby castle walls.

Former ironstone mines at Greetwell, just east of Lincoln, are now extensively quarried for limestone and provide sites for waders, such as Little Ringed Plovers. Despite their closeness to Lincoln, they seem to have been largely ignored by ornithologists.

4. The Southern Limestone Heath and Kesteven Clays

South of Lincoln, the limestone heath gradually broadens until it becomes widely covered with boulder clay beyond Grantham, forming a large region of some 400 square miles. The northern part is dry with few wooded areas and eighteenth century enclosures eliminated all traces of heathland. Golden Plovers winter regularly and Quail may be found in some summers. The clay region is heavily wooded and there are several streams and rivers flowing through the area, providing a more varied habitat for birds. A few species such as Nuthatch, Hawfinch and Marsh Tit have their county strongholds in this region.

At the Lincoln gap, the grassy, scrub-covered slope of the South Common attracts a few migrants such as Wheatears and other chats. A few small quarries in the Metheringham area sometimes hold breeding Little Ringed Plovers and a few passage waders. Some interesting woodland lies on the eastern edge of the heath at Potterhanworth and Nocton. Potterhanworth Wood is mainly coniferous, but the young plantations have breeding Grasshopper Warblers and Tree Pipits. Nocton Wood is a more varied, open, mixed wood with many warblers and tits. Areas of rhododendron bushes attract large numbers of roosting finches in winter and these often include many Bramblings.

In a gap in the hills at Ancaster, a few waders and wildfowl occur at the gravel pit and the Trust has a small reserve of sandy warrens, pits and heathland at Rauceby Warren which has recently attracted a number of rarities. Also in this area, grebes and wildfowl occur on lakes at the Sleaford ballast pit, Caythorpe and Culverthorpe.

There are several large areas of mature deciduous woods and parkland in the Grantham area. Belton Park is one of the few places where Sparrowhawks bred in the county during the period of near extinction and Hawfinches used to be regular in this area.

Another interesting area is Grimsthorpe Park, with its lake and mature oak woodland. A large flock of Canada Geese is resident and Great Crested Grebes nest on the lake. Nuthatches are common and a few Redstarts and Lesser Spotted Woodpeckers breed here.

There are extensive conifer plantations at Bourne and Morkery Woods and most of the usual woodland species may be found here, including a regular flock of Crossbills. Two small Trust woods in this area are Dole Wood, near Thurlby and Tortoiseshell Wood, near Castle Bytham. Both have a variety of breeding birds including Nuthatch, Nightingale, woodpeckers, warblers and tits.

A small reservoir at Denton has several pairs of Great Crested Grebes and has attracted a few migrant waders including Red-necked Phalarope. Great Crested Grebes also nest at the nearby Harlaxton Lake and an Osprey has been recorded there. Mining for ironstone in the Colsterworth area has created several quarries, but their ornithological importance is unknown.

5. The Ancholme Valley and Central Clays

In the northern half of the county, the central clay vale lies between the Cliff and the Wolds. This covers an area of 280 square miles extending from the former peaty carrs of the narrow Ancholme valley in the north and gradually broadening south to the River Witham.

Some wildfowl and waders occur on the South Ferriby pits, while the rivers and drains of the Ancholme valley attract a few wintering ducks such as Goldeneyes and Goosanders. This area must have formerly held large numbers of wildfowl as a decoy was operated on the western edge at Broughton.

The settling ponds at Brigg sugar beet factory have produced some interesting wader records in the past, although lately there has not been a regular series of records from there. The recently completed, but rather small, reservoir at Cadney is worth visiting. Already there have been some interesting records of wildfowl, waders and other birds. Another reservoir at Toft Newton is good for water birds in winter, although, since it is heavily fished, the disturbance is often too great for some species.

A few pairs of Curlews breed in rough grassland as far south as the River Rase, but most of the more interesting birds in the region are heath and woodland species.

Former areas of sandy heath and moorland close to the Wolds at Wrawby and Nettleton have been extensively planted with conifers and are not often visited by ornithologists.

A similar, but more popular, area is the extensive Willingham Forest, near Market Rasen. Coniferous woodlands dominate the area, although there is a succession from young plantations to mature trees. A few heathland species still exist in the more open areas, including Nightjars and Tree Pipits. Siskins are regular visitors. A fragment of the original habitat is maintained on the Trust reserve at Linwood Warren, where breeding species have included Redstarts and Long-eared Owls.

The clay woodlands of the extensive, but rather scattered, Bardney Forest are owned mainly by the Forestry Commission. Many of the woodlands have been planted with conifers, but areas of deciduous and mixed woodland still exist and there is a good variety of birds. In the 1960s, the young conifer plantations held very large numbers of Grasshopper Warblers, although these are now much scarcer. Many Woodcock breed in the area and Nightingales are common in some woods. Nightjars are scarce in the Forest, although they have occasionally bred near the Trust reserve at Little Scrubs, an area of old grassland amongst the woods.

In the Woodhall Spa district, there are still large areas of sandy heathland, although again, much has been planted with conifers. There are also some interesting woods of oak and birch, where Green Woodpeckers are as common as anywhere in the county. Two of the largest areas of heathland are Trust reserves. One of these, at Kirkby Moor, has extensive open areas of heather and bracken, and raptors such as Hen Harriers and Sparrowhawks are regular visitors. A small reservoir attracts a few wildfowl and other water birds and the woodlands and scrub have a variety of birds, including breeding Long-eared Owls in the conifer plantations. A nearby sandpit holds breeding Little Ringed Plovers and Sand Martins and attracts a few passage waders.

The other reserve at Moor Farm has an interesting range of habitats, with heath, woodland and a fairly extensive boggy area. Several pairs of Snipe nest and Siskins are regular winter visitors.

The reservoir at Revesby is a traditional nesting site for several pairs of Great Crested Grebes. There have been only a few other records from this area and the reservoir and surrounding woodlands would probably repay regular watching.

6. The Wolds

The chalk upland region of the Wolds covers an area of nearly 300 square miles, stretching from the Humber at South Ferriby in the north, to the edge of the Fens, where it is less than ten miles from the coastline. Much of the area lies above 400 feet, rising to over 500 feet in only a few places.

The pleasantly rolling hills are now intensively cultivated, with huge fields bordered by small, neatly trimmed, thorn hedges. Although there are few major areas of woodland, there are frequent copses and scattered hedgerow trees, so that some species, such as the Stock Dove, are very common. Before the enclosures of the eighteenth century, the Wolds was a wild area of scrub-covered grassland and heath. What little

Kirkby Moor — a wintering area for Sparrowhawks, Hen Harriers and the occasional Rough-legged Buzzard

Typical Wold scenery near Nettleton

Barton-on-Humber pits — a breeding site for Bearded Tits

permanent grassland remains is found mainly alongside streams in the valleys and on the steepest hillsides which defy ploughing.

In the north, the west facing escarpment is largely uncultivated and occasional Rough-legged Buzzards have found conditions suitable for wintering there, especially in the Bonby, Nettleton and North Willingham districts.

Some of the most extensive woodlands on the Wolds are those on the Brocklesby estate which stretch in a large ribbon from Great Limber south to the Pelham's Pillar, near Cabourne. The pillar commemorates the planting of over 12 million trees by the Earls of Yarborough in the first half of the nineteenth century. A large variety of mature mixed woodland exists there, but this once-popular area receives little attention from present day ornithologists.

Croxby Pond is another area which is visited less often nowadays, although its records go back many years. Good numbers of wildfowl are sometimes seen in winter and there have been several unusual records. Another wetland area worth visiting is Biscathorpe Fish Pond, in the Bain Valley. Access is easy as the lake is bordered by the 'Viking Way' — the long distance footpath which traverses much of the Wolds. Apart from wildfowl, the lake is interesting for breeding Reed Warblers and Yellow Wagtails, which are scarce in the Wolds and there used to be large Sand Martin colonies in nearby gravel pits. Great Crested Grebes nest at a few other fish ponds in the Bain Valley and Ospreys are fairly regular visitors.

On the eastern edge of the Wolds a few clear trout streams flow swiftly to the adjacent Marsh district. One of these, the River Lud passes through Hubbard's Hills, an attractive narrow wooded valley, at Louth. Single Dippers have been recorded here in several winters and Grey Wagtails are frequently present and nest occasionally. The beech woods also attract wintering Bramblings. Like many old Lincolnshire market towns, Louth has a large population of Swifts. Recently, many traditional nest sites have been lost as the older houses have had their roofs modernised. In the last few years, part of the population has found alternative sites by moving to houses on a council estate.

There are a few woodlands of interest on the south-eastern edge of the Wolds. Burwell Wood is mainly coniferous, but has a variety of birds including Sparrowhawks. A heronry in Muckton Wood is long-established and there is another in Willoughby Wood. The nearby Trust reserve at Hoplands Wood has a large population of warblers and tits, the latter being aided by a supply of nest boxes. Extensive parkland and woodland on the Well Vale estate has recently been opened as a nature trail. Redstarts have bred here and Hawfinches sometimes nest in the general area.

Many of the rougher valleys and hillsides in the Wolds have breeding Snipe and wintering birds such as Short-eared Owls and occasional Great Grey Shrikes. Typical of such areas are Sow Dale and the nearby Trust reserve and country park at Snipe Dales. Even quite small valleys are worth exploring, as one near Alford held two pairs of breeding Red-backed Shrikes in 1977.

Of all the regions in the county, this is perhaps the one most ignored by ornithologists. The main reason for this seems to be the large size and uniformity of much of the area, making it difficult to find sites in which to make concentrated observations.

7. The River Humber and Marsh District

The broad Humber estuary forms a natural boundary to the northern edge of the historic county. Tidal along the whole of its length of some 40 miles, the estuary was once fringed by extensive salt marshes. Only fragments of these now remain, mainly along the lower reaches. The river itself is considered in this section, along with the low-lying Marsh district between the Wolds and the Humber, and covers an area of about 210 square miles. A region of boulder clay near the Wolds is known as the Middle Marsh, whereas the coastal area of marine silt is called the Outmarsh.

The sheltered waters of the Humber form a natural refuge for seabirds during stormy weather and many interesting species may be seen from the bank of the river at such times. Scoters, skuas and Kittiwakes are regular visitors and, in exceptional conditions, species such as Manx Shearwaters, Gannets and Little Auks occasionally penetrate as far as the upper reaches.

The Humber begins at the confluence of the Trent and the Ouse in an interesting area known as Trent Falls. Since the Royal Society for the Protection of Birds established its nature reserve at the nearby Blacktoft Sands in Yorkshire, knowledge of migration in this area has increased enormously. The permanent warden has taken the trouble to provide detailed records of birds occurring in Lincolnshire on both the Trent and the Humber, as well as on an area of marsh at Alkborough. Trent Falls has proved to be an important area for wildfowl and waders and many seabirds have been recorded here. Vagrants have included a Collared Pratincole and White-winged Black Tern in 1977 and Britain's first Hudsonian Godwit in 1981.

Extensive sandbanks are uncovered at low tide in the upper reaches of the Humber. One of these, the Humber Wildfowl Refuge at Whitton, is now a statutory site established by Act of Parliament in 1985, and wardened by the Nature Conservancy Council (N.C.C.). It attracts large numbers of wildfowl and thousands of Pink-footed Geese used to roost here, although — as elsewhere in the county — numbers have become much reduced in recent years. It remains the most important site for Mallard in Great Britain.

A few miles downriver lies the most inaccessible part of the county, namely Read's Island. This low island, barely half a mile wide and a mile and a half long, is occupied by only one farm and a herd of deer. Few ornithologists have had the opportunity to visit the island, although it obviously has a rich avifauna. Marshy fields and rough grassland attract many birds including raptors, wildfowl and waders and there is much of interest throughout the year. Fortunately, many of the larger birds can be identified from the Humber bank. A pair of Dunlin nested in 1958 and Black-tailed Godwits have bred in some recent years. Several pairs of Short-eared Owls nest fairly regularly and harriers are frequent visitors. A few pairs of Wigeon have also bred on a few occasions. Such a site hardly needs the formal status of a nature reserve, since it is, in effect, a natural one. However, the island has even greater potential and perhaps could be managed so as to provide optimum conditions for breeding wildfowl and waders.

A series of old brickpits between Barton-on-Humber and East Halton forms one of the county's most important wetland areas. Many of the shallower pits are reed-filled and support a good breeding population of Reed Warblers and are host to large roosting flocks of hirundines. Several pairs of Bitterns have bred since the late 1940s and Bearded Tits have become established since 1968. The pits are also important for breeding Great Crested Grebes, Little Grebes, Water Rails and Pochard, while vagrants such as Little Bitterns and Golden Orioles occasionally occur. The Trust has a reserve on the west side of Barton and important areas on the east side are at Barrow Haven and Goxhill. Increased disturbance from fishing and boating and the construction of the Humber Bridge seem to have had a detrimental effect on the rarer breeding birds. An interesting area of saltmarsh between Goxhill and East Halton sometimes attracts a few Snow and Lapland Buntings and Richard's Pipit has also occurred there.

An important series of shallow pits containing many small islands is found at North Killingholme Haven. Water levels on this Trust reserve are controlled by means of sluices to provide optimum conditions for waders. The area is very popular with birdwatchers as good views can be obtained from the road and the Humber bank without disturbing the birds. A large variety of wildfowl and waders has been seen and attractive species such as Avocets are fairly frequent visitors. It is hoped that the latter may eventually find conditions suitable for nesting as good numbers now breed in north Norfolk. Spoonbills have also become a regular feature and up to six were present for several weeks in 1978. Rare waders have included Lesser Yellowlegs, White-rumped, Baird's and Sharp-tailed Sandpipers.

Oil refineries and chemical factories dominate the landscape between Killingholme and Grimsby. There are few good areas for birds, although an industrial pit at Immingham attracts fair numbers of wildfowl in the winter. One large pit at Killingholme has been used as a rubbish tip recently, and several Glaucous and one or two Iceland Gulls have been identified amongst the huge numbers of gulls feeding there.

An area of saltings and mudflats, known as Pyewipe Marsh, immediately west of Grimsby, is favoured by large numbers of feeding waders and wildfowl — especially Curlews and Shelduck. In winter, Grimsby Docks can hold interesting birds such as grebes and divers, while marine ducks including Scaup and Eiders regularly occur. At the eastern fish docks, extensive mudflats and a sewage outfall form ideal feeding conditions for many thousands of gulls in winter.

Small areas of bushes at Cleethorpes Boating Lake and a conifer plantation on the sea bank at Humberston provide cover for migrating passerines. Although quite small, these areas have produced several interesting records, including a Serin in song for several days at Cleethorpes, and an Arctic Warbler and two Parrot Crossbills at Humberston.

Between Humberston and Grainthorpe are extensive saltmarshes and mudflats at the mouth of the Humber. A large part of the marshes at Tetney is now an R.S.P.B. reserve. This was formed mainly to conserve the county's largest Little Tern colony, which is concentrated around an old chalk road constructed during the laying of an oil pipeline. A seasonal warden is employed by the R.S.P.B. to protect the terns and numbers have risen to more than 100 pairs in some years. Large numbers of waders roost on the saltings, and the marshes are important for wildfowl in winter. Short-eared Owls breed fairly regularly and other raptors, especially harriers, are frequent visitors. The Louth Canal reaches the sea at Tetney Lock and the bank and saltmarshes of the tidal Tetney Haven are regular sites for Lapland Buntings in autumn and winter.

A similar saltmarsh at Grainthorpe has, like Tetney, breeding Redshanks, Oyster-catchers and Shelduck, with the addition of a Black-headed Gull colony and a few pairs of Common Terns. The whole area is important for a flock of several thousand wintering Brent Geese based around the mouth of the Humber. The coastal fields there are perhaps the only really regular sites for wintering White-fronted Geese in the county.

There are few areas of significance inland in the Marsh District bordering the Humber, although woodlands and the lake in Brocklesby Park have attracted some interesting birds in the past. Some areas of grassland hold fairly large flocks of Golden Plover in winter and a few Quail appear in some summers. Large numbers of Collared Doves inhabit the Grimsby area while Bradley and Weelsby Woods have produced a few noteworthy birds, including one or two Hoopoes. A pair of Red-backed Shrikes bred successfully in the area in 1978. An attractive Trust reserve at Tetney Blow Wells always provides a selection of the commoner warblers in the breeding season.

Perhaps the most popular locality in the region is the 200-acre reservoir at Covenham which has been in existence since 1969 and attracts a large variety and number of wildfowl and other water birds. The south-east corner is a Trust reserve, so there is always a sanctuary for birds during sailing and other watersport activities. Up to 1,000 Mallard winter here and divers and the rarer grebes are regular visitors. Despite the steeply sloping concrete edges, many waders visit during spring and autumn migration. Black Terns and Little Gulls are regular, sometimes staying for long periods. There is always the chance of a rarity — a Gull-billed Tern stayed for a month in 1974, several White-winged Black Terns have been recorded and the county's only Whiskered Tern was seen in 1987.

8. The North Sea Coast and Marsh District

The Marsh District between the Wolds and the North Sea covers an area of 230 square miles, with a 28 mile coastline from Donna Nook at the Humber mouth, south to Gibraltar Point. Despite heavy pressure from the holiday industry, all the important natural areas on the coast have been saved from destruction — thanks to co-operation between the Trust, the Nature Conservancy Council and various local authorities. The coast is the most intensively studied area in the county and there are excellent opportunities for the naturalist along almost the whole of its length.

All the former inland marshes have long since been reclaimed and the drains and rivers flowing from the Wolds are all that remain. These do not attract many wildfowl, but are favourite wintering sites for Little Grebes. As in all areas of the county, the land is intensively cultivated, although some fairly large areas of permanent pasture remain. Many of these still retain the form of the old strip system of farming and wet areas between the strips often attract waders and wildfowl. Flocks of Curlews and other waders regularly flight from the coast to feed on the pastures and Golden Plovers are common in winter. A few wild swans sometimes remain during the winter.

The Humber coastline turns abruptly south at Donna Nook at its junction with the North Sea. This area south to Saltfleet Haven has recently become a Trust reserve. Here, the typical Lincolnshire coastal scenery begins, with wide sand and mudflats and grassy sand dunes often dominated by thick, almost impenetrable, thorny sea buckthorn scrub.

Covenham reservoir is an attractive site for wildfowl and waders

Brackish marsh and dunes at Donna Nook — many migrants and unusual birds have been recorded there

The dunes at Donna Nook are backed by an artificial sea bank, with an interesting area in between of marshes and shallow pools which are good for waders. The dunes attract large numbers of migrants and many unusual birds have been recorded. Birdwatchers visit the area almost daily, and members of the Cleethorpes Ringing Group kept observatory-style records for more than 20 years. The list includes five species of shrikes, while such eastern rarities as Pallas's Warbler, Siberian Rubythroat and Red-flanked Bluetail in successive years show that almost anything might be expected. A large proportion of all the county's Ortolan Buntings and Richard's Pipits have been seen there. Little Terns nest on shingle ridges on the open shore and Shore Larks and Snow Buntings occur in winter.

Access to the northern shore is restricted on weekdays when the R.A.F. bombing range is in operation, but the mudflats are more interesting for wildfowl and waders further south towards Saltfleet. A saltmarsh area there is a regular site for several thousand wintering Brent Geese and nearby are compact areas of dunes and scrub. The tidal inlet at Saltfleet Haven sometimes holds a few sea-ducks and the muddy banks are good for waders.

Reclamation north of Saltfleet has left an interesting area of inland sand dunes. These have been planted with conifers at North Somercotes Warren and there are some attractive willow-fringed pools. Migrants recorded here have included Hoopoes, Thrush Nightingale, Yellow-browed Warblers and Crossbills.

Between Saltfleet Haven and Mablethorpe are nearly five miles of unspoilt coastline forming the Saltfleetby to Theddlethorpe National Nature Reserve, which is managed jointly by the Trust and the Nature Conservancy Council. The wide variety of habitat and unlimited opportunities make this reserve very popular with birdwatchers. At the northern end, Redshanks and Oystercatchers nest on the saltmarsh, and extensive mudflats attract many gulls, terns and waders. The dunes are dominated by sea buckthorn, but there are clumps of elder and other bushes and open grassy areas. Large numbers of Whitethroats, Dunnocks and Reed Buntings nest, and thousands of Field-fares feed on the buckthorn berries in autumn. Several unusual migrants are seen every year. A large area of fresh water marsh consisting mainly of sedges and rushes can prove very interesting. A few pairs of Snipe and Water Rails nest in most years and several Hen Harriers occur in winter, sometimes roosting in the sedgemarsh. At low tide it is over a mile to the sea across the mudflats, but sea-watching here can be very rewarding. Sea-birds such as skuas, Gannets and shearwaters often pass by at very close range.

The coast south of Mablethorpe has been under attack from the sea for hundreds of years. Much of the original dune system was destroyed by the disastrous storm floods of 1953 and has been replaced by a concrete wall while stabilising groynes run into the sea at intervals along the shore. At Trusthorpe Point these have provided ideal conditions for a few wintering Purple Sandpipers, a species which would not normally find a natural niche in Lincolnshire. Sea-watching here is also worthwhile as the tideline is never far from the sea wall. Trusthorpe sewage farm, a few miles inland, attracts a few passage waders, while some wildfowl winter on Sutton brick pit.

The area between Sutton-on-Sea and Chapel St. Leonards is of outstanding interest to ornithologists. Sandilands Golf Course is good for ground-feeding migrants such as

Wheatears and pipits, and several Richard's Pipits have been recorded there. Huttoft Bank car terrace is a convenient place for sea-watching and a narrow strip of scrub-covered dunes here occasionally has a good variety of migrants. Anderby Creek is also an excellent area for migration. The dunes to the north of the village have been planted with many trees and a Great Spotted Cuckoo was seen here in 1971. South of the village there is an interesting area of sea buckthorn, elders and some reed-filled borrow pits.

The dunes in this area were breached by the sea in several places in 1953 and in order to repair them, clay was excavated from several pits near the sea bank. These have now become partially overgrown with reeds and several are Trust reserves. The most important ones are Huttoft Pit, Wolla Bank, near Anderby, and Chapel Pit. Large numbers of Reed Warblers nest and Bearded Tits are regular winter visitors. The shallow pits attract many wildfowl and have been good for waders in very dry years. A long list of rarities includes several Purple Herons and Spoonbills, Little Bittern and Great Reed Warbler.

A shelter on top of the sea wall at Chapel Point makes a comfortable sea-watching point and the dunes and gardens in the Chapel St. Leonards area would be worth investigation in the migration seasons. Ingoldmells Point is the most easterly part of this coastline and would probably also make a good point for sea-watching, although little appears to have been carried out.

Between Ingoldmells and Skegness there are good areas of dunes and scrub and a golf course, but the area receives little attention from birdwatchers, probably due to the number of holidaymakers and the attraction of other quieter sites. Nevertheless, such rare birds as Rufous Bush Robin and Subalpine Warbler have been recorded.

A good area of saltings at Seacroft is well worth visiting for waders, as Pectoral Sandpiper and other scarce species have occurred. Extensive shingle banks on the shore are also used as a late summer roost by gulls and terns and have included such interesting species as Mediterranean and Glaucous Gulls.

South of Seacroft, at the corner of the Wash, is the 1,000-acre Trust reserve at Gibraltar Point. Extensive areas of shingle, sand dunes with scrub, saltings and a freshwater marsh provide a good variety of habitats for birds. Information for the general visitor is available at the Visitors' Centre and there is a public hide at the freshwater mere. Facilities for research and education are provided at the Field Station, which houses a laboratory and accommodation for naturalists. An Observatory and Ringing Station has been in operation for 40 years, using Heligoland traps and mist nets to trap birds.

Many species of birds breed on the reserve including large numbers of Skylarks, Reed Buntings, Dunnocks and Whitethroats. A Little Tern colony is actively protected by a summer warden and there are good numbers of nesting Ringed Plovers. Spectacular roosting wader flocks are present in the autumn and raptors are frequent visitors. Few areas in the county are better placed for observing migration. Diurnal movements of Swifts, hirundines and other species are often spectacular and large falls of Continental night migrants such as Pied Flycatchers and Redstarts may often be seen in the autumn. Rarities can also be expected and amongst those recorded have

Heligoland trap and the Field Research Station at Gibraltar Point

Settling ponds at Bardney sugar beet factory — an important inland site for passage waders

been Sardinian Warbler, Isabelline and Lesser Grey Shrike, Citrine Wagtail, American Redstart and Rustic Bunting.

Recently, some very interesting records have been received from the Inner Dowsing Tower Lighthouse, about 12 miles off the Lincolnshire coast (53 degrees 20N, O degrees 34E), almost due east of Huttoft Bank. Thousands of birds are attracted by the light in spring and autumn and these have included many scarce species, with rarities such as Pallas's Warbler and Short-toed Lark. Although seabird movements have proved to be no larger than those seen from the shore, they have included most of the scarcer species such as petrels, Sabine's Gull and Roseate Tern.

9. The Fens and the Wash

The Fens occupy the whole of the south-east quarter of the county and form the largest region with an area of more than 700 square miles. They are bordered on the east by the great bay of the Wash, with its extensive saltmarshes and mudflats. These form by far the largest area of natural habitat left in the county. Much of the inland region was formerly peaty fenland, very low-lying and often completely flooded in winter, forming a paradise for wildfowl and other marshland birds. Attempts at partial drainage from the Middle Ages onwards did not meet with much success until an intensification of effort in the late eighteenth and early nineteenth centuries completely changed the landscape. In parallel with this, large areas of saltmarshes were gradually reclaimed from the sea and this process has continued to the present day.

The present-day Fens are a flat, featureless plain, intensively cultivated and inter-sected by a multitude of dykes, drains and ditches. Three major rivers, the Witham, the Welland and the Nene, flow through the region to the Wash. There is hardly any wood-land, few trees and bushes and an almost complete lack of hedgerows. The resulting avifauna mainly comprises ground-nesting and ground-feeding birds. In the breeding season, birds such as Skylarks, Reed Buntings and partridges are dominant, and in winter there are large flocks of Lapwings and gulls. Apart from the Wash, the most interesting areas for birds are largely man-made.

In the north-west of the region, a gradually narrowing strip of fenlands extends as far as Lincoln, alongside the River Witham. Until the 1960s, Lincoln sewage farm was a good place for passage waders, but modernisation has left it devoid of any suitable habitat. Amongst the many pipits and wagtails which feed here, a few Grey Wagtails can be found in most winters.

Long-eared Owls breed occasionally in an isolated copse alongside Branston Delph and Whinchats used to nest regularly in nearby farmland, even though the habitat did not seem typical of that which is normally required. At Branston Island, a bend in the River Witham has been cut off and the enclosed area is sometimes turned into a reservoir during flood conditions. Large numbers of wildfowl occur there during such times, but the reservoir usually remains filled only for short periods.

The settling ponds at Bardney sugar beet factory have proved to be one of the most important inland sites for passage waders in the county. All the usual species occur here, sometimes in good numbers, and there have been several scarce migrants and vagrants. Of a few American species, the most interesting was a Solitary Sandpiper in 1963, while a Sabine's Gull stayed for nearly three weeks in 1974. Both Little Ringed and Ringed Plovers nest in some years and there is a small Black-headed Gull colony, with occasionally a few pairs of Common Terns.

Large numbers of wildfowl occur in winter at Nocton Fen, but the main interest here is the regular appearance of Marsh Harriers in late summer and early autumn. Three or four are sometimes seen, often roosting together in a sugar beet field.

In the northern part of the region, the excavation of fen-edge gravels has produced an interesting series of pits. Those between Woodhall Spa and Tattershall have long been worked out and are now overgrown, although providing excellent habitat for grebes and other waterfowl and a variety of warblers. Larger pits at Kirkby-on-Bain and Tattershall are still being worked and there is a wide variety of habitat in both areas. Little Ringed Plovers bred for the first time in the county in this area in 1950 and still do so along with Ringed Plovers, Shelducks and Common Terns. A feral population of Greylag Geese has become established after introductions in the 1960s. A few waders occur on passage and there are good numbers of wintering wildfowl.

In severe weather, the River Witham usually remains ice-free and can then hold some interesting wildfowl such as Smew and Goosanders and occasionally grebes and divers. The stretch of river between Woodhall Spa and Chapel Hill can be easily viewed from the road running alongside the bank.

Also in this area is the only major area of deciduous woodland in the Fens at Tumby. Although rarely visited by birdwatchers, the woods hold a large variety of birds including Nightingales and all three woodpeckers, while there is also a major heronry in Troy Wood.

In the East Fen a few small woodlands exist on the sites of old duck decoys. One of these, at Friskney, is a Trust reserve and has a fine selection of mature trees. Part of the old pond has been re-excavated and is filled with reeds. Breeding species include Spotted Flycatchers, Reed Warblers and Tawny Owls. Many migrants pass through the wood, especially Willow Warblers, while occasional rarer species have included Golden Oriole, Firecrest and Crossbills.

In the Boston area, the River Witham and the larger drains attract a variety of birds including Kingfishers, wildfowl, Cormorants and Common Terns. The Hobhole drain, near its junction with the Witham, is of interest for its dense cover of bushes along the banks. This provides ideal habitat for wintering Long-eared Owls and up to ten can be found here every year.

A few small pits at Hubbert's Bridge, Gosberton and Surfleet are Trust reserves and birds occurring there include Reed and Sedge Warblers, wildfowl and a few waders. In the Spalding area a few waders occur on the sugar beet factory ponds and some interesting wintering waterfowl can often be found on the River Welland between Spalding and Deeping St. James.

Valuable fenland habitat was lost when the Welland Washes were finally reclaimed in the early 1960s. Garganey used to breed regularly and Black-tailed Godwits had done so on a few occasions. A similar, although much smaller, area of washes has been saved by the creation of Trust reserves at Baston Fen and Thurlby Fen Slipe alongside the River Glen. The habitat consists of flooded meadows with areas of marsh and small pits. In

*Wildfowl at
Kirkby-on-Bain
gravel pits*

*Gravel workings,
such as these at
Langtoft, provide
nesting sites for
Little Ringed Plovers
and Common Terns*

*Saltmarshes at
Freiston Shore*

spring, there is a good passage of Snipe and visitors include Bewick's Swans and Short-eared Owls as well as many other wildfowl and waders. Snipe and Redshanks breed regularly, as do several species of wildfowl. The nearby Bourne South Fen has proved to be a regular site for Dotterel in spring.

Another area of gravel excavated on the southern fringe of the county has produced a large area of pits. These are at Tallington, West Deeping, Langtoft and Baston Common and have all the usual birds associated with gravel pits. As on the northern edge of the Fens, there are Little Ringed and Ringed Plovers, Common Terns and feral Greylag Geese. Large numbers of wildfowl winter, including a regular flock of Goosanders. The lake at Deeping St. James is of interest for wildfowl and the large heronry in a nearby wood.

The muddy banks of the River Nene provide habitat for feeding waders and gulls, but the main attraction here used to be Wisbech sewage farm, which straddled the border between Lincolnshire and Norfolk. A great number and variety of waders has occurred there including many rare American species such as Wilson's Phalaropes, Stilt Sandpipers and a Semipalmated Sandpiper. Species such as Pectoral Sandpiper and Temminck's Stint were almost annual and other rarities have included White-winged Black Terns and Spotted Crakes. Breeding birds included many Shelducks and Moorhens and a few Black-headed Gulls and Shovelers. The sewage farm ceased to be used in the early 1980s.

The 35 miles of Wash coastline between Gibraltar Point and the Norfolk border, just beyond the River Nene, consists of continuous saltmarsh, fronted by wide mudflats at low tide. The sheer size and remoteness of the area makes it an ideal habitat for many species of birds at all times of the year. However, some disturbance is caused by bombing ranges at Friskney and Holbeach on weekdays. Also, most of the saltmarshes around the Wash are very popular with wildfowlers in winter.

In the breeding season, the commonest birds are Shelducks, Redshanks, Black-headed Gulls, Skylarks, Meadow Pipits and Reed Buntings. Other breeding species include Oystercatchers and Ringed Plovers, both of which often nest in coastal fields, and a few pairs of Short-eared Owls. Large numbers of migrant and wintering waders feed on the mudflats, gathering in immense roosting flocks at high tide. Wintering wildfowl include large numbers of Brent Geese and Wigeon and a regular flock of Pink-footed Geese. The saltmarshes are important sites for large flocks of wintering Twites and recently there have been large numbers of Lapland Buntings.

On the north-west side of the Wash, much of the saltmarsh has been reclaimed over the last ten years or so, drastically reducing the habitat for breeding birds. Even so, the area can be very rewarding where access to the new sea bank is possible, since much closer views can now be obtained of birds on the edge of the marsh and at sea.

Wainfleet and Friskney marshes have always proved to be very good areas for harriers. Hen Harriers are regular in winter and Marsh and Montagu's Harriers are seen in most summers, the latter occasionally nesting. Friskney is a good site for watching roosting waders on the highest tides. Spectacular flocks of Oystercatchers, Knot, Bar-tailed Godwits, Dunlin and other species often roost here and many others flight towards Gibraltar Point.

There are several other access roads at Wrangle, Benington, Butterwick and Freiston, all suitable for viewing the wildfowl and waders that occur all round the Wash. In autumn, sea birds such as skuas, shearwaters and Gannets can often be seen close to the sea bank on the highest tides, especially when northerly gales drive them into the shelter of the Wash.

Another popular and important area for birds is at the mouth of the River Witham. It is reached along a road from Fishtoft and by walking the final mile along the river bank. Good views can be obtained of Brent Geese and other birds from the hide recently constructed by Anglian Water and the Lincolnshire Bird Club. In winter, there is a flock of up to 100 Eiders, some often staying throughout the summer. Other wildfowl in winter include a flock of several hundred Goldeneyes. A few divers, grebes and other sea-birds can sometimes be found and rarities have included Sabine's Gulls, Black Guillemot and Marsh Sandpiper.

A huge area of mature saltmarsh lying between the outfalls of the River Witham and the River Welland comprises Frampton and Kirton Marshes, which are Trust, N.C.C. and R.S.P.B. reserves, and undoubtedly the most important sites in the Wash. Reclamation elsewhere has resulted in a concentration of many species here and the Black-Headed Gull colony, at its peak estimated at more than 20,000 pairs, is one of the largest in Britain. There is also a Common Tern colony and several hundred pairs of Redshanks. Shelducks sometimes make open nests on the saltmarsh and large numbers of other wildfowl occur in winter.

Many interesting birds occur at the Welland mouth. A walk along the southern bank gives good views across towards Kirton Marsh and this is one of the most remote areas in the Wash. Good numbers of Black Terns often feed there in autumn and birds of prey are seen quite frequently.

The south side of the Wash holds all the usual species and there are often very large flocks of Shelducks in winter and large numbers of roosting waders. Of particular interest is a wintering flock of several thousand Pink-footed Geese at Holbeach St. Matthew and Lutton Outmarsh which is now a National nature reserve.

The mouth of the River Nene does not attract as many wildfowl as the other rivers, but it is sometimes good for sea birds. Skuas often continue inland along the River Nene and the marshes and fields there are good for birds of prey. Between the river and the Norfolk border, Terrington Marsh is notable for its large numbers of wintering Pintails.

Distribution of Breeding Birds

Although the avifauna of the county is enriched by the occurrence of regular migrants and rare vagrants, it is the number of breeding species which really reflects the variety of habitats. Out of the total of over 350 species that have occurred in Lincolnshire, at least 150 have been recorded breeding, although some have not nested for many years and others now do so irregularly.

Until recently, the distribution of many species in the county was not fully known, although a few fairly accurate surveys had been possible for localised species breeding

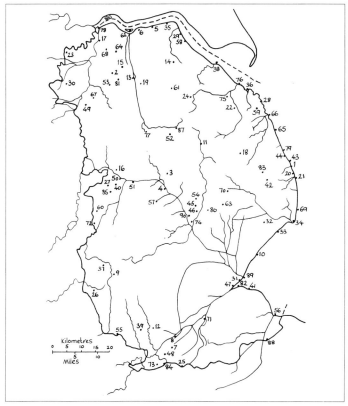

Fig 3. Sites of ornithological interest

Key:

1 Anderby Creek
2 Ashbyville Lake
3 Bardney Forest
4 Bardney Settling Ponds
5 Barrow Haven
6 Barton-on-Humber Pits
7 Baston Common Pits
8 Baston Fen
9 Belton Park
10 Benington Marsh
11 Biscathorpe Fish Pond
12 Bourne Woods
13 Brigg Settling Ponds
14 Brocklesby Park
15 Broughton Woods
16 Burton Pits
17 Burton Stather
18 Burwell Woods
19 Cadney Reservoir
20 Chapel Pit
21 Chapel Point
22 Covenham Reservoir

23 Crowle Waste
24 Croxby Pond
25 Deeping Lake
26 Denton Reservoir
27 Doddington Woods
28 Donna Nook
29 East Halton Pits
30 Epworth Turbary
31 Frampton Marsh
32 Friskney Decoy Wood
33 Friskney Marsh
34 Gibraltar Point
35 Goxhill
36 Grainthorpe Marsh
37 Grantham Sewage Farm
38 Grimsby Docks
39 Grimsthorpe Park
40 Hartsholme Park
41 Holbeach Marsh
42 Hopland's Wood
43 Huttoft Bank
44 Huttoft Pit
45 Kirkby Moor

46 Kirkby-on-Bain Pits
47 Kirton Marsh
48 Langtoft Pits
49 Laughton Common
50 Lincoln Ballast Pit
51 Lincoln Sewage Farm
52 Linwood Warren
53 Messingham Sand Quarries
54 Moor Farm
55 Morkery Woods
56 Nene Mouth
57 Nocton Woods
58 North Killingholme Pits
59 North Somercotes Warren
60 Norton Disney Woods
61 Pelham's Pillar Woods
62 Read's Island
63 Revesby Reservoir
64 Risby Warren
65 Saltfleetby/Theddlethorpe
   N.N.R.
66 Saltfleet Haven
67 Scotton Common

68 Scunthorpe Quarries
69 Seacroft
70 Snipe Dales
71 Spalding Settling Ponds
72 Stapleford Woods
73 Tallington Pits
74 Tattershall Pits
75 Tetney Blow Wells
76 Tetney Marsh
77 Toft Newton Reservoir
78 Trent Falls
79 Trusthorpe Point
80 Tumby Woods
81 Twigmoor
82 Welland Mouth
83 Well Vale
84 West Deeping Pits
85 Whisby Pits
86 Whitton Sands
87 Willingham Forest
88 Wisbech Sewage Farm
89 Witham Mouth
90 Woodhall Spa Pits

33

in relatively small numbers, such as the Heron and Great Crested Grebe. The situation has now changed considerably since the survey into the breeding distribution of all species in the British Isles undertaken by the British Trust for Ornithology during 1968-72. The survey was based on the 10km squares of the National Grid and was an undoubted success. There are 90 grid squares containing parts of Lincolnshire and the daunting task of organising full coverage in the county was ably undertaken by P.J. Wilson. The results have been published in *The Atlas of Breeding Birds in Britain and Ireland* (Sharrock 1976) where the distribution of Lincolnshire breeding species can be studied in detail and compared with the rest of the country. No maps have been reproduced in this work because of the imminent publication of the *Lincolnshire Bird Club Atlas*[i] which will show present distribution in much greater detail, as well as highlighting any changes since the B.T.O. Atlas.

Three categories are shown on the maps; confirmed breeding, probable breeding and possible breeding. Considering only the first two categories, it can be deduced that there were 117 breeding species in the county during the five year period of the B.T.O. survey. It is interesting to examine the extent to which these occupied the county as this will be useful in assessing future trends.

Very widespread species

A total of 41 species bred or probably bred in over 90 per cent of Lincolnshire's 10km squares: Mallard, Red-legged Partridge, Grey Partridge, Pheasant, Moorhen, Lapwing, Stock Dove, Woodpigeon, Turtle Dove, Cuckoo, Swift, Skylark, Swallow, House Martin, Pied Wagtail, Wren, Dunnock, Robin, Blackbird, Song Thrush, Mistle Thrush, Sedge Warbler, Whitethroat, Blackcap, Spotted Flycatcher, Blue Tit, Great Tit, Jackdaw, Rook, Carrion Crow, Starling, House Sparrow, Tree Sparrow, Chaffinch, Greenfinch, Goldfinch, Linnet, Bullfinch, Yellowhammer, Reed Bunting and Corn Bunting. All of these obviously find much suitable habitat in the county and most have quite large populations. Of the above, perhaps only the Lapwing is under any serious threat as more intensive farming methods have gradually reduced the number of safe nesting sites.

Fairly widespread species

A total of 26 species bred or probably bred in from 50-90 per cent of Lincolnshire's 10km squares: Mute Swan, Tufted Duck, Kestrel, Coot, Snipe, Collared Dove, Barn Owl, Little Owl, Tawny Owl, Sand Martin, Meadow Pipit, Yellow Wagtail, Grasshopper Warbler, Reed Warbler, Lesser Whitethroat, Garden Warbler, Chiffchaff, Willow Warbler, Goldcrest, Long-tailed Tit, Willow Tit, Coal Tit, Treecreeper, Jay, Magpie and Redpoll. Many of these are limited from being more widespread only by the lack of suitable habitat in a few areas of the county.

It is interesting to see the Collared Dove in this category after having first bred in the county in 1957. Rapid increases in numbers of Tufted Ducks and Redpolls have put them here after having been previously more local. In a predominantly farming county it is satisfactory to find that the Snipe can still breed over much of the area, although with further drainage the species is likely to continue to decline.

Fairly local species

A total of 30 species bred or probably bred in from 10-50 per cent of Lincolnshire's 10km squares: Little Grebe, Great Crested Grebe, Grey Heron, Canada Goose, Shelduck, Teal, Shoveler, Pochard, Quail, Water Rail, Oystercatcher, Little Ringed Plover, Ringed Plover, Woodcock, Curlew, Redshank, Black-headed Gull, Common Tern, Feral Pigeon, Long-eared Owl, Short-eared Owl, Nightjar, Kingfisher, Green Woodpecker, Great Spotted Woodpecker, Tree Pipit, Nightingale, Redstart, Marsh Tit and Hawfinch. These include several species whose distribution is restricted by the need for specialised habitats such as coast or heathland.

Many of the best of these habitats are now conserved as nature reserves, so that although a few species have very low populations they are in no immediate danger of being lost to the county. Little Ringed Plovers first nested in 1950 and they now occupy most of the suitable gravel pits and quarries in the county.

Very local species

A total of 20 species bred or probably bred in less than 10 per cent of Lincolnshire's 10km squares: Bittern, Greylag Goose, Wigeon, Gadwall, Pintail, Garganey, Montagu's Harrier, Sparrowhawk, Corncrake, Black-tailed Godwit, Sandwich Tern, Little Tern, Lesser Spotted Woodpecker, Black Redstart, Whinchat, Wheatear, Wood Warbler, Bearded Tit, Nuthatch and Red-backed Shrike. Many of these have difficulty in finding suitable conditions for breeding in the county and several do so only irregularly. Little Terns are maintaining their numbers thanks to the strenuous protection at several sites, although breeding success is very low in some years.

It is sad to see the Sparrowhawk in this category as it was once much more widely distributed in the county. A combination of poisonous chemicals and persecution reduced the population to a level from which until very recently it seemed unable to recover. Greylag Geese are now well-established after introductions in the last 20 years. Two other species became established again after absences of over 100 years. Bitterns bred regularly from the 1940s and Bearded Tits from the late 1960s. Both were widespread in the Fens before drainage eliminated all suitable habitat.

Irregular breeding species in the last 50 years

A further 18 species have bred irregularly in the county during the last 50 years: Pink-footed Goose, Barnacle Goose, Egyptian Goose, Mandarin, Scaup, Ruddy Duck, Marsh Harrier, Hobby, Kentish Plover, Dunlin, Common Sandpiper, Herring Gull, Arctic Tern, Woodlark, Grey Wagtail, Stonechat, Siskin and Crossbill. Few of these seem likely to form regular populations due to lack of suitable habitat and the fact that Lincolnshire is outside the normal range of most of them.

Former breeding species

Another 19 species have not bred in the county for over 50 years: Black-necked Grebe, Spoonbill, Red-crested Pochard, Red Kite, Hen Harrier, Goshawk, Buzzard, Merlin, Black Grouse, Spotted Crake, Crane, Great Bustard, Avocet, Stone-curlew, Ruff, Black

Tern, Wryneck, Pied Flycatcher and Raven. A few of these could perhaps breed again given the right conditions. Goshawks could possibly spread from the Midlands to some of the mature conifer forests such as Laughton or Willingham. Avocets have recently increased in Norfolk and there are a few suitable areas for nesting in the Wash and the Humber, where they are now occurring more regularly in spring and summer. The same applies to Ruffs, since they sometimes display in spring in a few areas that appear suitable for breeding.

Despite a total county breeding list of 154 species only just over 100 now do so regularly. This compares rather unfavourably with the 229 species that bred in Britain and Ireland during the period of the Atlas. With ever-increasing conservation efforts in the county, it should be possible to maintain this level, although special measures may be needed to ensure the survival of a few species with only a tenuous hold.

Black Tern — a former breeding species

Explanatory footnote to Part One

i   Due to be published, 1990

Part Two:
A history of birds in Lincolnshire

The county of Lincolnshire is rich in historic architectural and archaeological treasures so it is fitting that many details of its former spectacular avifauna have also survived over the centuries. Until comparatively recently much of the county was wild and uncultivated and a paradise for wildlife. The abundance and variety of birds was often a source of amazement to visitors and some were inspired to record valuable and detailed accounts of their impressions.

Some of these old records have been republished in various recent historical accounts of the county but most remain in rare manuscripts and early books that are often difficult to consult. For this reason many references have been left in their original form and supplemented by explanatory notes in the following historical review. This is intended to give a comprehensive picture of bird life in former times and to show how ornithology has gradually developed in the county until the present time.

St. Guthlac's Birds

Documented accounts of birds in Lincolnshire may be traced back over many hundreds of years. The earliest notes are associated with St. Guthlac who should perhaps be regarded as one of the county's earliest birdwatchers. A few years after the saint's death many interesting anecdotes about his life were recorded by the monk Felix, a modern translation of which has recently been published (Colgrave 1956).

Guthlac was born about 674AD. He spent his early youth as a warrior before entering the monastery at Repton in Derbyshire in order to study the lives of the hermits. This interest led him to seek a similar life and in his search for a wilderness he finally settled in the Fens on the island of Crowland early in the eighth century. Felix's description of the Fens vividly shows the suitability of Guthlac's choice for solitude in the centre of what was England's least inhabited area.

> There is in the midland district of Britain a most dismal fen of immense size, which begins at the banks of the River Granta, not far from the camp which is called Cambridge, and stretches from the south as far north as the sea. It is a very long tract, now consisting of marshes, now of bogs, sometimes of black waters overhung by fog, sometimes studded with wooded islands and traversed by the windings of tortuous streams.

Guthlac soon took an interest in the wild creatures all about him and his ability to tame them is given as an example of his patient character.

> Even the birds of the untamed wilderness came flying to his call and took food from his hand.

Two corvids that lived on the island were a constant nuisance to Guthlac, often entering his house and stealing or breaking objects. Their confiding and mischievous behaviour suggests that they were Jackdaws. When his visitors had some articles stolen by the birds, Guthlac was able to predict that they would be recovered as he knew that the Jackdaws would carry the items only a short distance before dropping them.

On another occasion two Swallows flew singing into his house and perched on his arms. Later they built a nest on a basket that he suspended under the eaves and thereafter the Swallows returned to nest each year. This must surely be one of the earliest instances of an artificial nest site being provided deliberately by man.

St. Hugh's Swan

One of the county's great religious figures, St. Hugh of Avalon, Bishop of Lincoln from 1186 to 1200 was involved in an interesting piece of ornithological history. Although he is best remembered for rebuilding and extending Lincoln Cathedral after devastation caused by an earthquake, the story of his pet swan has also survived the centuries. For details of the event we are indebted to the chronicler Giraldus Cambrensis, who was present in Lincoln during St. Hugh's final years and also wrote his biography. The relevant portions of Giraldus's manuscript were copied by the monk Adam of Eynsham and it is this work which has been translated into English (Douie and Farmer 1961).

Before coming to Lincoln St. Hugh had already gained a reputation as a lover of nature. At Chartreuse in France he tamed the birds and squirrels of the forests so that they would take food from his hand. Later, when at Witham Priory in Somerset, a bird regularly entered his cell and ate food that he provided. This was a *burneta*, a small brown bird, perhaps a Dunnock.

With this background it does not seem particularly remarkable that he should tame a swan so that it followed him around and fed from his hand. However, Giraldus had stressed the initial wildness of the swan which had arrived on the lake at the Bishop's Palace at Stow, near Lincoln in late September 1186. As well as being very large it was also aggressive, driving off and allegedly killing most of the other swans which were resident there. The swan was also of an unfamiliar type as it did not have the usual black knob of swans. Its bill was described as being flat and bright yellow; the head and neck were also yellow and Giraldus later described how the bird would fly about making loud noises. Clearly it was a Whooper Swan and the others were Mute Swans. Ticehurst (1957) regarded this as the earliest account of both species in Britain.

St. Hugh also used to visit Thornholm Priory in Lindsey and there the tits would leave the woods and perch on his arms and head while waiting to be fed.

All the above instances of taming wild birds have interesting parallels today. Feeding small birds by hand in gardens and parks has become a normal practice, although in earlier times it was regarded as something of a miracle. The Wildfowl Trust now undertakes regular mass feeding of Bewick's Swans on the Ouse Washes in Norfolk and at Slimbridge in Gloucestershire and the swans have become completely unafraid of the people who feed them.

Cranes and other birds as food

King John's association with Lincolnshire is most often remembered because of his disastrous last journey in the Wash when the baggage train carrying his valuables was swept away by the tide during a crossing of the River Nene. Other visits to the county were less unhappy, however, as they provided him with the opportunity to indulge in his favourite pastime of hawking. Spectacular sport was enjoyed by flying at Cranes with his Gyrfalcons which he had received as a present from King Philip of Norway. On one visit in about 1212, he took no less than nine Cranes with his Gyrs and 'in the joy of his heart regaled the poor in the neighbourhood with bread, meat and ale'. (Harting 1882).

Cranes and several other large birds of the marshes were highly esteemed as sources of food. Abundant supplies were taken from the Fenland areas of Lincolnshire and illustrations of this exploitation were contained in the list of provisions ordered by Henry III for various royal feasts (Ticehurst, 1934). In both 1249 and 1251 the Prior of Spalding and the Abbot of Crowland were asked to provide as many swans, Cranes, Heronshaws, Bitterns and wildfowl as might be obtained. Also for Christmas 1251 the sheriff and bailiff of Lincoln had to supply among other items 30 Cranes, 40 swans, 300 Partridges and 80 Pheasants.

On a smaller scale, but of equal interest, details of presents given to notable figures by Lincoln Corporation are recorded in the minute books of the Council (Lincolnshire Archives):

1537, 29th January Itm itt is agreed that mr mare & his bredern schall meite the Duke grace off Norffolk & gyff hym a present off two Craynes, two Swannes and two Pykys.

1548, 15th March And that ther was geven this yere for a present to the Duchysse of Suffolk & to the Duke hir son of the costs of the comen chambre, by the assent of the mayr & his brethern & diverse of the comen councell, that is to sey ij Cranes and iiij Swannes, and to therle of Rutland, iij Signetts, vj Bytters[i] & xvj Knotts.

1552, 9th June Tht is agreid in this secret councell that the Duke his grace of Northumberland schall have for a present of this cytye at his cumyng of the charge of the comen chambre iiij Cranes, sex Signetts, vj Bytters, xij Godwytts, ij dosen Knotts, ij grett Pykes, ij gret Breames & ij grett Tenches and ij persons schalbe sent into the countreys to provide the seid present and ther costs to be born of the comens.

1554, 20th July Itm it is agreid that the Quenes Attorney schall have a present of this cytye of ij Cranes and iiij Signetts and that the beror shall have mr recordors lettre wt hym & his present also.

1568, 22nd December Itm wher as mr recordor hath of late taiken paynes for the busines of this citie with certen of the Quenes maties privye counsellors, therefore it is agreid that he schall have a present against Crystmas next to be sent unto hym of ij ffatt Swannes or j ffatt Swan & a ffatt tyrkye cock of the charge of the comen chambre.

A similar example given by Thompson (1856) was taken from the Boston Corporation minute books:

1597 To be sent to the Lord Treasurer as a present, 1 dozen godwights, 5 dozen knots, and 1 dozen of puets[ii], at the Corporation's charge.

Some early attempts at conservation were made in 1534 when an act to avoid the destruction of wildfowl was introduced (Harting 1882). This prohibited:

...the taking of the eggs of any kind of wildfowl between the beginning of March and the end of June, under pain of imprisonment and a fine of twenty pence for every egg of Crane or Bustard, eight pence for eggs of Bittour[i], Heroune and Shovelard[iii] and a penny for the eggs of Mallard, Teal or any other wildfowl.

There is no doubt that Cranes bred in the Fens and Turner in 1544 claimed to have seen their young, although he may have been referring to Cambridgeshire. Evidence of them having bred in Lincolnshire is provided in local Fen laws of 1548 quoted by Thompson (1856).

No man to bring up any Cranebirds out of the East Fen unless he has witness thereof.

Mute Swans

A frequent source of food used to be the Mute Swan which could be bred in semi-captivity and produced large numbers of young. Although free-flying swans were regarded as the property of the Crown, many people kept pinioned birds on private lakes and engraved distinctive patterns on the birds' bills. Sometimes swans were stolen and there were often disputes over ownership. Attempts to solve these cases were made by special courts called Swan-motes, founded in the fifteenth century. In order to restrict swan ownership to people above a certain standing, the statute of 22 Edward IV was passed in 1483. This considerably upset the common people of Crowland who made their living from swans and other wildfowl as they were unable to grow crops in the marshes and fens which surrounded the town. However, they were given exemption from the act when they successfully appealed to the King (Ticehurst 1934):

... that all youre seid subgietts, inhabitaunts of Croyland aforeseid, by tyme out of mynde, have contynually used to have and occupie in the fennes and marche ther, greate games of Swannes of ther owne, by the whiche the greateste parte of ther relyf and lyvyng hath been susteyened in longe tyme passed, as is well knowen, the whiche games of Swannes, if by reason of the seid Acte shuld not be from hensforth occupied and had by the seid inhabitaunts, as they herebefore tyme used to have, shulde cause utter povertee and destruction of the seid inhabitaunts ther, forasmuche as the seid towne of Croyland standeth all in mersshe and fenne, and noon arable land nor pasture about it, soo that few or noon other profitts may or can be founde in the precincte of that towne, to the relyf of the seid inhabitaunts ther.

The swans, given as a present by Lincoln Corporation, were probably obtained from one of the several large pools within the city boundary. One of these, now drained, was called Swan-pool and some birds were likely to have been kept on Brayford Pool, which even today has one of the largest concentrations of swans in the county. The City had been granted rights to all stray swans within its boundaries by the charter of Richard III in 1484 (Birch 1911).

And that the same mayor and citizens, their heirs and successors aforesaid, for ever have treasure trove, waif and estray within the said county of the city aforesaid.

A council minute in 1520 shows how they intended to take advantage of this right.

1520, October Also it is agreid tht mr mayer & the privy concell off this citie schalhave auctorytye to elect & chese anable person to have the oversight wtin the presynct off this citie ffor sutch Swannes as be streyes & not knowne the owner, so tht all such Swannes may be takyn to thuse off mayster mayer & comyns accordyng to the Kynges graunt by hys chartur confirmyd.

At first the corporation may not have bothered with a swan-mark although perhaps to enable them to identify any lost along the rivers, it was later decided to obtain one, as recorded in the minute book:

1570, June 13 "Itm it is agreid tht a Swan marke schalbe bought for the corporation of this citie of Thomas Wynterborn, which was lately Wm Yatt's alderman deceased.

Thus in the sixteenth century the ownership and marking of swans had become more organised. Suitable parts of the county were divided into areas under the control of a Royal Deputy who kept a list of marks and their owners on a Swan Roll. Several of these Rolls still exist and one at Fulford Hall, Yorkshire covered the Lincolnshire coast marsh district in 1650. Another relating to the Fens in Elizabethan times contains the marks of many Lincolnshire owners (Lincolnshire Archives). Attached to these rolls were detailed lists of regulations concerning the marking of swans and penalties for failing to comply with them. Some of the earliest regulations were drawn up for the River Witham in 1524 and Sir Joseph Banks read a copy of these before the Royal Society in 1810. The 18 points listed are of interest not only for the details of marking but also for the bye-laws which in effect made the River Witham a conservation area. The penalties, which have been omitted from the following list, ranged from 3s 4d to £5.

The true copy of a Parchment Roll, touching the Swannery, delivered to me, W. Monson, by Mr. Matthew Nayler, now Officer thereof, under Mr. Secretary, this June, 1570, 12th Elizabeth.

1. These are the Ordinances made 24th day of May, in the 15th year of the reign of our Sovereign Lord King Henry the 8th (1524), by the Lord Sir Christopher Wylluby, Sir Edward Dimock, Mr. Goderycke, Robert Barrett, Pryor of Bardnay, Mr. Cleston, Mr. Penyngton, and other Justices of the Peace, and Commissioners, appointed by our Sovereign Lord the King, for the confirmation and the preservation of his Highness' game of swans, and signets, of his stream of Witham, within his County of Lincoln, with all other cryckes, or syckes, or diches, that do ascend, or descend, to, or from the said stream of Witham, viz. from a Breges, called Boston Breges, unto the head of the said stream, with all other moats, pounds and diches, within the said County, within the compass of the said stream, and in the parties of Kestevan, of whose grounds soever they be, either Lords Spiritual, or Temporal, or other of the King's subjects, of what degree soever they be of: and also for the keeping of the game of his Lords Spiritual and Temporal, and other of his subjects, that have swans and signets on the same stream, or waters, and the liberties thereof, or franchises of the same, and also for the conservation of fishing, or fowling with any nets, or dogs, or for laying of any dunings, or oyes, or nets, or for setting of lime twigs, or any other engine of the same stream, or waters, or within the liberties of the same, or for making of fish garths, or for making of pits or pounds for steping of hemp or flax, in the same stream or waters, whereby the said stream or waters may be corrupted, otherwise than as appointed by law, or statutes of this realm.

2. ... No person or persons having swans or signets, on or upon the said streams or water, or the liberties of the same, shall appoint or set no Swannerd for to row for him, or them, without the assent of the King's Swannerd, or his Deputy.

3. ... If the King's Swannerd doth mislike of the said Swannerd at any time, then it shall be lawful for the King's Swannerd for to discharge him and put him out presently, without any warning, and the King's Swannerd to appoint one to row for his masters, and the same Swannerd for to have the same fees that the other should have had, so that the King's Swannerd let his master know what was the cause of the same ...

4. ... The King's Swannerd, nor the Company, shall not go a rowing for to mark no signets, before the Monday after the feast of St. John Baptist (June 25th to July 1st) in every year ...

5. ... The King's Swannerd, or his Deputy, shall give warning unto the rest of the Swanners, when that be, or his Deputy will go a rowing, and what day or place they shall meet him or them for to go a merkinge, or foredrawing of any other swans, or signets, at any time within the year ...

6. ... The King's Swannerd, or his Deputy, shall keep one swan book, and that he shall not inroll no new merke, for no person, without the owner of the merke have freehold, according to the statute, and not without the counsell of two or three of the company besides, and he shall look that the mark shall not hurt no other mark in the book, and that the King's Swannerd shall not give or sell to no person, or persons, any mark that is within his book whether there be swans of the same mark or no, without it be the heir or next of kin ...

7. ... No Swannerd shall keep, or carry any swan book, but the King's Swannerd or his Deputy ...

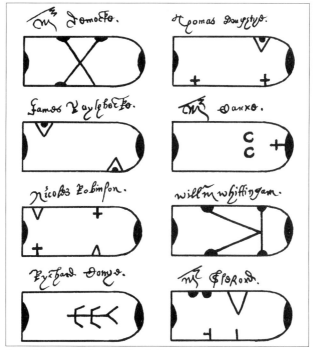

fig 4. Swan marks from the Banks' Roll

8 ... The King's Swannerd or his Deputy, shall have a book of the name of every Swannerd, and his masters, and so shall inroll in this same book every swan that is marked, and of what mark, and who is the owner of the swan mark, and that no Swannerd shall row for no masters, than his named within the same book, and that no Swannerd shall have no more masters than three, or four at the most ...

9 ... If the King's Swannerd, or his company, meet with any swans that hath young and no Swannerd for them and the mark in the book, then the company shall have one, and mark the rest after the sire and the dam, but if their mark be not in the King's book then all the signets shall be seized for the King, and if the Company find any flying swans, after the time of marking it shall be seized unto the King ...

10 ... After the King's Swannerd, and his Company, meet with any swans blounder mark, or double mark, they shall be seized for the King, until the Company have tried it; but if they have young, they shall be marked for the King, and the swanners shall not depart from the swan, until it be tried who hath the right unto her, and if they cannot try who owns her, the King's Swannerd shall set the King's mark on her ...

11 ... After the King's Swannerd and his Company begin to mark, there shall be no Swannerd depart away, or put by any swans from marking, unto the time the King's Swannerd have done ...

12 ... No Swannerd shall take any swans for his masters, after the time of marking, nor before the King's Swannerd or his Deputy, and one other Swannerd, or else two or three Swanners, and one or two other men that is the owner of swans with them ...

13 ... All Swanners shall have free power to go into all waters, ponds, moats, fenns, or marshes, for to breed or feed, in what corporation or liberty soever it be, Lords Spiritual or Temporal, or any other of the King's subjects, without hurt or trouble, of the same swans, or breaking of their nests, or stealing of their eggs, or killing them with bow or gun, or dog or any other engine, by day, or by night ...

14 ... No fisher, or other man that hath ground butting on any waters or stream, where swans may breed, or of custom have bred, shall mow, shear, or cut any thackets, reed or grass, within 40 feet of the swans nest or within 40 feet of the stream ...

15 ... The King's Swannerd of the stream of Witham, shall have free power and liberty to go with two or three of the Company, into any river, pond, or moats, within the County of Lincoln, or not, to look for swans, so that he or they give knowledge unto the King's Swannerd of the same country or waters, without hurt or trouble of any of the King's subjects in any wise notwithstanding ...

16 ... No persons shall hawk, nor hunt, fish with dogs, or set nets, or snares, or engines, for no fish, or fowl, in the daytime, or shoot in hand gun, or crossbow, between the feast of Philip and James, and the feast of Lammas (May 1st to August 1st) ...

17 ... No hemp or flax shall be steeped in any running water, nor within 40 feet of the water, nor any other filthy thing be thrown into running waters, whereby the waters may be corrupt, or no man to encroach on the running water, whereby the waters may be hurt ...

18 ... The King's Swannerd, or his Deputy, shall have full power and strength, for to view and search for all such offences, at all times, as he thinks meet for the same, and for such faults as is within these presents, and made by our law, found by them or any other person, that doth complain unto them of the same, it shall be lawful for the King's Swannerd to seize, and strain for the forfeitures of the same, and keep it to the King's use; and if any person or persons do present the same offence unto the King's Swannerd, he shall have the one moiety, the King or his Deputy the other moiety.

Some of the swan-marks reproduced from the Banks Roll show the variety of patterns employed to distinguish the many different owners *(fig 4)*. In his researches of the various Rolls still existing, Ticehurst (1957) was able to identify no less than 550 marks belonging to Lincolnshire people.

By the eighteenth century, the practice of marking swans had more or less died out although there is a reference to it in the Spalding Gentlemen's Society Minutes for 17th November, 1748. This recalls what may have been the last marking of cygnets in the Spalding area about 1710.

Camden's Britannia

A detailed description of Lincolnshire in the sixteenth century appeared in William Camden's *Britannia*, first published in 1586. This contained a brief section on the spectacular avifauna of the county, quoted below from Holland's first English translation, published in 1610.

All this Tract-over at certaine seasons, good God, what store of foules (to say nothing of fishes) is heere to be found! I meane, not those vulgar birds which in other places are highly esteemed and beare a great price, as Teales, Quailes, Woodcocks, Phesants, Partridges etc but such, as we have no Latin names for, the very delicate dainties, indeed, of service, meates for the Demigods, and greatly sought for by these that love the tooth so well, I meane, Puitts, Godwitts, Knotts, that is to say, Canutus or Knouts birds, (for out of Denmarke they are thought to fly thither), Dotterells, so named for their dotish foolishnesse, which being a kind of birds as it were of any apish kind, ready to imitate what they see done, are caught by candlelight according to foulers gesture, if he put forth an arm, so they also stretch out a wing: sets he forward his legge, or holdeth up his head, they likewise doe theirs: in brief, what ever the fouler doth, the same also doth this foolish bird untill it be hidden within the net. But these things I leave to their observation, who either takes pleasure earnestly to hunt after Nature's workes, or being borne for to pamper the belly delight to send their estates downe the throat.

And from a section on Crowland:

... yet the most gainful trade they have is by taking fish, and catching water foule, and that is so great, that in the moneth of August, they will spred a net and at once drawe three thousand mallards and wild ducks and such like together: and these pooles or watery plots of theirs, they use to terme their corne fields: for, they see no corne growing in five miles any way. In regard of this their taking of fish and foule they paid yeerely in times past to the Abbot, as now they doe to the King, three hundred pounds of our money.

This figure for the number of moulting ducks caught was no exaggeration, but truly reflected the vast numbers of wildfowl inhabiting the Fens, as confirmed by a note in the Spalding gentlemen's Society minutes for 20th June, 1728:

> Mr Stevens told the Soc. that the Duckers this day toke at one draught or push into a Nett one hundred and fifty five dozen (1,860) of Mallards, at their General Ducking in Deeping Fenn.

A grand total of 13,032 ducks were taken there in the three days of 20th, 21st, and 29th June.

Ruffs at Crowle

A remarkable pamphlet published in 1586 contained the first printed illustration *(fig 5)* and description of Ruffs made from live specimens obtained in Lincolnshire. Apparently this constituted the first British account of the species, as well as being the first time the title Ruff had been applied to *Philomachus pugnax* (Mullens 1919).

...In the yeare of our Lord God 1586, within the parish of Crowley nere adjoyning to the pastures of the Lordship of Hatfild in the Countie of Lyncolne, one Richard Wallar, and Richard Preston, of the same parish of Crowley, having set certaine Lime-twigges intangled and caught in the same seven great Foules, all of one bignes, & of intermixt coloures: the like whereof were never seen or heard of in any Countrie, by any man having hitherto seene them or their pictures: which being lively in their true colours purtrayed by one Blackborne a Paynter in Yorke, at the procurement of the right Worshipfull Sir Henry Lee Knight, are diversly amongst divers persons dispersed. Three of the same foules were brought and presented to the same Sir Henry Lee, then lying at his brother's house at Hatfild in Yorkshire.

Fig 5. Sixteenth century drawing of a Ruff at Crowle

The Fethers on their heads and fronts grewe and stood out, not unlike to the frysled haire of men and women: and the Fethers about their necke, being of divers coloures, grew and stood up very high, even, and formally like unto great Ruffes: and were hilde up with stiff quilles, as it were Wyers or Supporters, such as are now commonly used of our Gallants. These Foules going loose, seemed so careless of their libertie and to escape, that (though threatened by shaking and shoving with the handes, or otherwise) they woulde not shrinke from, or shunne any person: retayning still as it were one and the same countenaunce, their use was all three in rankwise and with great statelines to walke divers turnes up and downe in the Hall, and then eftsoones to stay and drawe all their heades and billes together. Standing so a long time, as it were in consultation or counsell of some weightie matter, and then to fall againe to walking, refusing to take, and not seeming to make any account of any meate, which they were oftentimes offered. In this order they continued until all three dyed one after another, about three days after their taking. When they were dead not any man with both his handes could scarse stirre one of their fethers about their neckes. Divers Foulers were sent for to see them, but neither could they tel what Foules they were, or ever had seene or hearde of the like...

Drayton's Poly-Olbion

Early in the seventeenth century another detailed description of the county was published as part of the *Poly-Olbion*, an account in verse of the counties of England and Wales. Written by Michael Drayton (1613-22), the verses may seem rather quaint but closer examination shows them to contain a surprising amount of information on the natural history of the county. Many birds are mentioned and most species are readily identifiable from Drayton's descriptions and details of behaviour. The account could only have been written with a comprehensive knowledge of the avifauna of the various parts of the county, as can be seen from the following sections on birds.

The part referring to Holland deals mainly with the Fens and the Wash:

My various Fleets for Fowle, O who is he can tell,
The species that in me for multitude excell!
The Duck, and Mallard first, the Falconer's onely sport,
(Of River-flights the chiefe, so that all other sort,
They onely Green-Fowle terme) in every Mere abound,
That you would thinke they sate upon the very ground,
Their numbers be so great, the waters covering quite,
That rais'd, the spacious ayre is darkened with their flight;
Yet still the dangerous Dykes, from shot do them secure,
Where they from Flash to Flash, like the full Epicure
Waft, as they lov'd to change their Diet every meale;
And neare to them ye see the lesser dibling Teale
In Bunches, with the first that flie from Mere to Mere,
As they above the rest were lords of Earth and Ayre.
The Gossander with them, my goodly Fennes do show
His head as Ebon blacke, the rest as white as Snow,
With whom the Widgeon goes, the Golden-eye, the Smeath[iv],
And in odde scattred pits, the Flags and Reeds beneath,
The Coot, bald, else cleane black, that whitenesse it doth bear
Upon the forehead star'd, the Water-Hen doth weare
Upon her little tayle, in one small feather set.
The Water-Woosell[v] next, all over black as jeat,
With various colours, black, greene, blew, red, russet, white,
Doe yeeld the gazing eye as variable delight,
As doe those sundry Fowles, whose severall plumes they be.
The diving Dob-chick, here among the rest you see,
Now up, no downe againe, that hard it is to prove,
Whether under water most it liveth, or above:
With which last little Fowle, (that water may not lacke,
More than the the Dob-chick doth, and more doth love the brack,)
The Puffin[vi] we compare, which coming to the dish,
Nice pallats hardly judge, if it be flesh or fish,
But wherefore should I stand upon such toyes as these,
That have so goodly Fowles, the wandring eye to please.
Here in my vaster Pooles, as white as Snow or Milke,
(In water blacke as Stix,) swimmes the Swanne, the Ilke[vii],
of Hollanders so tearm'd, no niggard of his breath,
(As Poets say of Swannes, who only sing in death)
But oft as other Birds, is heard his tunnes to roat,
Which like a Trumpet comes, from his long arched throat,
And tow'rds this wat'ry kind, about the Flashes brimme,
Some cloven-footed are, by nature not to swimme.
There stalks the stately Crane, as tho' he march'd in warre,
By him that hath the Herne[viii], which (by the Fishy Carre)
Can fetch with their long necks, out of the Rush and Reed,
Snigs, Fry, and yellow Frogs, whereon they often feed;
And under them againe, (that water never take,
But by some Ditches' side, or little shallow Lake
Lie dabling night and day) the pallet-pleasing Snite[ix],

The Bidcocke[x], and like them the Redshanke, that delight
Together still to be, in some small Reedy bed,
In which these little Fowles in Summers time were bred.
The Buzzing Bitter sits, which through his hollow Bill,
A sudden bellowing sends, which many times doth fill
The neighbouring Marsh with noyse, as though a Bull did roare;
But scarcely have I yet recited half my store:
And with my wondrous flocks of Wild-Geese come I then,
Which look as though alone they peopled all the Fen.
Which here in Winter time, when all is overflow'd,
And want of sollid sward inforceth them abroad,
Th'abundance then is seene, that my full Fennes do yeeld,
That almost through the Isle, do pester every field,
The Barnacles with them, which wheresoere they breed,
On Trees, or rotten Ships, yet to my Fennes for feed
Continually they come, and chief abode do make,
And very hardly force'd my plenty to forsake:
Who almost all this kind doe challenge as mine owne,
Whose like, I dare averre, is elsewhere hardly knowne.
For sure, unlesse in me, noone yet ever saw
The multitudes of Fowle, in Mooting time they draw,
From which to many a one, much profit doth accrue.
Now such as flying feed, next these I must pursue;
The Sea-meaw[xi], Sea-pye[xii], Gull and Curlew heere do keepe,
As searching every Shole and watching every deepe,
To find the floating Fry, with their sharpe-pearcing sight,
Which suddenly they take, by stouping from their height,
The Cormorant then comes, (by his devouring kind)
Which flying o'r the Fen, imediately doth find
The Fleet best stor'd of Fish, when from his wings at full,
As though he shot himselfe into the thicned skull,
He under water goes, and so the Shole pursues,
Which into Creeks doe flie, when quickly he doth chuse
The Fin that likes him best, and rising, flying feeds.
The Ospray oft here seene, though seldom here it breeds,
Which over them the Fish no sooner do espie,
But (betwixt him and them, by an antipathy)
Turning their bellies up, as though their death they saw,
They at his pleasure lye, to stuff his glutt'nous maw.
The toyling Fisher here is tewing of his Net:
The Fowler is imployed his lymed twigs to set.
One underneath his Horse, to get a shoot doth stalke,
Another over Dykes upon his Stilts doth walke:

The description of Lindsey includes birds that would be found in the Isle of Axholme, the Wolds and on the River Humber.

For neere this batning Isle in me is to be seene,
More than on any earth, the Plover gray, and greene,
The Corne-land loving Quayle, the daintiest of our bits,
The Rayle, which seldome comes, but upon Rich mens spits:
The Puet, Godwit, Stint, the pallat that allure,
The Miser and doe make a wastfull Epicure:
The Knot, that called was Canutus Bird of old;
Of that great King of Danes, his name that still doth hold,
His appetite to please, that farre and neere was sought,

For him (as some have sayd) from Denmarke hither brought:
The Dotterell, which we thinke a very daintie dish,
Whose taking makes such sport, as man no more can wish;
For as you creepe or cowre, or lye, or stoupe, or goe,
So marking you (with care) the Apish bird doth doe,
And acting every thing, doth never marke the Net,
Till he be in the Snare, which men for him have set.
The big-boon'd Bustard then, whose body beares that size,
That he against the wind must runne, e're he can rise:
The Shovler[iii], which so shakes the ayre with saily wings,
That ever as he flyes you still would thinke he sings,
These Fowles, with other Soyles, although they frequent be,
Yet are they found most sweet and delicate in me.

Spoonbills nesting in the Fens

Among the more spectacular of fenland birds, Spoonbills bred in Britain until the seventeenth century, so it is interesting to find evidence that they did so in Lincolnshire. Dugdale's treatise on the history of drainage of the Fens (1772) included a map of South Holland dated 1662. Unusually for such a map, a wood near Crowland was marked as:

Dousdale Holt where many White Herons do breed..

That these were indeed Spoonbills is confirmed by Charleton, writing in 1668. He listed alternative names for Spoonbill as Spoonbill'd Heron and White Heron, *Ardea alba*.

Ray and Willughby

One of the earliest books on the status of birds in Britain was Ray's *The Ornithology of Francis Willughby* published in 1678. This was based mainly on Willughby's observations, but Ray included some of his own notes and there are several interesting references to Lincolnshire.

Crane — common in the Fens of Lincolnshire ...
... They often come to us in England: And in the Fen-Countries in Lincolnshire and Cambridgeshire there are great flocks of them, but whether or no they breed in England I cannot certainly determine, either of my own knowledge, or from the relation of any credible person...
Knot — About the beginning of Winter they are said to come into Lincolnshire, where they continue two or three months about the Sea-shores, and away again. They fly in flocks. Being fed with the white bread and milk they grow very fat, and are accounted excellent meat. King Knout is reported to have been so fond of them, that from him they got the name of Knots or Knouts.
Ruff — They breed in Summertime in the Fens of Lincolnshire and Crowland. They are fattened with white bread and milk, like Knots, being shut up in close dark rooms: For let in but the light upon them, presently they fall a fighting, never giving over till one hath killed the other, especially if any body stand by. The Fowlers when they see them intent upon fighting, spread their Nets over them, and catch them before they be aware.

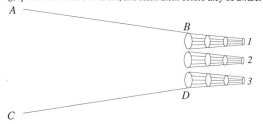

Fig 6. Plan of nets for catching moulting ducks

Black Diver or Scoter — In the Wash in Lincolnshire it is found plentifully.

Shoveler — In one which Mr.Willughby saw at Crowland, the head was very dark, lightly tinctured with a deep shining green.

Mallard — In the Fens in the Isle of Ely, Norfolk, and Lincolnshire, about Crowland and elsewhere, Ducks, Wigeons, Teal and other birds of this kind, at what time they moult their feathers and cannot fly, are taken yearly in great numbers in Nets placed after this manner. *(fig 6)*

AB, CD are nets extending a great length in form of a wall or hedge, inclining to one another, at the further end of which, before they concur in an angle are placed 1,2,3 or more conoideal Nets, like tunnelling Nets for Partridges. Which things being so prepared, and the day for fowling set, there is a great concourse of men and boats. These drive the Birds, now unable to fly, into the grounds enclosed in the nets with long Staves and Poles, and so by degrees into those Conoideal Tunnels, 1,2,3 disposed, as we said in the angle. By the way many are knocked down by the boatmen and other rabble with their poles, others and more are driven upon the side nets AB, CD. These belong to them who own the nets (for the nets for the most part have several owners) those fall to their shares that killed them. Those which are cooped up, and driven into the end tunnels 1,2,3 , belong to the Lord of the Soil. To one fowling sometimes you shall have four hundred boats meet. We have heard that there have been four thousand Mallards taken at one driving in Deeping Fen.

Our countrymen (imitating, as I suppose, the low Dutch, who were authors of the invention) in maritime and fenny places, in Pools prepared by a new artifice and fitted with their channels and nets, and stored with coy-ducks, take yearly in the winter-time duck and Mallard, Wigeon, Teal, and other birds of the duck-kind in great numbers.

A place is to be chosen for this purpose far remote from common high-ways, and all noise of people, and in which those birds are wont in great numbers to frequent. Having pitched upon a convenient place, prepare a large pool A, set round with willows and reeds *(fig 7)*. On the north side N, or the south side S of this pool draw as many ditches or channels I,I,I, (Pipes they call them) as you, please or think needful; let them be broad at the pool, and by degrees narrower till they end in a point. Along these channels on each side at little distances thrust into the banks rods or

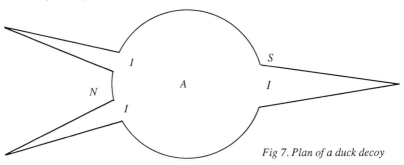

Fig 7. Plan of a duck decoy

wands of wood, and bending them over-head bind them together by pairs all along in form of an arch or vault from the beginning of the channel to the end. As the channels grow narrower so the bows are made lower and lower. The poles thus bent in fashion of bows are to be covered with nets cast over them, and so the pipes are made. These arches or vaults end in long cylindrical nets kept strecht by hoops like bow-nets, that end which respects the arch being open, the other shut.

Ray also described in detail the methods by which the wild ducks were enticed onto the pools by the use of tame coy-ducks. The mouth of each pipe was baited with hemp seed and the ducks were gradually driven into the funnel trap by the fowler and his dog.

Lincolnshire duck decoys

The first decoys were constructed in England about 1650 and the vast Lincolnshire marshes and fens provided ideal sites for such devices. Moulting ducks could only be rounded up in summer, but the new method enabled large numbers of wildfowl to be captured from the huge wintering population.

At least 40 decoys existed in the county and much of the catch was sent to London markets. Records only exist for a few decoys but it is probable that at their peak in the eighteenth century, a total of between 100,000 and 200,000 ducks was taken each winter. Drainage of the Fens caused most decoys to be abandoned early in the nineteenth century, although a few struggled on with diminishing yields before they became uneconomical.

Details of many of the Lincolnshire decoys are given in Payne-Gallway's *Book of Duck Decoys* (1886) and the sites of some of them are shown on old maps of the county, such as Bryant's (1828) and Greenwood's (1830). Traces of some of them still exist today, although in most cases the only link with the past is the retention of the name Decoy Farm. However, one or two ponds have survived and at a few sites the decoys

Key:

1 Keadby
2 Ashby
3 Twigmoor
4 Broughton
5 North Kelsey
6 Freshney Bog
7 Farlesthorpe
8 South Carlton
  and Burton
9 Skellingthorpe
10 Nocton
11 Timberland
12 North Kyme
13 South Kyme
14 Sempringham (4),
  Aslackby and
  Dowsby
15 Deeping (5) and
  Bourne
16 Cowbit
17 Fleet
18 Leake
19 Wrangle (3)
20 Friskney (5) and
  Wainfleet (2)
21 Hagnaby

Fig 8. Sites of duck decoys and fenland areas in Lincolnshire

have become woods, characterised by their regular shapes.

The location of all known Lincolnshire decoys is shown in *fig 8*, which also shows the extent of the Fens before drainage. Grid references given in the following list are as accurate as possible although in a few instances they are only the site of the decoy farm.

In the north west of the county, the only decoy in the Isle of Axholme was at Keadby (SE 820120). According to Stonehouse it was still being worked in 1839. Just across the River Trent one of the most successful decoys was that at Ashby (SE 866081). Traces of it still remain today and it was the last decoy to be operated in the county. When Cordeaux visited it in 1882 the catch was still averaging about 3,000 ducks each season and the owner, Mr. Tacey, informed him that in one recent winter he had taken over 6,000 birds. A previous owner, Captain Healy, kept detailed records for the 35 winters from 1833-4 to 1867-8. A total of 95,836 ducks was caught during this period, an average of over 2,700 each winter, and in two years over 6,000 birds were trapped. Most of these were Mallard (48,664) and Teal (44,568) with smaller numbers of Shoveler (285), Pintail (278) and Gadwall (22). The success of this decoy when most others had long since failed was no doubt due to its proximity to the River Trent and the Humber. Others in the same general area were at Twigmoor (SE 940060), in the Ancholme Carrs at Broughton (SE 978111), where a wood still exists on the site, and at North Kelsey (TF 025995).

In the Marsh district between the Wolds and the sea there were only two decoys. One of these was in Freshney Bog (TA 235085) near Great Coates and the other in Farlesthorpe Fen (TF 487752) near Alford.

Three decoys were situated in the Trent Valley just west of Lincoln. Two of these at South Carlton (SK 932755) and Burton (SK 943746) were owned by Lord Monson. The association of the area with wildfowl continues today since the attractive Burton gravel pits almost on the site of the old decoy are leased by the Trust from the present Lord Monson. The decoy at Skellingthorpe (SK 942717) may have been one of the oldest in the county and a pond still exists on the site. An interesting document in the Lincolnshire Archives shows that the decoy was leased to Humphrey Wilkinson in 1693 for 21 years at an annual rent of £16-10s. At the end of the period he was obliged to:

> reasonably and quietly leave, surrender and yield upp (the decoy) so well and sufficiently repaired ... together with twenty drakes and fourscore tame ducks as are sufficiently taught and instructed to come into the pipes of the said decoy.

Another document records the lease of Skellingthorpe decoy to the Rt. Hon. John Lord Monson in 1783 at a yearly rent of £10. It ceased to be worked about 1840.

The majority of Lincolnshire decoys were situated around the edge of the great fen which comprised almost the whole of the south-eastern part of the county. Four decoys were in the fens bordering the River Witham between Lincoln and Boston. These were at Nocton Fen (TF 093653), Timberland (TF 174594), North Kyme (TF 183527) and South Kyme (TF 198480). South Kyme is mentioned in poems written by William Hall who lived in the fens during the second half of the eighteenth century. These give an interesting impression of life in the fens and the following extracts are quoted from

Payne-Gallway (1886).

> Born in a coy, and bred in a mill,
> Taught water to grind, and Ducks for to kill;
> Seeing Coots clapper claw, lying flat on their backs,
> Standing upright to row, and crowning of jacks;
> Laying spring nets for to catch Ruff and Reeve,
> Stretched out in a boat with a shade to deceive.
> Taking Geese, Ducks, and Coots, with nets upon stakes,
> Riding in a calm day for to catch moulted drakes;
> Gathering eggs to the top of one's wish,
> Cutting tracks in the flags for decoying of fish.

> Pray, sirs, consider, had you been
> Bred where whole winters nothing's seen
> But naked floods for miles and miles,
> Except a boat the eye beguiles;
> Or Coots, in clouds, by Buzzards teaz'd.
> Your ear with seeming thunder seiz'd
> From rais'd decoy, — there Ducks on flight,
> By tens of thousands darken light;

> Kyme God knows,
> Where no corn grows,
> Nothing but a little hay,
> And the water comes,
> And takes it all away.
> Where Ducks by scores travers'd the Fens,
> Coots, Didappers[xiii], Rails, Water-hens,
> Combined with eggs, to charge our pot
> Two furlongs circle round the spot.
> Fowl, fish all kinds the table grac'd,
> All caught within the self same space;
> As time revolv'd, in season fed,
> The surplus found us salt and bread;
> Your humble servant, now your penman,
> Liv'd thus a simple, full-bred Fen-man.

Further south was a group of four decoys situated close together in Sempringham Fen (TF 142324, TF 144323, TF 149328 and TF 158324) with others nearby at Aslackby (TF 141310) and Dowsby (TF 134300). It seems likely that such closely grouped decoys belonged to one owner and were so placed in order to increase their catching efficiency. Birds disturbed from one decoy would be likely to drop onto one of those nearby. In any event Dowsby decoy was very successful for records show that 13,180 ducks were taken between 1st October 1765 and 1st April 1766 and sold for 7s. a dozen.

In the south of the county, there was a group of five decoys in Deeping Fen (TF 180210, TF 180208, TF 184204, TF 195198 and TF 176187) and one nearby in Bourne Fen (TF 168205). Others in this area were at Cowbit (TF 264195) and in Fleet Fen (TF 358165), the latter being destroyed by the construction of the South Holland drain in 1793. The remaining decoys were all situated around the edge of the East Fen. One was at Leake (TF 385539), three at Wrangle (TF 428562, TF 424558 and TF 422548), five at Friskney (TF 437565, TF 449569, TF 453575, TF 464576 and TF 464572), two at

Wainfleet (TF 440579 and TF 444577) and one at Hagnaby (TF 437608). Pennant in 1768 stated that ten of these decoys had recently sent a total of 31,200 ducks to the London markets in one winter. Traces of several of the decoys exist in some of the woods in the Friskney area. One of them is now a Trust reserve (TF 464572) and its pond has been partially re-excavated. The decoy was owned by several members of the Skelton family (a famous name in decoy construction and operation) and was once one of the most successful in the county, producing about 7,000 ducks in a good season. By 1866 the total had declined to 1,100 and the decoy ceased to be worked after 1878.

The Spalding Gentlemen's Society

The formation of the Spalding Gentlemen's Society early in the eighteenth century provided an opportunity for the commencement of what may be described as the first formal ornithology in the county. Among the many subjects of interest to the members, natural history formed a considerable part of the proceedings and was recorded in detail in the early minute books from 1710 to 1758. The interest in birds was often stimulated by the examination of unusual specimens obtained in the local fens, although it is evident that the members could not put a name to some of them. In an age when the classification and identification of birds was still in its infancy, it is to the credit of the various secretaries that they provided brief descriptions of most specimens. These have enabled many of them to be identified specifically, thus making a valuable addition to our knowledge of birds in south-east Lincolnshire around 250 years ago.

On 13th June 1728 one member recorded that the heronry formerly at Wykeham Hall had moved to Fullney Hall, a distance of two miles. In September of the same year an account was given of a diving bird on the local canal (from the description clearly a Great Crested Grebe) and the secretary showed its skin on 3rd October, after it had been killed by some boys. Another member brought a Brambling on 19th December which he had shot on the local marshes.

In 1729 the secretary showed the skeleton of a Bittern on 6th February (no doubt a common bird in the fens) and another grebe (probably Great Crested) on 27th March. More interesting was a smaller grebe shown on 17th April that had been taken by a fowler in the fens. This was described as the size of a Teal with eyes and flesh around them of a bright red colour and feathers of a colour of melting copper. A Slavonian Grebe seems more likely than a Black-necked, as the species was also said to be rare in those parts except in severe winters.

In 1730 a specimen of an Avocet was shown on 9th July followed by a Water Rail on 26th November, both birds being well described. A Cormorant and a white gull were exhibited on 4th February 1731.

Members of the Society were shown a live brown eagle in January 1732. This had been captured in Nocton Woods and the secretary recorded that its wingspan measured seven feet (it was later identified as an immature White-tailed Eagle). A tern exhibited on 12th September 1734 may have been an immature Arctic as it had very short legs and a black bill. A drake Shoveler was shown on 18th December 1735. A woodpecker presented to the Society on 3rd November 1737 was probably a Lesser Spotted, as it was described as speckled black and white with a scarlet head. Interest in albinism was shown by the recording on 17th August 1738 that a white Coot had been captured in Spalding, and on 1st March 1739 that a black and white Rook had been shot at Moulton.

A valuable series of records began with the presentation to the Society on 24th September 1741 of a Corncrake which had been shot in the neighbourhood by one of the members. The secretary showed the members a Great Grey Shrike on 7th February 1745 and recorded that it had been shot in Spalding. A Wryneck was shot at Fullney on 10th April 1746 and shown to the Society on the same day, a full description being recorded in the minutes of its behaviour, structure and plumage.

On 29th January 1747 the treasurer recorded that he had procured a live female merganser which had been shot on Cowbit Wash (as likely to have been a Goosander as a Red-breasted Merganser). On 31st May of the same year he exhibited a live male Hawfinch and recorded that several had been taken in the area in the previous winter. The skins of a Moorhen and a Green Woodpecker were presented to the Society on 14th January 1748.

On 6th April 1749 one of the members showed a hawk which he had winged (from the description probably a Sparrowhawk) and a week later exhibited the skins of a Heron and an ash-coloured diver which was probably a Red-throated.

On 21st November 1751 the secretary showed the members the skin of a bird shot on the salt-marsh near Fosdyke. It was well described and clearly a male Snow Bunting also being recorded in the minutes as a winter visitor occurring in flocks. A Bittern shot in some reedy ground was shown on 21st September 1752 and the secretary exhibited a Treecreeper on 29th January 1756 and recorded that it had been killed by a cat in a member's garden.

Eighteenth Century publications

The eighteenth century saw the publication of several books describing the status of birds in Britain and some of them contained interesting accounts of birds in Lincolnshire. An early book was Albin's *A Natural History of Birds* (1731), although some of the details were taken from Ray. Of particular interest is the statement that Bearded Tits were found in the Fens of Lincolnshire and an immature Dotterel illustrated in Volume II was said to have been taken in the county. Much of our knowledge of Lincolnshire birds in the eighteenth century can be attributed to Pennant, who made several visits to the Fens sometimes staying with Sir Joseph Banks, the explorer and naturalist, on his estate at Revesby. The following extracts are taken from Pennant's *British Zoology* (vol. *II*) (1768):

Ruff. These birds are found in Lincolnshire, the Isle of Ely, and in the east riding of Yorkshire, where they are taken in nets, and fattened for the table, with bread and milk, hempseed, and sometimes with boiled wheat; but if expedition is required, sugar is added, which will make them in a fortnight's time a lump of fat; they then sell them for two shillings or half a crown a piece.

Dottrel. These birds are found in Cambridgeshire, Lincolnshire and Derbyshire; on Lincoln-heath, and on the moors of Derbyshire they are migratory, appearing there in small flocks of eight or ten only in the latter half of April, and stay there all May and part of June, during which time they are very fat, and much esteemed for their delicate flavour.

Mallard. They abound in Lincolnshire, the great magazine of wildfowl in this kingdom; where prodigious numbers are taken annually in the decoys. The Lincolnshire decoys are commonly set at an annual rent, from five pounds to

Dotterel were recorded as early as the sixteenth century

Ruffs were common in the West Fen in the eighteenth century

Knots used to be captured for food

twenty pounds a year. They contribute principally to supply the markets of London. Amazing numbers of ducks, wigeons and teal are taken.

Red-breasted Shoveler. We are indebted to Mr. Bolton for the description of this bird, who informed us that it was sometimes taken in the decoys of Lincolnshire.

Crane. This species was placed in the folio edition of the Zoology, among the British Birds, on the authority of Mr. Ray, who informs us that in his time they were found during the winter in large flocks in Lincolnshire and Cambridgeshire; but on the strictest enquiry we learn, that at present the inhabitants of those counties are entirely unacquainted with them; we therefore conclude, that these birds have forsaken our island.

Small Spotted Water-Hen. Breeds in Lincolnshire where it is known by the name of quail. *(No doubt the reference is to Spotted Crake.)*

In his *Tour in Scotland* (1771), Pennant described a brief visit made to the county in 1769. In this account he took the opportunity to describe the fens and the birds found there from his knowledge acquired during previous visits.

The fen called the West Fen, is the place where the Ruffs and Reeves resort to in the greatest numbers; and many other sorts of water fowl, which do no require the shelter or reeds or rushes, migrate here to breed, for this fen is very bare, having been imperfectly drained by narrow canals which intersect it for great numbers of miles. These the inhabitants navigate in most diminutive shallow boats; they are in fact the roads of the county.

The East Fen is quite in a state of nature, and gives a specimen of the country before the introduction of drainage: it is a vast tract of morass, intermixed with numbers of lakes, from half a mile to two or three miles in circuit, communicating with each other by narrow reedy straits: they are very shallow, none are above four or five feet in depth, but abound with fish, such as Pike, Perch, Ruff, Bream, Tench, Rudd, Dace, Roach, Burbot, Sticklebacks and Eels. It is observable that once in seven or eight years, immense shoals of Sticklebacks appear in the Welland below Spalding, and attempt coming up the river in form of a vast column. They are supposed to be the collected multitudes washed out of the fens by the floods of several years; and carried into some deep hole, when over-charged with numbers, they are forced to attempt a change of place. They move up the river in such quantities as to enable a man, who was employed in taking them, to earn, for a considerable time, four shillings a day, by selling them at half-penny per bushel. They were used to manure land, and attempts were made to get oil from them. The fen is covered with reeds, the harvest of the neighbouring inhabitants, who mow them annually, for they provide much better thatch than straw, and not only cottages, but many good houses are covered with them. Stares[xiv], which during winter resort in myriads to roost in the reeds, are very destructive, by breaking them down by the vast numbers that perch on them. The people are therefore very diligent in their attempts to drive them away, and are at great expense in powder to free themselves of these troublesome guests. I have seen a stock of reeds harvested and stacked worth two or three hundred pounds which was the property of a single farmer.

The birds which inhabit the different fens are very numerous: I never met with a finer field for the zoologist to range in. Besides the common Wild-duck, wild Geese, Garganies, Pochards, Shovelers and Teals, breed here. I have seen in the East Fen a small flock of the Tufted Ducks; but they seemed to make it only a baiting place. The Pewit Gulls and Black Terns abound: the last in great flocks almost deafen one with their clamours: a few of the great Terns[xv], or Tickets, are seen among them. I saw several of the Great Crested Grebes on the East Fen, called there Gaunts, and met with one of their floating nests with eggs in it. The lesser crested Grebe, the black and dusky Grebe[xvi], and the Little Grebe, are also inhabitants of the fens; together with Coots, Water-hens, spotted Water-hens[xvii], Water-rails, Ruffs, Redshanks, Lapwings or Wipes, Red-breasted Godwits[xviii] and Whimbrels. The Godwits breed near Washenbrough; the Whimbrels only appear for about a fortnight in May near Spalding, and then quit the country. Opposite to Fossdyke Wash, during the summer, are great numbers of Avosettas, called there Yelpers, from their cry: they hover over the sportsman's head like the Lapwing, and fly with the necks and legs extended.

Knots are taken in nets along the shores near Fossdyke in great numbers during winter, but they disappear in the spring. The Short-eared Owl visits the neighbourhood of Washenbrough, along with the Woodcocks, and probably performs its migration with those birds, for it is observed to quit the country at the same time: I have also received specimens of them from the Danish dominions, one of the retreats of the Woodcock. This owl is not observed in this country to perch on trees, but conceals itself in long old grass; if disturbed, it takes a short flight, lights again, and keeps staring about, during which time its horns are very visible. The farmers are fond of the arrival of these birds, as they clear the fields of mice, and will even fly in search of prey during the day, provided the weather is cloudy and misty.

But the greatest curiosity in these parts is the vast Heronry at Cressi-Hall, six miles from Spalding. The Herons resort there in February to repair their nests, settle there in the spring to breed, and quit the place during the winter. They are numerous as Rooks, and their nests so crowded together, that myself and the company that was with me counted no fewer than eighty in one tree.

Pennant evidently had difficulty in identifying some of the smaller, less well marked birds and corresponded with Gilbert White over the identity of a warbler he had shot at Revesby. White, one of England's greatest naturalists, was a master at observing subtle details, differences in behaviour and song patterns. His letters to Pennant were published in *The Natural History and Antiquities of Selbourne in the County of Southampton* (1789). It is interesting to note that White had spent a week in the county in 1746 and had been impressed by the fens. His letters illustrate his painstaking and thorough research in proving conclusively that Pennant's bird was a Sedge Warbler.

To Thomas Pennant, Esquire.
XXII Selbourne, Jan.2, 1769.
In your account of your error with regard to the two species of herons, you incidentally gave me great entertainment in your description of the heronry at Cressi-hall; which is a curiosity I never could manage to see. Fourscore nests of such a bird in one tree is a rarity which I would ride half as many miles to have a sight of. Pray be sure to tell me in your next whose seat Cressi-hall is, and near what town it lies. I have often thought that those vast extents of fens have never been sufficiently explored. If half a dozen gentleman, furnished with a good strength of water-spaniels, were to beat them over for a week, they would certainly find more species.

XXIII Selbourne, February 28, 1769
I return your thanks for your account of Cressi-hall; but recollect, not without regret, that in June 1746 I was visiting for a week together at Spalding, without ever being told that such a curiosity was just at hand. Pray send me word in your next what sort of tree it is that contains such a quantity of herons' nests; and whether the heronry consists of a whole grove or wood, or only a few trees.

XXIV Selbourne, May 29, 1769
One of my neighbours lately brought me a new *salicaria*, which at first I suspected might have proved your willow-lark, but, on a nicer examination, it answered much better to the description of that species which you shot at Revesby, in Lincolnshire. My bird I describe thus: 'It is a size less than the grasshopper lark; the head, back, and coverts of the wings, of a dusky brown, without those dark spots of the grasshopper lark; over each eye is a milkwhite stroke; the chin and throat are white, and the underparts of a yellowish white; the rump is tawny, and the features of the tail sharp-pointed; the bill is dusky and sharp, and the legs are dusky; the hinder claw long and crooked.' The person that shot it says that it sings so like a reed sparrow that he took it for one; and that it sings all night; but this account merits farther enquiry. For my part I suspect it is a second sort of *locustella*, hinted at by Dr. Denham in Ray's letters.

XXV Selbourne, Aug 30, 1769
I have taken a great deal of pains about your *salicaria* and mine, with a white stroke over its eye and a tawny rump. I have surveyed it alive and dead, and have procured several specimens; and am perfectly persuaded myself (and trust you will soon be convinced of the same) that it is no more or less than the *passer arundinaceus minor* of Ray. This bird, by some means or other, seems to be entirely omitted in the British Zoology; and one reason probably was because it is so strangely classed in Ray, who ranges it among his *picis affines*. It ought no doubt to have gone among his *aviculae cauda unicolore*, and among your slender-billed small birds of the same division. Linnaeus might with great propriety have put it into his genus of *motacilla*; and the *motacilla salicaria* of his *fauna svecica* seems to come nearest to it. It is no uncommon bird, haunting the sides of ponds and rivers where there is covert, and the reeds and sedges of moors. The country people in some places call it the sedge bird. It sings incessantly night and day during the breeding time, imitating the notes of a sparrow, a swallow, a skylark, and has a strange hurrying manner in its song. My specimen corresponds most minutely to the description of your fen *salicaria* shot near Revesby.

XXVI Selbourne, December 8, 1769
You admit, I find, that I have proved your fen *salicaria* to be the lesser reed-sparrow of Ray: and I think you may be secure that I am right; for I took very particular pains to clear up that matter, and had some fair specimens; but, as they were not well preserved, they are decayed already. You will, no doubt, insert it in its proper place in your next edition.

Pennant included the species in vol IV (1770) and his illustration is clearly a Sedge Warbler. A few other interesting notes were included in this volume.

Sedge Bird. Frequents fens of Lincolnshire.
Tree Sparrow. Common near Lincoln, Spalding, etc...
... Lesser Crested Grebe. Very common in the fens of Spalding, where it breeds; lays four or five small white eggs, and makes its nest not unlike that of the Great Crested Grebe. Length to rump one foot; extent of wing twenty two inches. Bill turns up a little; lorum naked and black; irides red. Behind each eye a long tuft of ferruginous feathers pointing backwards; feathers on the head, cheeks and throat full and black; secondaries white; sides under the wings as far as the rump a bright ferruginous colour. Belly white and glossy; outside of the legs dusky, inside greenish.

The above seems to prove that Black-necked Grebes once bred commonly in the fens of Lincolnshire, which is perhaps not so unreasonable. However, modern authorities on the status of British birds seem to have overlooked this. It is sometimes erroneously stated that the species was not recorded breeding in Britain until the early twentieth century.

Latham's *A General Synopsis of Birds* (vol III, 1783) provided the first evidence of a rare vagrant occurring in Lincolnshire. A Rose-coloured Starling had been shot at Grantham a few years earlier and was stated to be in the possession of Sir Joseph Banks.

Walcott's *Synopsis of British Birds* (1789) contained a few more interesting records not previously mentioned.

Stone Curlew. Mostly found in Norfolk, Hampshire, Lincolnshire and some parts of Kent.
Bearded Tit. Marshy situations with reeds including Cowbit in Lincolnshire.
Bean Goose. Bill white except at base and end being black, upper parts and coverts bluish grey, legs reddish flesh. Migrates in autumn into Lincolnshire and Yorkshire, feeding much on green wheat.
Pochard. Common in fens during the winter; some said to breed in those of Lincolnshire.

The description of Bean Goose indicates a Pink-footed, so that the status of the latter may have been similar to that of today.

The Nineteenth Century

Donovan's *The Natural History of British Birds* (1794-1819) included a description of a male Ring-necked Duck purchased in the Leadenhall Market, London, in January 1801. It was said to have come from Lincolnshire as were many of the ducks on sale there, Leadenhall being the chief outlet for wildfowl caught in the county's decoys. It is strange that this has never been accepted as a valid British record, particularly as it was the type specimen and would hardly have been imported from its native North America. Donovan also recorded that Brent Geese were sometimes plentiful in winter in the Lincolnshire marshes and that Greylag Geese still bred in large numbers in the fens.

Details of the status of many birds in the county were given in Montagu's *Ornithological Dictionary* (1802), although most of the information was similar to that published by previous authors. Early in the century, however, he paid a visit to the county exploring the fens before they were finally drained, and the coast near Skegness. His original observations were included in a supplement published in 1813.

Montagu found Black-headed Gulls:

plentiful in the breeding season, inhabiting the most swampy parts along with Snipes, Redshanks and Ruffs.

Redshanks were particularly common near Spalding and Black Terns were abundant in the fens, but he did not find any Black-tailed Godwits. One of the aims of the expedition was to discover as much as possible about Ruffs and the practice of catching them and fattening them for the table. He stated that Ruffs could still be found near Crowland and Spalding and in the East and West Fens between Boston and Spilsby, but they were by no means plentiful. Decreases had taken place due to drainage and enclosures and he correctly predicted that Ruffs would cease to breed as agriculture increased.

Montagu had difficulty in locating any of the Ruff-catchers but eventually he found a fowler near Spalding who showed him the method of trapping the birds, using stuffed decoys and a clap net. He also bought several from a feeder at Cowbit, who showed him a room where he kept about seven dozen males and a dozen females. Another feeder from Spalding said he had once set off for Ireland with 27 dozen packed into baskets carried upon two horses. Seven dozen were delivered to the Duke of Devonshire at Chatsworth in Derbyshire and seventeen dozen were taken on to Dublin for the Marquis of Townsend, three dozen having died on the way.

Of his visit to the coast, Montagu remarked:

Near Skegness, at a point called Gibraltar there is an isolated part of a marsh, where Oystercatchers breed in such abundance, that a fisherman informed us he had taken a bushel of eggs in a morning.

He was also surprised to see a large flock of Oystercatchers in the middle of the breeding season, but was told that a high tide had swept away their eggs, together with those of Ringed Plovers and Little Terns. Montagu had discovered what was to become, 140 years later, Lincolnshire's premier nature reserve. Today only odd pairs of Oystercatchers nest there, but Ringed Plovers and Little Terns still breed in good numbers and endure the same hazards from the vagaries of the sea. During his visit to the county he found Lesser Whitethroats and Garden Warblers quite common and observed a Wryneck near the coast.

A rather haphazard list of birds seen in the neighbourhood of Louth was published by Bayley in 1834. He intentionally omitted some common species and it is little more than a bare list of some 80 species. His area obviously included the nearby coast and among the few species for which he mentioned any status, Quail, Velvet Scoter, Long-tailed Duck, Hoopoe and Waxwing were described as rare and the Dotterel as plentiful. Several rarities such as Crane and White Stork are included without any useful detail although he claimed to have seen the latter three times in the previous ten years.

Stonehouse's *History and Topography of the Isle of Axholme* (1839) contains a section on birds, although his summary of the species which used to inhabit the Isle before the drainage includes a few dubious species. More interesting are a few of his own observations from there and the neighbouring part of north-west Lincolnshire. Bitterns still occurred in the early part of the century and he shot two on Burringham Moors in 1817 and once found a nest containing four eggs. He also stated that Marsh Harriers continued to frequent the Isle and recorded finding a nest with three young at Lindholme in 1836. Ruffs could still be found on Burringham Moors and he saw some in 1819 and was shown a dozen which a fowler had trapped and intended to fatten for the London market.

A paper by Alington entitled *Ornithology of Lincolnshire* was published in the Naturalist in 1852. This gave a brief summary of birds in the county in former times including extracts from Camden. Amongst a few original observations he noted that Nightingales were spreading to the north of the county and that he had found Oyster-catchers nesting on the Humber bank. He also listed about 100 species that he had seen at Croxby Lake, all of which seem quite likely to have been genuine, although he did not give any details of status apart from stating that Golden Plovers occurred in large flocks. Of a few species, which would only have been scarce visitors, he recorded Avocet and Great Northern Diver.

Records of birds in Lincolnshire in the nineteenth century were frequently published in journals such as the *Naturalist*, *Zoologist* and *Field*. A large proportion of these records were of birds that had been shot, although a few field ornithologists began to emerge in the second half of the century.

One of Lincolnshire's finest ornithologists, John Cordeaux, lived at Great Coates near Grimsby. In addition to studying migration in the north-east of the county, he also made frequent excursions to the Yorkshire coasts. His *Birds of the Humber District* (1872) dealt with an area almost identical to the present county of Humberside. Much original material about the birds of north Lincolnshire was included, although it is sometimes difficult to determine whether some records refer to Yorkshire or Lincolnshire. A revision in 1899 summarized all the additional information and presented a comprehensive analysis of migration on the coast. An account of his life has recently been published (Pashby 1985).

Towards the end of the century an equally fine ornithologist, G.H. Caton Haigh, began regular visits to the coast at Tetney and North Cotes. He shot many rare birds including several new species for Britain, such as Radde's and Greenish Warbler, and showed that vagrants such as Yellow-browed and Barred Warblers occurred with some regularity. However, he was also an excellent field observer and meticulously recorded details of migrants in his diaries. These have been deposited in the British Museum at Tring and cover nearly 50 years from 1888.

Brogden's *Birds of Spalding and the South Lincolnshire Fenland* was edited by Cordeaux and appeared in the *Naturalist* in 1900. It presented a concise and useful summary of the status of all species occurring in that area.

Drainage and enclosure of many of the wilder parts of the county early in the century had put pressure on many species, but some of the larger birds of prey managed to survive on the remaining heaths and in the larger woods. However, these were increasingly sought after by taxidermists and were heavily persecuted by gamekeepers.

Writing in the *Field* in 1886, Elmhirst recalled how sixty years earlier he had helped his father to exterminate a colony of Hen Harriers on the sandy moors near Market Rasen. His father had acquired the shooting rights of over 50 square miles of land from the Earl of Yarborough and systematically waged war against all so-called vermin. The harriers nested in large areas of gorse and they were shot or trapped on their nests. Elmhirst remembered that on one moor at Middle Rasen no fewer than 26 birds, including young, were destroyed in a single day and a total of at least 50 were accounted for in one year.

In his *Fens and Floods of Mid-Lincolnshire* (1882), Padley described how the Kite had suffered a similar fate near Lincoln. Until a few years previously, they had bred in Tumby and Fulsby Woods and also at Branston, Nocton and Blankney. However, a 'bird-fancier' from London moved into the neighbourhood and relentlessly shot each pair until not one remained.

Some examples of the intensity of game-bird shooting in the county can be found in early game-books (Lincolnshire Archives). On the Syston Estates near Grantham totals of 11,588 Partridges and 10,745 Pheasants were shot in ten winters between 1863-73. At Grimsthorpe, October to November totals for seven years from 1898 to 1904 included 5,000 Partridges and 46,000 Pheasants. As is the case today, many of these birds, especially the Pheasants, would have been released after artificial rearing but the total number of birds shot each year in the whole county in the late nineteenth century must have been enormous.

Shorebirds were also captured in large numbers, but the effect of this was less serious due to the huge wintering populations. Several plover decoys existed in the north-east of the county. Clap nets were used to catch mainly Lapwings and Golden Plovers, attracted to the catching area by live, tethered decoys. Members of the Stubbs family operated such decoys between Tetney and Conisholme and they provided many interesting records of scarce migrants.

All around the mudflats of the Wash huge nets on stakes were used to catch migrant and wintering wildfowl and waders. In a highly descriptive account of life at Friskney in 1889, Dixon recorded his impressions of a visit to see the nets in action on the shore. These were left up all winter and caught most birds on the darkest nights. A visit at dawn revealed the night's catch. This included several Dunlins, Knots and other waders, a Fulmar, two Leach's Petrels, a Wigeon and a Great Crested Grebe. Many of these had been drowned.

The Twentieth Century

An attempt to summarize the status of birds in another part of the county was made by Peacock in a series of four papers on the Birds of North-west Lindsey which appeared in the Naturalist between 1902-1908. However, his list was very incomplete (a fifth part was never published) and lacked the conviction of earlier lists by Cordeaux and Brogden.

The *Transactions* of the Lincolnshire Naturalists Union, formed in 1893, began to appear regularly from 1905 and these early volumes sometimes contained articles on birds. Another ornithologist of note, the Rev. F.L. Blathwayt, was secretary of the Vertebrate Zoology section of the Union for many years. His interest in the distribution of birds led him to study them in parts of the county such as the Lincoln area which had previously been neglected. He published an interesting paper on the birds of Scotton

Common (1906) but his major contribution was the first complete annotated list of the birds of Lincolnshire (1915) which appeared in the *Transactions* for 1914. Blathwayt highlighted the need for more observations to be made in the southern half of the county but unfortunately he left Lincolnshire in 1916.

For the next 25 years or so the vast majority of records in the *Transactions* were still confined to the north of the county. The few notable exceptions were when there were surveys of colonial species such as Herons, Great Crested Grebes and Rooks. A census of breeding Kestrels and Sparrowhawks in 13 parishes in the north of the county was made by Cox, May and Davey in 1932. At that time both species were fairly common, but the results are particularly valuable today now that the Sparrowhawk is recovering again after becoming virtually extinct as a breeding bird in the county. Material for a book on the Reed Warbler was obtained by Brown at North Cotes when he was stationed there during the Second World War.

After 1945 there was a gradual increase in interest of birds in the county and many new areas were visited regularly such as the Wash and inland gravel pits and sewage farms. On the coast the establishment of Gibraltar Point bird observatory in 1949 soon showed what a splendid area that was for the study of migration.

A further stimulus occurred with the publication in 1955 of the county's first comprehensive avifauna: *The Birds of Lincolnshire* by Smith and Cornwallis. Much new information on the status of birds in the county had been obtained since Blathwayt's list and this was skilfully presented. However, it soon became apparent that many species had been under-recorded in the past, thus masking their true status in the county.

Particularly noteworthy has been the increase in records of sea-birds since regular sea-watching has become established at several sites along the coast. The use of mist-nets to catch birds has enabled ringers to operate almost anywhere in the county, increasing the variety and numbers of birds ringed and adding greatly to our knowledge of migration.

Such was the progress in Lincolnshire ornithology that Cornwallis was already preparing a revision only ten years after the publication of the *Birds of Lincolnshire*. After his death in 1969 this 'supplement' was brought up to date and edited by Atkin and Townsend (Cornwallis 1970).

Interest in breeding birds was stimulated by the British Trust for Ornithology's *Common Bird Census*. Several different habitats have been studied in Lincolnshire and have provided interesting data on densities and population compositions as well as indicating fluctuations from year to year. Some of the results have been published in the *Transactions*.

A major achievement in the field of breeding distribution was the *B.T.O. Atlas* work undertaken in the county from 1968-1972 (Sharrock 1976). The results were an outstanding success and form a basis for understanding breeding distributions of all species in the county as well as providing a base line for monitoring future changes.

A new development in 1979 was the formation of the Lincolnshire Bird Club. The Club aims to stimulate interest in and co-ordinate ornithological studies in the county. It also publishes an illustrated annual *Bird Report*, with articles on surveys, ringing and other topical features as well as a comprehensive specific list. A major undertaking in the 1980s has been the compilation of a Breeding Atlas[xix] surveyed in much greater detail than was previously possible. The Atlas should provide a valuable basis for conservation measures and assessment of both short-term and long-term trends.

The winters of 1981/82, 1982/83 and 1983/84 were devoted to intensive counting of all species throughout the county for the B.T.O.'s *Atlas of Wintering Birds in Britain and Ireland* (Lack 1986). In Lincolnshire this was a model of co-operation between members of the B.T.O., L.B.C. and L.N.U. with additional help especially on reserves from the Trust, R.S.P.B. and N.C.C. The results form an essential companion volume to *The Atlas of Breeding Birds in Britain and Ireland* for understanding bird distributions on both local and national scales.

Today, so widespread is the interest in birds in the county that no significant ornithological event can pass unnoticed. With ever-increasing conservation measures and a recent more widespread awareness of the importance of the natural environment, the future for birds in the county seems much more optimistic than was the case only a few years ago.

Explanatory footnotes to Part Two

i   Bittour, Bytter = Bittern
ii   Puet, Puitt, Pewit = Black-headed Gull
iii   Shovelard, Shovler = Spoonbill
iv   Smeath = Smew
v   Water-Woosell = Dipper
vi   Puffin = Manx Shearwater
vii   Ilke = Whooper Swan
viii Herne = Grey Heron
ix   Snite = Snipe
x   Bidcocke = Water Rail
xi   Sea-meaw = Common Gull
xii   Sea-pye = Oystercatcher
xiii Didapper = Little Grebe
xiv Stare = Starling
xv   Great Tern = Common Tern
xvi Lesser Crested Grebe, Dusky Grebe = Black-necked Grebe (summer, winter)
xvii Spotted Water-hen = Spotted Crake
xviii Red-breasted Godwit = Black-tailed Godwit
xix Due to be published, 1990

Part Three: The Systematic List

We have researched old and modern literature, periodicals, newspapers, diaries, letters and much unpublished data in an attempt to reassess every record of significance. Many old records cannot be fully-authenticated due to the length of time which has now elapsed, while certain others were considered to be unreliable by comparison to modern standards of recording. The lists of Cordeaux, published in 1872 and 1899, and that of Blathwayt in 1915 were very important contributions to our earlier knowledge of birds in Lincolnshire, although there were some records apparently unknown to these authors. Smith and Cornwallis in their 1955 list concentrated on the status of birds during the present century and the more readily known earlier records of rarities. Much recourse has been made to these lists and we have rechecked all references given by these authors and by those of more localised lists.

Descriptions of rarer species have been re-examined and a number of records previously published with erroneous dates have been amended. Species not quite fully-authenticated or of questionable origins are given in Appendices 1 and 2. We have deleted one species, the Ivory Gull, from the county list and our reasons for doing so are to be found in Appendix 3. Since 1958 all records of rare birds in Britain have been considered by the Rare Birds Committee of *British Birds*. All relevant records in our list have been accepted by the Committee except in one or two cases where it is stated that a decision is still awaited.

All records up to 31st December 1988 are included, these comprising 357 species accepted to the list. The sequence and nomenclature adopted follows that of the 1977 *List of Recent Holarctic Bird Species* by Professor Dr. K.H. Voous.

We have assessed the status of each species occurring during the last ten years and have termed relative seasonal abundance as follows:

Rare	1-10 birds,
Scarce	11-100 birds,
Fairly common	101-1,000 birds,
Common	1,001-10,000 birds
Numerous	10,001-100,000 birds
Abundant	over 100,000 birds

For all but the most sedentary species, the term 'resident' has largely been omitted from the text, as its usage often hides the fact that different populations of a species may frequent the same areas in alternate seasons.

Individual records are given for all species recorded fewer than ten times in the county. Up to three observers' names are mentioned for each record of species noted on one to three occasions or for the first county record when there are up to ten occurrences. The appropriate occurrence of a species is numbered when there are fewer than 20 British records.

The origins of vagrants are given only for those species whose breeding range does not include any part of Europe. Subspecies are normally indicated as showing the characteristics of a certain race, unless a specimen was obtained or sufficiently distinct differences exist, such as in the Carrion and Hooded Crow.

Ringing recoveries have been extracted chiefly from those published by the British Trust for Ornithology, the Lincolnshire Naturalists' Union, the Lincolnshire Bird Club and the Wash Wader Ringing Group. The recovery records of Gibraltar Point Bird Observatory and the Cleethorpes Ringing Group have also been consulted. The selective publication of recoveries in recent years may have resulted in the omission of a number of records relevant to Lincolnshire.

Red-throated Diver *Gavia stellata*
A fairly common winter visitor on the coast, most numerous from late September to mid-April. Early immigrants sometimes arrive in August and stragglers in the spring may be present until early May. There are several records of birds on the sea during the summer months and some of these have been in full breeding plumage. It occasionally occurs on inland waters, particularly during adverse weather.

Black-throated Diver *Gavia arctica*
A winter visitor and passage migrant in very small numbers. Coastal records are concentrated in the Wash and at the mouth of the Humber. Fewer birds occur on the more exposed parts of the coast and the species is a very infrequent wanderer to inland waters. Many divers on passage at some distance from the shore are not readily identifiable. Some of these birds are undoubtedly Black-throated so that it is probably not as scarce as records suggest.

The earliest arrivals occur from about the third week of September and a distinct peak is reached in January and February. Passage birds may be seen until late April although odd ones have been reported during the summer months.

Great Northern Diver *Gavia immer*
A very scarce passage migrant and winter visitor with only one or two records in some years. In the nineteenth century it was said to be more frequently recorded than the Black-throated but during the last 25 years the reverse has been the case. This may be the result of improved observation standards raising the number of definite Black-throated

Diver sightings, rather than any true change in status.

The Great Northern tends to arrive earlier in the autumn than the preceding species. Several have been recorded in late August, but September is the main month for the first arrivals. The period from November to January produces the majority of reports followed by a sharp decline during February. Very little spring movement has been observed but occasional birds may occur during the summer months. It seems to favour the open coastal waters rather more than the estuaries and occurs only infrequently inland.

White-billed Diver *Gavia adamsii*
A very rare vagrant. An adult bird was found dead by M.R. Plant on Friskney Marsh in the Wash on 26th March 1976. The species breeds in Arctic Russia, Siberia and Alaska.

Little Grebe *Tachybaptus ruficollis*
A fairly common summer resident and winter visitor. In some areas it is more numerous than the Great-Crested Grebe and usually breeds on a wider variety of smaller waters than that species. It regularly nests on lakes, gravel pits, small ponds, rivers and canals. Although well distributed in the county it is most numerous on the pits along the south bank of the Humber. Some of the breeding sites are occupied throughout the year, unless freezing conditions drive the birds to the coast, reservoirs and larger lakes.

Immigrants arrive from September to November and are most obvious in coastal localities. The open sea is largely shunned even in severe weather but it occurs on the more sheltered estuaries, tidal creeks and docks.

One ringed at Sutton Bridge in October 1966 was recovered in Cheshire in January 1967 and a young bird ringed in Essex in July 1953 was found at South Killingholme in December of the same year.

Great Crested Grebe *Podiceps cristatus*
A fairly common breeding species and winter visitor. Large numbers bred in the Fens before the final drainage early in the nineteenth century and nesting apparently ceased in the county until about 1900, when single pairs occupied the Lincoln L.N.E.R. Pit, Denton Reservoir, near Grantham and a site near Spalding. Since then there has been a fairly steady increase in the number of breeding pairs. At least eight waters were known to be occupied by 1914 and censuses were taken in 1931, 1952/53, 1965 and 1975. It is not known how complete the earlier counts were, but those of 1965 and 1975 probably give an accurate assessment of its recent status. In 1931 there were 26 pairs at 12 sites but there was an apparent decrease to 16 pairs at nine sites in 1952/53. In 1965 106 adults were located on 24 waters and most of this increase could be attributed to the occupation of recently excavated gravel pits in the southern part of the county. By 1975 this number had more than doubled when no fewer than 100 pairs were present on most of the suitable waters in the county. Since then further increases have occurred.

The majority of summer residents leave the breeding waters early in the autumn and resort to the larger reservoirs, estuaries and open sea coast, returning to the nesting sites in February and March. Gravel pits and the larger waters are the most favoured breeding

Black-throated Diver

Red-necked Grebe

areas although many more than formerly now nest on some fenland rivers and drains. During this period one or two non-breeding birds are occasionally seen on the sea.

At Covenham Reservoir about 30 birds were found dead from an unknown cause in late October 1974.

One unusually long-lived bird, ringed in Essex in April 1966, was found dead at Theddlethorpe in March 1978 and another ringed at Deeping St. James in March 1977 was found dead in Cheshire in October 1983.

Red-necked Grebe *Podiceps grisegena*

A winter visitor in very small numbers which may occur in small influxes particularly during periods of freezing weather conditions. Most of the records are from coastal localities but inland records are not unusual. Early arrivals have occasionally been observed from the beginning of August but the main immigration takes place from September to November. Return passage occurs in March and early April though a few birds sometimes remain until early May. There are two recent summer records. One was seen at Humberston on 4th July 1981 and there was one at Covenham Reservoir from 11th to 14th June 1982.

Significant hard weather influxes were recorded in January and February 1865 and January and February 1937. More recently there was an influx of over 100 birds during severe weather in mid-February 1979.

Slavonian Grebe *Podiceps auritus*

A rare but regular winter visitor to coastal and inland waters. It was stated by Cordeaux to have been common in the Humber in winter, and in recent years most of the records have been from this area and the north-east coast.

The second week of September usually marks the earliest arrivals and records are spread fairly evenly until March. A very early bird was seen at Bardney from 21st to 25th July 1961 and it has been noted several times in August during recent years. There are no records in spring after early May. Small cold weather influxes occurred in the north of the county in February 1932, in late January 1937, and in January and February 1979.

Black-necked Grebe *Podiceps nigricollis*

A rare passage migrant and winter visitor. Pennant (1768-70) stated that the species bred commonly in the Fens near Spalding and it is possible that it may well have done so until the early nineteenth century but modern authorities seem to have overlooked this.

There is a paucity of early records. One was found in a stack-yard at Thoresway near Caistor on 19th January 1850 and another was obtained at Bourne in January or February 1864. One was shot at Deeping St. James on 31st January 1875 and in the autumn of 1882 three birds were obtained near Lincoln. Another was shot at Horncastle Brick Pits on 2nd July 1901. There are no further records until 1954 but since then the species has occurred more regularly and is now seen annually, due no doubt to an increase in the activity of observers. Only a minority of birds occur during the winter months, most of the records referring to autumn migrants from August to November. A return passage on a smaller scale takes place in spring and recently several pairs in breeding plumage have been recorded in May and June.

In contrast to the Slavonian Grebe the records of this species are more or less equally divided between the northern and southern halves of the county, particularly on the coast of the Wash in the south. Most of the sightings in the north have been at Covenham Reservoir, where it has been a regular visitor since 1970.

Fulmar *Fulmarus glacialis*

A fairly common offshore visitor which has been recorded more frequently during the remarkable increase and expansion of range of the species in Britain this century.

In the late nineteenth century it was described as an uncommon autumn and winter visitor along the coast although it was more regular and common on the North Sea fishing grounds. Nowadays Fulmars are generally present along the coast between mid-March and early November with maximum numbers in August and September, but birds may be seen at any time of the year. Some of these birds are undoubtedly visitors from Yorkshire which was first colonised in 1922, and from Norfolk where breeding occurred from 1947.

Dead Fulmars are often washed ashore in the winter and early spring and in February and March 1962 a large wreck, including a high proportion of dark and intermediate phases, was recorded on the North Sea coasts of Britain and the Continent. At least 47 birds were reported from the Lincolnshire coast and several of these were dark-phase birds. An exceptionally heavy northerly passage of several hundred birds was observed on the coast during a period of strong northerly winds between 17th and 20th September 1977 and also included one or two dark-phase examples. An unusually large spring movement was noted at Huttoft on 30th April 1978 when 272 flew south.

Inland records are rather infrequent and usually refer to storm-driven birds in the autumn. One of these individuals found at Saxilby near Lincoln had been ringed as a nestling on the Isle of Man three weeks earlier in August 1946.

Cory's Shearwater *Calonectris diomedea*

A rare vagrant. One flying south at Saltfleetby on 14th August 1985 was seen by B.M. Clarkson and M.J. Tarrant. Another flying north at Huttoft on 20th August 1988 was seen by C. R. Casey and S. Keightley.

Great Shearwater *Puffinus gravis*

A rare and irregular vagrant in autumn and winter that has been recorded on ten occasions. The first bird reported by A. Thomson was captured near Spalding and sent to London Zoo in the autumn of 1882. One was shot on Holbeach Marsh in December 1893 and another suffered a similar fate in the Welland estuary on 27th November 1902. One was found dead at North Cotes by Haigh though the date is unrecorded. Two were seen off Anderby Creek on 15th September 1968 and one which was considered to have been dead for about three weeks was found in the Wash at Gedney Drove End on 28th February 1970. One was identified at Gibraltar Point on 15th September 1974 and others were seen at Trusthorpe near Mablethorpe on 28th September 1975 and at Donna Nook on 17th September 1977.

Sooty Shearwater *Puffinus griseus*
An autumn visitor to coastal waters generally in small numbers. An increase in the amount of sea-watching in recent years has produced an annual series of records from late July to early December, but mainly between late August and the end of September. Most movements are northerly. An unusual winter record was one picked up alive about one mile inland at North Cotes after a north-easterly blizzard on 2nd January 1941.

It was said to have been seen not infrequently earlier in the century and a scarcity of records between 1930 and 1960 is probably due to a lack of observers. More than usual were seen in 1908 and 1968 but the largest numbers were in 1976 when at least 50 were recorded and in 1977 when over 100 were seen.

Manx Shearwater *Puffinus puffinus*
A scarce coastal visitor mainly in autumn though fairly common in some years particularly during stormy weather. Small parties often occur and although sometimes noted in June most records are between July and the third week in October with stragglers into November. Spring occurrences in April and May are infrequent and generally involve only small numbers.

Several have been found at inland localities during the autumn. Two of these had been ringed as nestlings shortly before on Skokholm, Pembrokeshire and had been carried inland by south-westerly gales.

The western Mediterranean race, *P.p. mauretanicus*, known as the Balearic Shearwater, has been identified three times at Gibraltar Point on 5th October 1963, 1st August 1971 and 15th September 1976 and twice at Saltfleetby on 28th July and 26th August 1984.

Storm Petrel *Hydrobates pelagicus*
A rare and irregular vagrant recorded once in spring. Most of its appearances have been after heavy gales between late September and mid-December. It occurred slightly more often in the late nineteenth century.

Small numbers were reported in several autumns from 1869 to 1889 when storm-blown birds were picked up at some inland and coastal localities. Unusual numbers along the whole east coast of England in November 1883 resulted in at least four Lincolnshire records. With the exception of a few individuals coming to shore on boats, there are no more records until one at the Witham Mouth on 14th December 1957. Since 1971 there have been 14 records. Most of these have been seen between late August and October apart from one at Huttoft on 5th April 1975 and one found dead at Anderby Creek on 25th January 1987.

Leach's Petrel *Oceanodroma leucorhoa*
A rare vagrant from September to November with occasional records in December and January. It is rather irregular occurring chiefly after gales, usually later in the autumn and less infrequently than the Storm Petrel.

A good number of the earlier reports are of birds obtained well inland in the south of

Manx Shearwater

Cormorant

the county and on the coast of the Wash particularly at Friskney where several were netted by bird-catchers up to 1881. During a large wreck in 1952, mainly on the west coast of Britain, at least seven individuals were found in the county. Two of these were in late September and the remainder were picked up dead in early November. Since 1960, there have been about 38 records including several inland and the only spring occurrence of two at Donna Nook on 22nd May 1984.

Gannet *Sula bassana*
A common coastal passage migrant in autumn with smaller numbers at other times of the year. Spring birds usually occur singly or in very small parties from late March until the end of May. A few birds fishing offshore in summer are probably from the Yorkshire colony. Regular passage extends from late July to early November.

Peak numbers, sometimes of several hundred birds, occur in late August and September. Storms may drive birds well into the Humber and some individuals are occasionally found inland.

The majority of birds in autumn are immature, but wintering birds, which are only rarely brought close to the shore by adverse weather conditions, are invariably adults.

One ringed as a nestling at the Bass Rock colony in the Firth of Forth in July 1958 was found at Ingoldmells in August 1959.

Cormorant *Phalacrocorax carbo*
A fairly common visitor chiefly from autumn to spring. It has been recorded in sizeable flocks much more frequently during the last few years.

Passage on the coast in autumn is most marked from late August until early December with a return movement in March and April. Wintering birds concentrate in the Humber and the Wash but small numbers also occur on inland waters particularly during bad weather. Birds regularly flight from the Humber to fish in Covenham Reservoir where up to 80 have been counted. A few immature birds remain on the coast during the summer. There are a few spring records of birds showing characteristics of the continental race, *P.c. sinensis*.

Seven birds ringed as nestlings on the Farne Islands, Northumberland have been recovered in Lincolnshire and there are single recoveries from Anglesey and Wigtownshire.

Shag *Phalacrocorax aristotelis*
A scarce visitor from autumn to spring mainly to coastal waters but sometimes inland. It was formerly quite rare and irregular but it has been noted much more often in recent years following significant increases at the east coast breeding colonies in Scotland and northern England.

Records are fairly evenly spread although peak passage is indicated by rather more birds in October and March. Stragglers in spring are sometimes seen until early May and there is a report of one at Gibraltar Point on 30th June 1965.

Occasionally there are minor influxes. Large parties were 30 at Holbeach in October 1961, 25 at Covenham Reservoir in February 1976, 24 there in January 1984, 20 at

Donna Nook in January 1985 and 26 at Saltfleetby in March 1988.

Eight nestlings ringed in Fife, one in Lothian, five in the Farne Islands and one in Caernarvon have been recovered in the county.

Bittern *Botaurus stellaris*

A very scarce breeding species and a rare but fairly regular winter visitor. Formerly it was a familiar resident of the Fens, the Isle of Axholme, the north-west and the Marsh district in the north-east of the county. Drainage and reclamation of its haunts caused a decline and finally the extinction of breeding birds in all areas by about 1825 — except in the Isle of Axholme where the species survived until about 1850. It has continued to occur as a regular winter visitor in very small numbers chiefly from mid-September to mid-April.

Breeding Bitterns became re-established at several reed bed sites close to the Humber Bank in the early 1940s but the first nest was not found until 1949. In good years up to six pairs have bred though there has been a recent sharp decline with no proof of breeding during the last ten years. Some sites have been destroyed and increased disturbance from fishing and boating suggests that future breeding will be rather precarious.

Little Bittern *Ixobrychus minutus*

A rare vagrant recorded on nine occasions. One shot in the county some years before 1872 was recorded by Cordeaux but he made no mention of any locality. A gamekeeper shot one near Gainsborough on 20th May 1870 and another bird shot at Ludford early in the present century was presented to Louth Museum. An immature bird trapped and ringed at Goxhill was present from 12th to 16th August 1953. One at Wolla Bank Pit near Chapel St. Leonards from 21st to 26th May 1964 was part of an influx concentrated mainly in the south of England; a larger influx in 1970 produced one at Burton Gravel Pit on 13th May. An immature bird at Birchwood, Lincoln on 26th August 1976 was found dead on the following day. One was seen at Barton on Humber on 23rd June 1977 and another was present at East Halton, near Killingholme from 19th to 29th April 1978.

Night Heron *Nycticorax nycticorax*

A rare vagrant recorded on eight occasions. One was shot by H. Stubbs on the foreshore at Tetney on 26th November 1888. Another bird stayed on a drain at Boston from 13th to 19th November 1973. One at Skegness from 30th December 1979 to 1st January 1980 was found dead on 4th January. It had been ringed as a nestling on the Black Sea coast of Russia in the previous June. One occurred at Saltfleetby on 14th May 1983 and another was seen near Goxhill from 8th to 12th October 1986. Two arrived off the sea at Gibraltar Point on 14th May 1987 and remained until the following day. In 1988, one was seen at Wainfleet on 1st June and a juvenile at Boston from 1st November to at least the end of December had been ringed as a nestling in the feral colony at Edinburgh. Apart from the Saltfleetby and Wainfleet birds, all the records were of immatures.

Squacco Heron *Ardeola ralloides*

A rare vagrant with no recent records. According to Morris (1851-58) there was a

Bewick's Swans

Night Heron

Lincolnshire specimen prior to 1850 but he gave no further details. Cordeaux (1899) recorded one that was shot at Fillingham Lake near Gainsborough in June 1861. An immature bird was shot on the Humber Bank at Great Coates by R.J. Pearson on 29th September 1910.

Cattle Egret *Bubulcus ibis*
A rare vagrant. One feeding with cattle at North Hykeham, Lincoln from 12th to 26th October 1986 roosted nearby at Apex Pit. It was seen by S. Shucksmith, M. Davies, R.J. Campey and other observers. Seven others occurred in Britain during the same autumn.

One said to have been obtained locally was purchased at a sale in Boston about 1865 and eventually presented to Lincoln Museum. One shot near Spalding on 1st October 1935 and another in the North Killingholme area from September to November 1936 may have related to several birds released from Whipsnade Zoo, Bedfordshire in 1935.

Little Egret *Egretta garzetta*
A rare vagrant, recorded with certainty only during recent years. Blathwayt (1915) referred to two nineteenth century specimens, both thought to have been obtained locally, but no details have been found. One was seen by M.T. Barnes and G.M.S. Easy on Kirton and Frampton Marshes on 23rd July 1966. There was a large spring influx of this species and other southern herons to Britain in 1970 when two were observed at Donna Nook on 5th May, followed by single birds at North Cotes on 25th May and 29th June and at Marton, near Gainsborough on 29th May. A smaller influx in 1973 produced one at North Killingholme from 6th to 17th June and one on Holbeach Marsh on 3rd June and 29th July. There have been at least five records since then in spring and autumn and one in the Wash from August 1987 to April 1988 and again from August to December 1988.

One found dead at the mouth of the Welland on 15th September 1979 had been ringed as a nestling in the Netherlands two months earlier.

Great White Egret *Egretta alba*
A very rare vagrant. One was seen by G.P. Catley, J.T. Harriman and other observers at Messingham, near Scunthorpe on 7th and 8th August 1979. Yarrell (1871-85) recorded one alleged to have been killed in the county during the early nineteenth century. No date or locality has been traced unless the record refers to one said to have been shot in the Fens in the mid-1830s and preserved in one of the Lincolnshire collections. One in Louth Museum mounted by Kew may possibly have been obtained locally.

Grey Heron *Ardea cinerea*
A fairly common breeding species, passage migrant and winter visitor. Colonies in the county have often been counted but apart from censuses in 1928, 1954 and 1964 and regular assessments since 1967, earlier histories of the heronries are often incomplete. Some sites are traditional and several have had quite chequered pasts. Attempts have been made to reduce numbers at some of the colonies particularly in the late nineteenth and early present centuries to protect trout farms and other fishing interests. Most sites

have also been affected at some time or another by the felling of older trees thus causing shifts to neighbouring woodlands. The species is also very vulnerable in hard winters and severe decreases may be evident in the succeeding breeding seasons.

Early reference to heronries seldom made any mention of the numbers of birds present, though Pennant (1771) described one at Cressy Hall, near Spalding as vast and with 80 nests in one tree. Cordeaux listed six colonies in 1870 and cited three more known to have been occupied shortly before then. Five heronries were recorded by Harting in 1872 and he gave counts of 40 pairs at Haverholme Priory, near Sleaford and 30 pairs at Manby Wood, near Brigg. By 1908 Blathwayt reported 66 pairs at six sites but he stated that additional smaller colonies were also in existence.

The British Trust for Ornithology organised its first census of heronries in England and Wales in 1928 and county results showed that there were 150 pairs in eight colonies with the highest counts of 42 pairs at Willoughby Wood, near Alford, and 34 pairs at Muckton Wood, near Louth. Some sites were possibly overlooked in this census but a comprehensive count in 1954 produced a new peak of 315 pairs at 15 colonies. Of the significant colonies Muckton still held 34 pairs and one at Wharton Wood, near Gainsborough had increased from 20 to 61 pairs. New large breeding sites were at Troy Wood, near Horncastle with 55 pairs and at Deeping St. James with 89 pairs.

A rapid reduction to about 200 pairs was noted soon after the 1954 census due mainly to large decreases at three of the main heronries at Muckton, Wharton and Deeping St. James. The species fared particularly badly during the severe winter of 1962/63 and a further decline to an estimated 100 pairs was evident by the following season. The population recovered to around 200 pairs from 1965 to 1967 but decreased slightly to 160 to 175 pairs at seven or eight heronries until 1971. Mild winters in the 1970s no doubt favoured the Heron and a gradual increase occurred each year until there were about 300 pairs at 11 colonies by 1977. During the last ten years there was a peak of 380 pairs in 1984 and 1985.

Six heronries in the county can be termed as of significant size in the last ten years. These are at Thornton Abbey, Muckton Wood, Willoughby Wood, Doddington, near Lincoln, Troy Wood and Deeping St. James. The smaller heronries are often only in existence for a few years and some of these appear to serve as overflow sites from the larger colonies in years of peak population. Solitary pairs are sometimes located and it seems quite probable that some small colonies are overlooked. An interesting record concerns a pair that reared three young at a reed bed site in the Wash area during 1936.

After the breeding season birds disperse and parties of juveniles form in the coastal districts. Autumn immigrants may begin to arrive at about this time but it is impossible to distinguish early migrants from local post-breeding birds. Later in the autumn, mainly from late August to early November, Herons may occasionally be seen arriving at the coast from the east. Return passage in April and May is usually poorly defined and migrants heading out to sea are only seldom observed.

The only ringing recoveries indicating the origin of these European immigrants are of two birds ringed as nestlings in southern Sweden and found in Lincolnshire in winter. There are a number of local recoveries all of birds ringed as nestlings. County-bred birds have been recovered in all of the neighbouring counties and also in Cumbria, Cleveland,

Lancashire, Staffordshire, Gloucestershire and Worcestershire. Birds found in the county between autumn and spring have originated from colonies in Northumberland, Berkshire, Buckinghamshire, Bedfordshire, Oxfordshire and Suffolk. Three birds reared in Lincolnshire have been recovered abroad in their first or second winters, one in north-west France and two in northern Spain.

Purple Heron *Ardea purpurea*
A rare vagrant usually in spring from April to early June. One was shot on the River Witham at Hykeham, near Lincoln by Reverend J. Metcalfe in the latter half of the nineteenth century and one is said to have been shot on Kirton Marsh in 1919. One at Brocklesby on 31st July 1952 was joined by a second bird from 12th to 31st August with one still present on 1st September. Since 1968 there have been at least 14 records mainly on the coast between Donna Nook and Chapel Pit with inland records at Tattershall and Messingham. A first winter bird was also noted at Deeping St. Nicholas from 6th to 30th November 1986 when it was found dead.

Black Stork *Ciconia nigra*
A rare vagrant. One at Freiston Shore on 25th April 1984, seen by J.W. Fox and R.A. Spiers, is the only record.

White Stork *Ciconia ciconia*
A rare vagrant. One was shot on the coast at Marshchapel in June 1832. There was an influx of White Storks mainly to south-east England in the spring of 1967 and a party of three appeared at Marshchapel on 21st May. One frequented fields near the Wash coast at Benington, Freiston and Frampton from 27th November to mid-December 1968 and one that made a protracted stay in the Stickney area in the Fens from 29th April to 12th June 1971 occurred during another widespread arrival of the species into Britain. One was seen at Gibraltar Point on 1st June 1976 and another flew north-west over Denton Reservoir on 6th April 1983. In 1986 two birds were following silage cutters at Holbeach Hurn on 9th and 10th June.

Glossy Ibis *Plegadis falcinellus*
There are six records of this rare vagrant. The first was shot on Read's Island in the autumn of 1869 by R. Pilkington. In 1881 an immature male was shot at Skegness on 9th September and another bird was obtained there on 27th October. One frequented the marshes of Tetney and North Cotes on 29th September 1923 and another was seen at Saltfleetby on 5th November 1975. One seen flying south at Gibraltar Point on 16th May 1976 was presumably the bird that arrived at Wisbech sewage farm later in the day and remained until 18th May.

Spoonbill *Platalea leucorodia*
A rare visitor chiefly in the spring and early summer, less often in autumn and exceptionally in winter. During the last 20 years it has occurred almost annually, but there are few records for the nineteenth century and the early part of the present century.

It probably occurred regularly before drainage of the Fens and even nested in the county until at least the middle of the seventeenth century, as it did elsewhere in England. The evidence for this is on a 1662 map of South Holland included in Dugdale (1772) where a wood near Crowland is marked as 'Dousdale holt where many White Herons do breed'. Blathwayt (1915) gave only two nineteenth century records but we have traced eight occurrences between 1826 and 1864. Six of the birds were shot. In 1911 two were seen at Tetney Haven in early November and one was shot at the mouth of the Welland on 13th November. One was seen at North Cotes in October 1912 and two occurred there in 1915. Another bird is said to have been seen at Gibraltar Point at some time prior to 1914.

There were no further records until 1945 when a party of five appeared at North Cotes in January. Since 1949 about 80 birds have been observed, chiefly along the coast of the Humber and in the Wash. The largest group was of six at North Killingholme in June 1978. It has been noted mainly from late April to early July with rather fewer records from August to early November. One bird also wintered at Gibraltar Point in 1984/85. A bird that stayed at North Killingholme from 26th June to 3rd August 1975 had been colour-ringed as a nestling in the Netherlands in June 1972. Another nestling ringed in the same area in 1984 was seen at Grainthorpe in April 1987.

Mute Swan *Cygnus olor*

A fairly common and widespread resident that is found on many inland waters ranging from large lakes, gravel pits and reservoirs to rivers, canals and drains in both urban and rural localities. Only very small numbers appear on the coast and some of these birds could be immigrants from Scandinavia judging by their wary behaviour. The Mute Swan is considered to have been indigenous in the Fens as well as in other parts of East Anglia before it was domesticated in the Middle Ages but many have now reverted back to a wild state.

The British Trust for Ornithology organised a breeding census in 1955 when 106 pairs were located in the county. A repeat census in 1961 showed a decline to 84 pairs and this was attributed to the destruction of 80 badly oiled birds at Lincoln in 1960, although national population levels also decreased between 1955 and 1965 due mainly to hard winters. By 1983 a recovery to 109 pairs had taken place. Non-breeding flocks occur at several places in the county particularly at Lincoln, in the Humber and on the Welland. Winter peaks on the Welland exceed 250 birds in some years.

Some birds are completely sedentary, breeding pairs remaining on their territorial waters throughout the year and ringing recoveries show that many movements are only local.

The greatest distance travelled by a Lincolnshire-ringed bird was 60 miles to the south by a juvenile ringed at Tetney in July 1962 and controlled in Cambridgeshire in April 1963. An immature bird ringed at Spalding in January 1962 was controlled 50 miles to the north-west in Nottinghamshire in May 1968. In addition three other birds have been recovered in Nottinghamshire and one was found in Northamptonshire.

Bewick's Swan *Cygnus columbianus*

A fairly common passage migrant and a winter visitor in small numbers though nowhere does it winter regularly. Flocks are often larger than those of the Whooper and although up to 130 have been counted, most parties are of 20 birds or less. The species has clearly increased in the county during the present century. It was recorded less regularly in the last century but in some winters, for example 1870/71 and in December 1890, larger numbers occurred. The first signs of any increase were during the late 1920s. A large influx of birds into England in the 1938/39 winter was followed by regular wintering of birds in the Ouse Washes in Cambridgeshire and regular sightings of transient flocks through Lincolnshire.

Habitats favoured in the county are similar to those of the Whooper; chiefly reservoirs, gravel pits, sewage farms, lakes, rivers and coastal waters. Arable land and flooded pastures are often frequented for feeding purposes. A few birds arrive during the second half of October but most immigrants appear in November.

Further influxes, dependent on the weather, may occur during the winter. Return passage in spring is from late February to the end of March, with odd stragglers later in the spring. One was present at North Killingholme during July 1952 and another was at Messingham throughout the summer of 1986.

Several birds ringed at Slimbridge, Gloucestershire have been reported in the county. One of these, colour-ringed in December 1978, was seen in the Netherlands in March 1981, then at Saltfleet Haven in February 1982 and in West Germany one month later. One ringed at Caerlaverock on the Solway in February 1982 was recorded in the county in March 1985.

Whooper Swan *Cygnus cygnus*

A fairly common passage migrant and winter visitor to coastal districts and inland waters. Early birds may be encountered from the first week of October but the main arrivals occur later in the month and in November. Most birds pass through the county as mid-winter counts are generally much lower than those for autumn. Numbers increase slightly again on a light return movement in March and occasionally during April. One was present on the Brayford Pool, Lincoln on 30th June 1982. Parties are generally quite small often of ten or less but sometimes larger herds of up to about 50 birds are present.

One ringed in Iceland in June 1980 was seen at Gibraltar Point on 21st to 24th October then at the Ouse Washes on 26th October of the same year.

Bean Goose *Anser fabalis*

A very scarce winter visitor. Most records are from the coastal districts but it has occurred occasionally inland. Early nineteenth century records of large numbers are not reliable as it is evident that much confusion existed between this species and the Pink-footed Goose. Groups tend to be rather small, up to five birds being normal, and the largest flock to appear consisted of 15 birds at Trent Falls in December 1976. A very early bird was seen at Gibraltar Point on 5th September 1960, otherwise it is usually noted from about the second week of October until early March. Birds belonging to both *A.f. fabalis* and *rossicus* have been identified in the county.

Two Dutch-ringed birds have been recovered at Holbeach. One ringed in late August 1958 was shot in January 1962 and the other bird ringed in February 1969 was shot in February 1970.

Pink-footed Goose *Anser brachyrhyncus*

The commonest grey goose despite a dramatic decline in wintering numbers during the last few years. The regular large flocks of 5,000 or more which used to appear on the Humber and Wash no longer occur. Now much smaller numbers are seen with flocks of over 1,000 usually remaining for only short periods. The main wintering population appears to be staying in Scotland and this may be due to disturbance and a lack of food in the county caused by changes in farming methods. Until the 1960s large numbers used to arrive in September and by November they were to be seen in thousands on the upper reaches of the Humber and in the Wash.

The Humber birds roost on the mudflats in the river and flight to the Wolds as well as lowland fields where they feed on stubble, young corn and small potatoes. Birds which frequent the Wash formerly occurred in very large numbers on Croft Marsh, near Gibraltar Point but during the last few years the main flock of around 2,000 birds has been on Holbeach Marsh. During the course of the winter there is much shifting about of the population and numbers can vary greatly. By late March most birds have left the county although a few may be seen in April. There are several records of pricked birds remaining through the summer. In 1975 at Messingham, near Scunthorpe a female which had arrived during the previous autumn laid and incubated a clutch of infertile eggs.

There are many ringing recoveries relating to birds wintering in Lincolnshire. At least 45 birds ringed on the breeding grounds in Iceland and one from eastern Greenland have been recovered in the county and one or two birds ringed in Lincolnshire have been found in Iceland and Greenland. Movements of ringed birds within the British Isles include 50 between the county and Scotland, in addition to several involving Lancashire, Yorkshire, Norfolk, Cambridgeshire and Gloucestershire.

White-fronted Goose *Anser albifrons*

A scarce but regular winter visitor chiefly to the Humber and the Wash estuaries. Traditional small flocks occur at North Cotes and Holbeach in many years and although most parties seldom exceed ten birds, up to 50 are sometimes present.

Our wintering birds belong to the nominate race, *A.a. albifrons,* which breeds in north-east Russia and Siberia but single birds showing characteristics of the Greenland race, *A.a. flavirostris,* were recorded at Gibraltar Point on 5th December 1950, Tetney on 2nd January 1964, Donna Nook on 23rd January 1969 and at Holbeach on 16th February 1972. Birds have been recorded as early as 28th September but few arrive before November with peak numbers generally present during January. Most individuals have departed by early March but stragglers may occasionally be encountered in April.

One ringed at Slimbridge, Gloucestershire in February 1958 was recovered at Tetney in December 1958.

Lesser White-fronted Goose *Anser erythropus*
A very rare vagrant. An adult bird seen by W. Tinsley and recorded by Peter Scott joined a pinioned pair of the same species at Holbeach Marsh for one day in January 1943. Cordeaux (1899) recorded one on a stall in Grimsby market about 1874. He considered it likely to have been shot locally but the record cannot be accepted in the absence of any details of origin.

Greylag Goose *Anser anser*
A scarce winter visitor and a fairly common feral resident. Before the drainage of the Fens the Greylag was a common breeding species that was exploited by the fenmen. The young goslings were frequently captured and domesticated and the wild stock probably became extinct in the Fens between 1770 and the early 1800s. Since then the Greylag has continued to be a scarce winter visitor from late September to early May. It occurs in most parts of the county though mainly on the coast. Introduced feral birds have recently become established in the Fens. A resident flock has colonised Kirkby-on-Bain gravel pit since the 1960s and now numbers up to several hundred birds, with similar numbers in the Deeping St. James area. Breeding was first recorded near Bardney in 1957 and now occurs regularly at Kirkby-on-Bain as well as at Tattershall and at several pits around Deeping St. James with isolated pairs in several other suitable areas in the county.

One ringed at Dumfriesshire in June 1976 was shot at Kirkby-on-Bain in December 1980.

Snow Goose *Anser caerulescens*
One seen near Boston by N.W. Moore on 31st January 1942 may have been of wild origin. There are several other records but most of these have probably been escaped birds since some of them have been very tame and others have occurred in summer, often with feral Canada and Greylag Geese. Few of the 20 or so records during the last 20 years have been in the winter.

Canada Goose *Branta canadensis*
A common resident originally introduced to private parks and lakes during the eighteenth and nineteenth centuries. Discovery of new waters was limited by its sedentary behaviour but since the 1940s it has increased and spread due to artificial dispersion. Flocks may wander about the countryside both during and outside the breeding season.

The strongholds in the county include Grimsthorpe Park and Denton Reservoir, where the flocks may number up to 500 birds. A few pairs have colonised several gravel pits away from the main concentrations and it is becoming more widespread as a breeding species especially in the north of the county. An adult of one of the smaller races was seen at New Holland and Barton-on-Humber in August and September 1986 and at Burton Pits in November.

A Derbyshire bird transported and released in Lancashire in June 1957 was recovered on Holbeach Marsh in August 1960. One from Leicestershire was released in Gloucestershire in June 1953 where it was still present in July 1956, but in May 1961 it was recovered at Riseholme, near Lincoln. Another bird trapped at Messingham, near Scunthorpe in April 1976 had been ringed in Inverness in the previous July.

Barnacle Goose *Branta leucopsis*
A scarce winter visitor which has been recorded in all but four of the last 30 years. It was apparently rare and irregular during the latter part of the nineteenth century and the early years of the present century but occasionally small flocks occurred in the Humber, as in December 1867.

Many of the recent records are of single birds or very small parties of up to 20 birds, although in 1981 there were flocks of 52 at North Cotes between 27th February and 3rd March and 48 at Holbeach from 22nd to 28th February. In 1984 there were 79 at Donna Nook from 25th to 29th January and 35 at Gibraltar Point on 29th January.

The first birds in autumn usually appear during early October and although most birds have departed by mid-March there are several records until the third week of May. Records in summer probably refer to escapes as does the attempted breeding by a pair at Chapel Pits in 1982 and 1983. It is most regular in the estuaries of the Humber and the Wash but there are several reports of inland occurrences.

One ringed in the Solway Firth, Dumfriesshire in February 1963 was found dead at Donna Nook in October 1970.

Brent Goose *Branta bernicla*
A numerous winter visitor to the Wash with smaller numbers present on the north-east coast. Early birds may arrive before the end of August but in most years small parties occur during October, followed by larger numbers from late November to early February. Dwindling numbers are usually present until the end of April but exceptionally there are good-sized flocks in the Wash until late May. There are a few recent records of birds seen during the summer.

During the last half of the nineteenth century the Brent Goose was quite numerous on the Lincolnshire coast although numbers were related to the severity of the weather. The light-bellied race, *B.b. hrota*, which breeds in Spitsbergen and on Franz Josef Land was a not infrequent visitor to the north-east coast particularly during hard winters, but after 1917 when there was a flock at North Cotes in February it occurred mostly singly and as an irregular vagrant. Since 1979 this race has been recorded annually in small numbers on the north-east coast and in the Wash.

The dark-bellied race, *B.b. bernicla*, breeds in Arctic Russia and Siberia and was stated to have been particularly common on the coast during the last century. From the early 1930s this population suffered a large decrease and reached its lowest level by the early 1950s. The decline was blamed upon over-shooting and the loss of its principal food, eel grass *(Zostera spp.)* although this plant appears never to have been common in Lincolnshire where its main food is a species of *Enteromorpha*. The recovery of eel grass in western Europe plus better protection measures improved the species' status during the 1960s. Large flocks have been recorded feeding on coastal fields of grass and winter cereals since 1981/82 and a few birds have occasionally wandered further inland.

Brent Geese

Mallard

In the last few years the flock on the north-east coast between Tetney and Saltfleetby has numbered up to 3,000 birds, while the Wash population has exceeded 15,000 in some winters. A bird showing the characteristics of the race *B.b. nigricans* which breeds in the Nearctic and north-east Siberia was seen at Donna Nook on 21st and 23rd January 1982. Another at Kirton Marsh on 19th February 1987 is still under consideration by *British Birds*.

One ringed at Benington in February 1967 was found dead in southern Sweden in October 1974. Two birds ringed in Denmark in April 1963 were found dead in the Wash in January and February 1965.

Red-breasted Goose *Branta ruficollis*
There are three or four records of this rare vagrant from Siberia. One was seen by B.M. Clarkson at Covenham Reservoir on 1st October 1978. One was present between North Cotes and Saltfleet from 25th to 29th November 1984 and in 1985 perhaps the same bird and sometimes a second were seen in the Wash between Gibraltar Point and Leverton from 9th February to 3rd March.

Egyptian Goose *Alopochen aegyptiacus*
A species that has been kept in captivity in England since the eighteenth century and has been found in a feral state for over 100 years. Most county records presumably originate from the population of East Anglia though some may have escaped from local wildfowl collections.

F. Stubbs (1929) recorded one shot by a farmer at North Cotes about 1880 and subsequently preserved. A party of six birds frequented Gibraltar Point between 13th August and 6th October 1973 and what was probably the same flock was seen at Mablethorpe on 14th October and at Donna Nook on 17th November. Three were seen at Gibraltar Point on 20th October 1974 and five were noted there on 30th October 1976. Up to nine birds have been recorded annually since 1977, chiefly from October to February, but also during the rest of the year. Most of these occurrences were on the coast although there are a few inland records. A resident pair at Grimsthorpe Park from 1980 to 1985 nested on at least one occasion.

Ruddy Shelduck *Tadorna ferruginea*
A very rare vagrant though most recent records probably relate to escaped birds. An invasion of the species into Britain in the summer of 1892 resulted in the first county record. A female was shot by a Cleethorpes gunner at Humberstone Fitties on 1st September and was verified by F. Stubbs. A party of three birds occurred on the Trent on 20th October 1898 and one that was shot is now in the Lincoln Museum. Another bird was obtained at North Cotes on 30th August 1919. During the last 30 years there have been many records especially of paired birds but none are acceptable as genuinely wild birds.

Shelduck *Tadorna tadorna*
A common breeding species and a numerous winter visitor particularly to the Humber

estuary and the Wash. Numbers have increased considerably since the last century, mainly due to protection in Britain and on the Heligoland Bight moulting grounds.

Around the turn of the century small numbers nested in the coastal dunes and on the sandy warrens in the north-west of the county but breeding in the Wash was recorded only irregularly probably as a result of poor coverage of the area at that time. At present it has spread to a number of inland gravel pits, sewage farms and other suitable areas, as well as breeding in small numbers along the open coast. Good numbers nest in the Humber from Donna Nook as far as the River Trent but the main population breeds in the Fens and the Wash.

In 1969 a census of the Wash by K. Atkin (1970) produced an estimated 385 pairs of Shelducks between Gibraltar Point and the county border. Most pairs nest in rabbit burrows, haystacks and derelict buildings but exceptionally nests may be found in the open on the salt marshes of the Wash.

After the breeding season most adult and non-breeding birds make the annual moult migration to the North Sea coast of Germany. Small flocks may be observed moving to the east between late June and August and only a few adults remain behind to care for creches of ducklings. Some concentrations of young birds may be quite large; for example 1,000 were present at Wisbech sewage farm in July 1974. Migrants return to the estuaries from late October to December and large gatherings of several thousands are a regular winter feature, especially in the Wash. Some migrants are probably of west coast origin as small parties occur occasionally on some inland waters.

Ducklings ringed in the Fens have been recovered in their first or second winters in Londonderry, County Clare, Carmarthen, Glamorgan, Lancashire and Cornwall. Two more were recovered in France in their first winters and another bird ringed in July 1962 was found dead in the Netherlands in December 1967. A juvenile ringed at Holbeach in August 1959 was caught and released in the Heligoland Bight ten years later and a duckling ringed at Tetney in July 1965 was found dead in the same area in October 1968. A Danish juvenile marked in August 1962 was found dead at Holbeach in April 1963 and another ringed in southern Sweden in July 1970 was recovered long dead at Grimsby Docks in June 1974. A duckling ringed in Dorset in July 1956 was found dead at Saltfleet in December 1960. One ringed in West Germany 1975 was found dead on Wrangle Marsh in March 1986.

Mandarin *Aix galericulata*
This species was admitted to the British List in 1971 following the successful establishment of feral birds particularly in south-east England. Doubtless the county records are incomplete as some observers have probably not bothered to report sightings. One was present at North Killingholme Pits in late July 1964. An immature male was trapped at Deeping St. James on 13th August 1973 and another was trapped at the same locality on 30th August 1974. A pair was present at Deeping on 10th January 1975 and by that year it was said to be a fairly frequent visitor to the various pits in the south of the county from feral flocks in Northamptonshire. During the last ten years there have been about 20 records at all times of the year. A pair bred near Tallington in the early 1980s.

Wigeon *Anas penelope*

A numerous winter visitor and passage migrant especially to the Humber and the Wash. A few occasionally summer in the county and breeding has been recorded several times. It is one of the most common ducks in winter. Small numbers begin to arrive in coastal areas in late August and September and by the end of November it is well distributed although in varying numbers according to food, weather and persecution. It frequently associates with flocks of Brent Geese on the mudflats and large flocks sometimes gather on the sea. Smaller numbers winter at several inland sites especially where there are flooded grasslands as at Baston Fen. Other flocks occur on gravel pits such as those in the Lincoln area. The largest numbers usually occur during severe winters particularly when sub-zero temperatures persist on the continent. Exceptionally 17,000 birds were present at Holbeach Marsh in December 1981. Wintering birds start to dwindle in February and most have departed by early April, although light passage continues until late May or even early June.

Breeding has occurred on several occasions but as with other wildfowl, feral birds may form a proportion of the records. It nested at Scotton Common in 1898 and again in the north-west of the county in 1926 and 1927. A pair bred at Deeping Pit in 1955 and single pairs bred at Kirkby-on-Bain and Read's Island in 1972. Two nests were found on Read's Island in the following year and in 1975 a pair bred successfully at Baston Fen.

Ringing recoveries indicate that many of our wintering birds come from Finland and the area eastwards across Russia. Migrants ringed in Denmark, Belgium and the Netherlands have been shot in the county. One ringed at Deeping Lake in April 1957 was recovered in north-west Italy in March 1958. Some of the immigrants winter farther west in the British Isles as shown by the recoveries of Lincolnshire-ringed birds in Cumberland, Pembrokeshire, Caernarvonshire and Fermanagh.

American Wigeon *Anas americana*

A rare vagrant from North America. The only definite county record is of a male located at Covenham Reservoir by E.J. Mackrill on 12th February 1974. It was subsequently seen by many observers during its stay until 24th February. At a meeting of the Zoological Society in April 1838 a male was exhibited and said to have been taken in the Lincolnshire Fens in the winter of 1837/38. As the bird was bought in a London market the authenticity of its origin is in some doubt though many ducks were sent to London from Lincolnshire.

Gadwall *Anas strepera*

A fairly common winter visitor and passage migrant that has increased during the last 40 years. Blathwayt (1915) knew of no recent records and merely quoted 22 birds taken in winter at the Ashby Decoy between 1833 and 1868.

An attempt was made to introduce this species in Lincolnshire about 1915 but this was unsuccessful. One was shot on the Welland in November 1924. It was more regularly recorded from 1933 onwards, chiefly from October to December on inland waters in the north of the county. Numbers have continued to increase and it is now quite regular from August to April with several pairs present in summer. It was more numerous than usual in 1973 when about 50 birds were seen but since 1980 there have been regularly over 100 records annually.

Most records are from freshwater sites and birds are encountered on the sea only infrequently. A pair bred at Roughton Moor, near Woodhall Spa in 1963 and since then there have been breeding records from near Tattershall in 1986, Burton Gravel Pits in 1987 and 1988 and near Baston Fen in 1988.

Birds ringed on passage in the county have been recovered in subsequent winters in France and the Netherlands and another bird was recovered in Nottinghamshire. One ringed as a duckling in Czechoslovakia in June 1975 was shot at Brigg in December of the same year. Fully-grown birds ringed in France and the Netherlands have been recovered in Lincolnshire in winter.

Teal *Anas crecca*

A fairly common but somewhat local breeding species and a numerous winter visitor and passage migrant. The main nesting areas are in boggy parts in the north-west of the county with smaller numbers occupying gravel pits and other suitable areas in the south. Elsewhere breeding records are usually irregular and restricted to isolated pairs in temporarily favourable situations. On passage and in winter it is more widespread occurring on inland waters of all sizes, in the estuaries and on the coast. According to Cordeaux in 1899 there had been a recent decrease in the numbers wintering in the county and Haigh remarked on a large decrease in the 1920s but these may only have been short-term declines.

The first autumn arrivals occur on the coast in late August and immigration continues until the end of November. Many of these birds pass into the Humber and large concentrations gather in the upper reaches of the river. Small movements may be seen during the winter particularly during hard weather. Spring passage chiefly from early March to mid-May is generally on a small scale.

Males showing characterisitics of the North American race *A.c. carolinensis,* known as the Green-winged Teal, were seen at Gibraltar Point on 11th November 1984 and 28th March 1985, and at Goxhill Marsh on 23rd April 1986 and Messingham from 29th November to 10th December 1988.

Birds ringed in western Britain in winter have been recovered in Lincolnshire, probably on return passage to the continent. These include two from Pembrokeshire, seven from Gloucestershire, two from Dorset and one from County Down. One ringed on autumn passage in the county was recovered later in winter in North Wales. Teal wintering in the county have originated from breeding grounds in Iceland, France and Midlothian. Two ringed on autumn passage on the north-east coast were recovered in France in subsequent winters and one ringed there in December 1962 was recovered in Germany in November 1965. One ringed on the Wash in March 1978 was shot in Denmark in 1980.

Mallard *Anas platyrhynchos*

The most numerous and widespread duck in the county. It is a common breeding species nesting regularly on many lakes, ponds, streams and rivers as well as in the marshes, on arable land and in copses and plantations. Numbers are augmented by large arrivals from Europe in autumn when it becomes abundant on reservoirs and other inland waters and also in the estuaries. It is plentiful on the open sea only during freezing conditions.

Both as a breeding bird and winter visitor, Mallard numbers were evidently immense in former times. Before drainage of the extensive fenny tracts of Lincolnshire the birds contributed a great deal to the livelihood of the fenmen. Thousands of young, flightless birds and moulting adults were rounded up and driven into nets in the late summer. Large numbers were also trapped in the 40 or so duck decoys in the county in the eighteenth and early nineteenth centuries. Immigration on a vast scale into the Fens is referred to in old accounts. Even in the late nineteenth century after extensive drainage and improved cultivation, Mallard movements were still often quite spectacular. Smith and Cornwallis (1955) thought that breeding birds had decreased during the present century, but since the early 1960s there appears to have been a recovery in many areas.

Winter visitors arrive from the end of September to early December, with the bulk of immigrants occurring from late October to mid-November. Return movement in spring is much less pronounced, chiefly between mid-March and late April.

Ringing recoveries show that some of our wintering birds originate from the Low countries and around the Baltic Sea. An adult ringed at Deeping St. James in July 1973 was shot one year later in Austria and one ringed at North Witham in February 1962 was shot near the Black Sea in Russia in November 1972. Two birds ringed in the Fens in autumn were shot in Rumania in subsequent winters. The most remarkable recovery concerns a juvenile ringed at Crowland in September 1962 and shot in Alberta, Canada in December 1965. This was the first recovery of a British-ringed duck in the New World.

Pintail *Anas acuta*

A fairly common passage migrant and common winter visitor. It has bred on two occasions. Numbers tend to fluctuate but it is more frequently recorded than formerly. In the latter half of the nineteenth century it was described as being not uncommon in some years but irregular in occurrence, but by the 1920s there had been a definite decrease on the north-east coast. During the last 30 years, however, the species has occurred regularly sometimes in sizeable flocks, particularly in the estuaries of the Wash. Recently there have been up to 400 at Holbeach Marsh and 3,000 at Terrington Marsh in winter.

Counts in the Humber, along the coast and on inland waters reveal mainly small numbers but a well-marked passage is in evidence. First arrivals in autumn are in late August and birds move through until late November or early December. Return movements last from the beginning of March to early May. Summering birds are very rare. Single pairs bred in the Fens in 1940 and again in 1952.

Four birds ringed at Deeping St. James have been recovered. One ringed in March 1956 was found at Arkangel in Russia in May 1958 and another ringed on the same day was reported from the Netherlands during the winter of 1960/61. One ringed as a juvenile in September 1956 was recovered in the Karelian S.S.R. in September 1961. One trapped in February 1966 was shot in Renfrewshire in January 1967. A juvenile ringed in the Netherlands in September 1961 was recovered at Humberston five weeks later.

Garganey *Anas querquedula*

A scarce but regular passage migrant and now only an infrequent summer visitor. A few pairs nested in the north-west of the county particularly at Scotton Common at least until 1914 and probably until 1918. Several pairs occurred in most springs at Ashby Decoy and records show that 29 were trapped there between 1834 and 1868. Breeding was not recorded again until 1940, when two pairs were reported in the Fens. One pair nested at Goxhill in 1948 when another pair almost certainly bred in the Welland Washes.

Between 1951 and 1962 regular breeding of up to five pairs occurred in the Welland Washes until drainage of the area destroyed the nesting habitat. During the last few years summering pairs have been noted only occasionally. Definite breeding was proved at Skellingthorpe, near Lincoln in 1958, at Lincoln sewage farm in 1960, at Baston Fen in 1967 and 1980 and at Killingholme in 1981 and 1987. Single pairs have possibly bred at several other sites in recent years.

Spring passage of very small numbers is chiefly from the second week of April to the third week of May but early birds sometimes arrive in the second half of March. A good proportion of birds in spring are paired so that the paucity of breeding records is probably due to a lack of suitable habitat. Return passage in autumn lasts from late July until the end of September with occasional stragglers remaining in October. Numbers are again usually rather small, parties seldom exceeding ten birds, but a flock of 30 occurred at Tetney on 11th August 1951 and 15 were seen at Gibraltar Point on 19th August 1985. Migrants have been recorded regularly since about 1940. Prior to that date the species occurred only rarely on passage. Coastal observers described the Garganey as a rare migrant during the latter half of the nineteenth century and the early part of the present century.

One bird ringed in Belgium and two from Holland have been recovered in Lincolnshire and one ringed at Deeping St. James in early August 1973 was shot in south-west France two months later.

Blue-winged Teal *Anas discors*

There are five records of this North American species though escapes from captivity cannot be discounted. An immature male joined a wildfowl collection at Sudbrook, near Grantham on 10th September 1941 and was still present on 23rd October 1947, although it had sometimes flown away for short periods. It was recorded by A.W.S. Dean and was also seen by P.P.L. Stevenson. A male was seen near Lincoln on 22nd April 1947 and one or two were present at Wisbech sewage farm from 11th September to 8th October 1978. Another was present at Huttoft pits from 26th to 30th September 1982.

Shoveler *Anas clypeata*

A fairly common breeding species with increased numbers on passage but scarcer in winter. A very small population nested in the county in the late nineteenth century but Cordeaux in 1899 stated that there had been some increase and spread in breeding range in recent years. During the early part of the present century good numbers bred at Twigmoor and Scotton Common with smaller numbers elsewhere. There has been a general national increase and spread since about 1900 and this has certainly been the trend in Lincolnshire, although the population has probably remained fairly static in recent years. The main breeding strength lies in the Fenland areas with smaller numbers on the heaths of the north west and along the bank of the Humber. Spasmodic breeding occurs in other suitable areas, though seldom in eastern coastal districts.

Immigration begins in late July and continues to the end of November, peak numbers occurring during September. Parties on migration tend to be small but concentrations of 100 or more are sometimes recorded. Return movements on a smaller scale last from late February until early May.

Several birds ringed on passage have been recovered. One ringed at Deeping St. James in early March 1966 was recovered in Russia, west of the Urals eight weeks later and one ringed at Wisbech sewage farm in August 1966 was recovered on the Siberian Plain in September 1968. Two March-ringed birds from Deeping have been recovered in Denmark in subsequent autumns. Three ringed in autumn were shot in France later in winter and a juvenile from Sutton Bridge in August 1965 was shot in Italy in March 1966. One ringed in September 1966 was recovered in south-east Spain in November 1967. A bird ringed at Deeping in April 1957 was in County Clare the following winter. A duckling ringed at Grimsthorpe, near Bourne in 1973 was shot in Gloucestershire in December of the same year and another duckling ringed at Tetney in 1971 was found dead in Essex in May 1973. A breeding adult ringed in Essex in June 1963 was at Barton-on-Humber in the following November.

Red-crested Pochard *Netta rufina*
A rare vagrant that has been noted increasingly during recent years and almost annually since 1967. Some of the records almost certainly refer to escapes from waterfowl collections. A male shot near Boston in January 1826 was only the second British record. Another was shot in the same district in early 1854.

There were no further records until April 1937 when five were present at Tetney. A pair established a territory and a nest containing four eggs was found on 19th May. On a later date there were six eggs but the clutch was eventually destroyed by rats. Correct identification was confirmed by examination of shells and down by F.C.R. Jourdain. These birds were considered likely to have escaped from Woburn Park in Bedfordshire where Red-crested Pochards had been bred and allowed to fly freely for a number of years before this date.

It is interesting to note, however, that there has been a spread in breeding range to the north-west across Europe and breeding was first reported in Denmark and the Netherlands in the early 1940s.

One was seen at the L.N.E.R. Pit, Lincoln on 24th November 1957 and at least three birds occurred at Tallington Pits, near Stamford during November and December 1959. One stayed at Langtoft Pit, near Bourne from 16th to 23rd May 1960, then there were no records until 1967. Since then, however, it has been recorded in all but four years with up to three records annually. Most have occurred from October to April with a few in summer. The majority of records are from pits in the southern half of the county.

Pochard *Aythya ferina*

A scarce breeding species and a common winter visitor and passage migrant, chiefly to inland waters. In the late nineteenth century breeding birds were confined to a few pairs in the area around Scawby and Twigmoor, with spasmodic nesting in the Spalding district. Despite a national increase and spread of Pochard and an increase in wintering birds in the county there was no obvious change in the nesting numbers until about 1960. Since then it has bred regularly in the Lincoln area and around Barton and Barrow-on-Humber with more irregular breeding at Huttoft, Wisbech sewage farm and gravel pits in the south of the county.

The increase in winter visitors has been more marked since 1960 and quite large flocks of 100 to 300 birds are not unusual on some waters. An exceptional flock of 700 was counted at Whisby Gravel Pit, near Lincoln on 27th February 1972 and up to 500 have been seen in recent winters in the New Holland area. Many of these assemblies contain a clear preponderance of males. Immigration from the Continent occurs in October and November and return passage is recorded from late February to April.

Birds ringed at Deeping St. James in winter have provided a good selection of recoveries. Thirteen birds have been recovered in Russia between 54N and 64N, and as far as 67E although one exceptional bird ringed in February 1966 was shot near Madagan by the sea of Okhotsk about 60N 150E in September 1968. Five birds have been recovered in Poland with two in Germany and single birds in France and Finland. One was wintering in Portugal a year later and another bird ringed on passage in November 1973 was shot in Portugal five weeks later. Birds wintering elsewhere in Britain in subsequent years have been reported in Staffordshire, Somerset, Dorset and County Cavan. One ringed in the Netherlands in November 1958 was shot near Louth in December 1962. One ringed in Czechoslovakia in July 1972 was shot at Boston in the following December and a duckling ringed at Lake Engure in White Russia in June 1966 was shot at Brocklesby in January 1969.

Ring-necked Duck *Aythya collaris*

A very rare vagrant from North America although the possibility of escapes from captivity cannot be excluded. A male was recorded by D. Suddaby at Messingham, near Scunthorpe from 3rd to 23rd June and on 6th to 20th October 1979. Either this bird or another was also seen at Barrow Haven by G.P. Catley on several dates between 24th October and 3rd November 1979. What was perhaps the same bird reappeared in 1980 at Nettleton on 17th February and again at Messingham on 23rd February and from 10th to 24th April and then in 1981 between 25th May and 6th June. In 1988, a male was in the Barton-on-Humber and Barrow Haven area on 17th and 18th June and presumably the same bird at New Holland from 24th November to 3rd December. Donovan first described this species from a male found in Leadenhall market and said to have been obtained in Lincolnshire in January 1801. It is unfortunate that the exact origin of the type specimen should remain unknown.

Ferruginous Duck *Aythya nyroca*
A rare vagrant recorded on ten occasions although the inclusion of birds escaped from captivity cannot be ruled out. In 1929 S.A. Cox recorded one or two at Newsham Lake on the Brocklesby Estate from 3rd to 24th February. A male was seen at Holywell, near Stamford from 25th to 27th December 1957. A female was shot at Baston Pits, near Bourne on 21st November 1959 and in the following year an adult frequented Goxhill Marsh from 4th to 26th September. A male was present at Wisbech sewage farm from 22nd July to 10th August 1972 and other males were recorded at Boston between 16th and 24th March 1974, at Covenham Reservoir on 4th and 5th November 1974, at Chapel Pit on 11th July 1976 and from 24th to 30th January 1980, and at Killingholme on 5th and 6th March 1981.

Tufted Duck *Aythya fuligula*
A fairly common breeding species and a common winter visitor and passage migrant. A huge national increase and spread at the beginning of the late nineteenth and early twentieth centuries has certainly been reflected in the county. A few pairs were suspected of nesting in the north-west from the 1890s onwards but there was no proven breeding record until 1920. During the next 30 years small numbers bred regularly in that area, spreading and increasing further from the 1960s onwards. Breeding is now recorded on a wide variety of inland waters from most parts of the county, with a population of several hundred pairs. Good numbers of non-breeding birds also spend the summer on many waters.

Wintering flocks have also become more numerous in recent years, rapidly exploiting gravel pits, new reservoirs and even quite small ponds. Flocks in excess of 100 birds are not uncommon and over 300 have been counted on some waters in mid-winter. Numbers are nearly always small on the open sea where it associates with parties of Scaup.

Flocks begin to assemble on the larger inland waters in July and August and the first winter visitors appear in September, passage continuing until November. Return migration of small numbers is recorded on the coast from early March until mid-May.

Birds ringed on passage and in winter at Deeping St. James have been recovered in subsequent winters in Norway, Sweden, Germany and Poland and in summer in Finland and in the Pechora Valley in Russia. Single birds have also been recovered in France in March, Czechoslovakia in August and Ireland in September. A duckling ringed at Wisbech sewage farm in 1969 was caught in northern Norway in May of the following year. One shot near Spilsby in December 1971 had been ringed as a duckling in the Ukraine two years earlier.

Scaup *Aythya marila*
A coastal winter visitor and passage migrant which occurs uncommonly inland. There is one breeding record. In mild winters numbers are usually rather low but during severe weather very large flocks may occur, particularly in the Wash and the Humber. Cordeaux recorded the species as the commonest duck in the Humber and flocks of a thousand or more were recorded there in several winters in the late nineteenth century. Although it is still fairly common in some winters, numbers are probably not as high as in former

Goldeneyes

Tufted Ducks

Long-tailed Duck

times.

Immigration on the coast lasts from late September to the end of December. Birds begin to disperse in March and passage migration continues until late April or early May. A few non-breeding birds are occasionally encountered in the summer months. On 7th August 1944, P.E. Brown found a female with seven young in a creek on Tetney Marsh. On a later date he managed to catch one of the ducklings and from his detailed description and measurements the identification was confirmed. The brood was last seen on 29th August.

One ringed at Deeping St. James in October 1960 was recovered in Denmark in January 1964 and a juvenile ringed at Oulu, Finland in July 1965 was shot near Barton-on-Humber in December of the same year.

Eider *Somateria mollissima*

A fairly common visitor that has increased markedly during the last 25 years and now occurs at all times of the year. It particularly favours the estuaries of the Humber and the Wash and quite large non-breeding flocks have been recorded in the Wash in summer. Early in the present century it was a rare but regular winter visitor to our coasts.

British and European populations have increased dramatically during the last 100 years but after the large scale exploitation of the Eider for food during the 1939-45 war the species was no more than a very rare vagrant until the early 1950s when increased protection brought a rapid return to former breeding numbers.

Despite thriving numbers on the Farne Islands in Northumberland there are no ringing recoveries in Lincolnshire from this area and it is considered that our birds possibly originate from the flourishing colonies in the Netherlands.

Since 1952 flocks have become more frequent on the coast and although most groups are rather small, up to 100 is not unusual and occasional gatherings of up to 500 are now recorded. An exceptional flock of 900 occurred at Freiston Shore in March 1986. Of the non-breeding flocks in the Wash during the summer over 200 have been counted at the Witham Mouth. Birds have penetrated the Humber as far as Trent Falls and Eiders have also been noted flying up the Trent. There are only a few other inland records.

Long-tailed Duck *Clangula hyemalis*

A rather scarce but regular winter visitor and pasage migrant on the coast. It is recorded annually at Covenham Reservoir but remains very rare on other inland waters. The majority of birds are immature with usually one or two birds at a time but parties of up to ten are sometimes noted. The first immigrants arrive in the first week of October, passage continuing until the end of November. Return movements last from March to early May. One was present at Covenham Reservoir from 6th July to 16th October 1983.

Smith and Cornwallis (1955) stated that it was apparently irregular but earlier accounts by Cordeaux (1899), Blathwayt (1915) and others give the impression that its status has probably not changed significantly over the years. Unusual numbers occurred in the Humber in October and November 1887 when many were reported to have been shot. More recently in 1988, there were up to 12 at Covenham Reservoir in December and up to 60 at the Witham Mouth in November and December.

Common Scoter *Melanitta nigra*

A common passage migrant and winter visitor. A few birds remain off the coast throughout the summer. It has evidently declined in the county since the late nineteenth century. Cordeaux and Haigh recorded immense flocks of thousands in autumn and at regular winter feeding grounds particularly off the north-east coast and in the Humber Mouth.

Migration on the coast usually begins in early July and continues regularly until November or sometimes early December. Most passage is to the north and many parties move into the Humber especially in the early part of the autumn. As the river narrows some of these flocks have been recorded at quite considerable height and it seems very likely that this is the start of overland passage to the west coast of Britain. Flocks have also been noted heading inland at Holbeach, in the Wash and small numbers seen quite regularly on some inland waters probably relate to birds on overland passage.

Coastal flocks in recent years have seldom exceeded 300 birds although in 1976 the species was more numerous than usual when up to 1,500 were present offshore at Theddlethorpe during November. Over 1,000 also occurred at Donna Nook in November 1983.

Velvet Scoter *Melanitta fusca*

A scarce but regular winter visitor that may be fairly common in some years. Main immigration is from September to November with a lighter return movement from late March to mid-May. Occasional birds remain in the summer. It is one of the most maritime of our wintering ducks with several inland records mainly at Covenham Reservoir during the past 25 years. It frequently associates with flocks of Common Scoters but numbers are generally small. Exceptionally, there were 100 at the mouth of Grainthorpe Haven on 12th October 1916 and good numbers were present offshore at Theddlethorpe between 13th November and 11 December 1976 with a maximum of 100 on 21st November.

Goldeneye *Bucephala clangula*

A fairly common winter visitor chiefly from mid-September to early May. Non-breeding birds are occasionally seen in summer and early immigrants may arrive in August in some years. Passage migration is indicated by maximum numbers being present in November and again in March and April but high counts have been made in mid-winter during severe weather on the continent.

There has been some increase in recent years. Immatures form the majority of immigrants but adults are by no means scarce. It is well-distributed on inland waters as well as on the coast. The largest concentrations occur in the Wash where flocks of 100 to 300 are now regularly counted and 460 were present at the mouth of the Witham on 11th March 1973. Up to 270 have also occurred in the Humber recently and up to 150 at Covenham Reservoir.

An adult female ringed in central Sweden in June 1957 was recovered at Sleaford in the following January.

Smew *Mergus albellus*
A winter visitor in variable numbers from late October to mid-April although most birds appear in January and February. It may be fairly common during severe winters but in most years it is rare or occasionally absent. It is most regular in the estuaries of the Humber and the Wash and on inland waters rather than on the open coast. In recent years it was most numerous during January to March in 1956, 1963, 1985, 1986 and 1987. As in other members of this genus, female and immature birds occur much more frequently than adult males.

Red-breasted Merganser *Mergus serrator*
A winter visitor and passage migrant in small numbers. The first arrive on the coast in late July and passage migrants are regularly noted until November. Wintering birds are almost entirely confined to the coast, inland records being rare and irregular and typically during severe weather. Spring passage is only light and lasts until early May although occasional birds remain throughout the summer.

Goosander *Mergus merganser*
A fairly common winter visitor, chiefly from the end of October to early April with occasional records in summer. Peak numbers usually occur during severe winters and although it is recorded mainly on inland waters it is also regular on the coast and in the Humber. The pits in the Deeping St. James and Tallington areas usually hold the main wintering parties and up to 80 birds have gathered there in recent years.

Ruddy Duck *Oxyura jamaicensis*
A scarce visitor with a recent small breeding population. This North American species was admitted to the British List in 1971 after a feral population had become established in several areas in western England. The original colonists are believed to have been birds which escaped from the Slimbridge collection in the 1950s and 1960s. The first county record was at Burton Gravel Pits, near Lincoln on 25th October 1964. It is possible that not all the early occurrences have been noted but there were about 20 records until 1983. Since 1984 one or two pairs have bred at Barrow Haven and Barton-on-Humber with a small resident flock of up to 25 established there. Pairs have summered at several other sites in the county, with breeding proved at Fulstow in 1987 and Burton Gravel Pits in 1988.

Honey Buzzard *Pernis apivorus*
A rare and irregular passage migrant mainly in autumn. About half of the 58 records have been during September but it has occurred in every month from April to October.
Many autumns produce no appearances but four were shot in September 1896, three were shot and another seen in September and October 1908, three were seen in September and October 1976 and five in September and October 1980. Unusually there were records of at least four birds in May 1986. Most of the recent records are from coastal localities whereas earlier occurrences were chiefly inland but this probably reflects the more concentrated observations along the coast during the last 20 years.

Black Kite *Milvus migrans*
A very rare vagrant. One was seen by G.P. Catley at East Halton, near Goxhill on 18th
May 1979. In 1988 one was seen by B.A.Wright near Skegness on 14th April, and then
there were several reports of perhaps the same bird at Gibraltar Point until 12th and 13th
May when good views were obtained of one there and at Wainfleet by D.R. Bromwich,
A.G. Ball and several other observers.

Red Kite *Milvus milvus*
Now only a very rare vagrant, probably of continental origin. In former times it was a
familiar and well-distributed species in the county. Persecution by gamekeepers and
others in the nineteenth century and the clearance of some of the larger woodlands
perhaps contributed to its decline.

In the first half of the nineteenth century it was still not uncommon in several areas.
In the 1820s it was said to have been common in the large woods near Louth and until
the 1850s Kites were a regular feature in the Isle of Axholme and in the woodlands
around Lincoln, Horncastle and Wragby. Four or five pairs frequented these woodlands
in the late 1850s, clutches of eggs being taken annually until 1859, and the final attempt
to nest was in Bullington Wood, near Wragby in 1870.

After this date there are very few birds on record. One was seen at Bottesford, near
Scunthorpe in 1875 and at least one was seen over the Humber marshes on 28th August
1878. One was shot at Croft Bank, Skegness in 1883 and two were present at North
Somercotes from 9th to 11th October 1886. Many years elapsed before there were any
further sightings. One was seen at Old Leake in the East Fen on 9th April 1969 and what
was probably the same individual was present at East Keal, eight miles away, on 12th
April. Since 1972 there have been 20 records mainly from December to April with single
occurrences in June, August and October. Nine of these were in 1988, between mid-
February and mid-April, although perhaps only five or six birds were involved.

White-tailed Eagle *Haliaeetus albicilla*
Formerly this species was an occasional autumn and winter visitor but there has been
only one record since 1933. There are 17 definite records and a futher nine unidentified
eagles, most of which were probably White-tailed. Positive records are as follows: an
immature bird obtained at Nocton, near Bardney in January 1732 was in the collection
of Grantham Museum; one was seen in the Ancholme Carrs about 1819; one, apparently
immature, frequented the foreshore at Great Coates for almost a week in the autumn of
1862; an immature male was shot at Edenham, near Bourne on 2nd November 1883;
one was present at Beesby, near Grainsby from 8th to 17th December 1896; an immature
was shot at North Somercotes on 10th October 1902; (this is the specimen now in the
Louth Museum and labelled as Golden Eagle); an immature was seen at Grainsby Park
on 27th and 28th February 1904; one trapped at Manton Warren, near Brigg on 9th
February 1916 had been present for about a week previously; one was shot at Norton
Place, near Gainsborough in mid-November 1916; an immature frequented Grainsby
Park from 28th February to 2nd March 1917; another appeared at the same locality on
25th December 1920; one was shot on Kirton Marsh in December 1921; one was at

Grainsby at the end of February 1923; there was one at Skegness in January 1925; one which came in off the sea at Grainthorpe on 5th January 1927 was probably the same bird seen in that area in late February and early March and in 1933 an immature male was shot at Aswarby, near Sleaford on 16th March. The one recent record was of an immature flying south along the coast on 27th October 1985 and seen at Grainthorpe, Saltfleetby and Gibraltar Point.

Records of unidentified eagles are as follows: one was shot in the county and reported in the Gentleman's Magazine for November 1784 but no diagnostic features were given; one, said to be Golden, was seen in the Horncastle area in 1854; another shot at Gautby, near Bardney on 8th November 1890 was the subject of considerable identification problems; one was seen at Grainthorpe between 28th and 31st October 1893; another at Marshchapel was present for a few days until 3rd November 1894; one, said to be Golden, was shot at Stoke, near Grantham just prior to 1900; one was seen at Grainthorpe on 15th November 1923 and in 1926 there was one on 19th January in the Saxby and Appleby area, near Scunthorpe and another at North Cotes in autumn.

Marsh Harrier *Circus aeruginosus*

A scarce but regular visitor from spring to autumn and recently re-established as a breeding species. The Marsh Harrier formerly bred in the Fens and other marshy areas and succumbed quickly at the advent of drainage of these vast tracts. There are no records of when it ceased to nest in the county, but it is unlikely to have survived much beyond the middle of the nineteenth century. Some were regularly seen in the north-west in the early 1800s and Stonehouse found a nest with three young in the Isle of Axholme in 1836.

One in the Grantham Museum was said to have been obtained in Ruskington Fen on 12th October 1829 and there are three specimens from the Scotton Common area obtained about 1850 in the Lincoln Museum. One occurred at Great Coates on 8th March 1875 and in 1880 one from Wyeham, near Grainsby was received by a Louth taxidermist. There were no further records until 18th November 1935 when one was seen at North Cotes.

After 1945 one or two birds began to appear in most years and from the mid-1950s it has become much more regular. Most birds are immatures and occur between late April and October with concentrations of sightings in May and August. The coastal marshes provide the bulk of the records which are continuing to increase. Inland occurrences are also becoming more regular and up to five have been present at Nocton Fen in recent autumns. There have been several instances of birds wintering in the county, especially in the Wash.

In 1962, a pair nested at Grainthorpe and managed to rear four young to the flying stage. Recently a small breeding population has become established in the south of the county, increasing from one pair in 1983 to three to four pairs in 1987 and two pairs in 1988. Over 20 young have been reared during this period.

A nestling ringed in Norfolk in June 1958 was recovered at Holbeach in September of the same year. A nestling ringed in Suffolk in July 1984 was found dead at Pinchbeck two months later and another nestling ringed in Kent in 1983 was breeding in

Lincolnshire in 1985.

Hen Harrier *Circus cyaneus*

A scarce winter visitor and passage migrant, chiefly to coastal marshes, fields and sand dunes from late September until early May. There are several recent instances of birds being seen during the summer.

In the early nineteenth century it was a widespread and locally common breeding species on a number of commons in the north of the county. Improved drainage, cultivation and persecution resulted in its decline. An account by Reverend E. Elmhirst in *The Field* describes its abundance in the Market Rasen area in the 1820s and the vigilant efforts made to exterminate the species from its nesting areas. Twenty six birds were once obtained in a single day on the Middle Rasen moor and during one year no fewer than 50 were destroyed in the same area. Following such wanton destruction it is hardly surprising that there appear to be few breeding records after 1830. The final pair bred successfully on Raventhorpe Common, near Scunthorpe in 1872.

Since then it has been largely confined to the coast and a few inland areas in autumn and winter. Numbers are fairly small although there were more than usual in October 1919 and in the winter of 1926/27. During the last 20 years there has been an increase in records with largest numbers at roosts. Most of these contain up to about six birds although one in the Wash has recently been used by up to 18 birds.

In the 1974/75 winter a bird with unstreaked rufous underparts frequented the Saltfleetby to Donna Nook area. It was seen well by a number of observers and although it closely corresponded to an immature of the North American race, *C.c. hudsonius*, the possibility of the bird being an aberrant colour phase of the nominate race, *C.c. cyaneus* cannot be discounted.

Four ringed birds have been found dead in the county. A nestling from Kincardineshire in July 1970 was recovered at Wainfleet in September 1973. One ringed in Orkney in July 1971 was found at Sutton Bridge in January 1972. A nestling ringed in the Netherlands in June 1972 was recovered at Marshchapel in December of the same year and another nestling ringed in Sweden in July 1984 was found dead at Holbeach Marsh in May 1985.

Montagu's Harrier *Circus pygargus*

A rare but regular passage migrant and summer visitor. Early records in the nineteenth century are unreliable as it is evident that much confusion existed between this species and the Hen Harrier. There appear to be no definite old breeding records but it may have been a former inhabitant of the Fens.

One shot at North Cotes on 9th October 1935 was the first recorded during this century but since 1949 it has been seen almost annually particularly in the Wash. A pair attempted to breed at Saltfleetby in 1951 and a pair nested successfully at the Nene mouth in 1956. In 1965 two pairs bred at Wainfleet, one pair rearing two young. A pair also bred unsuccessfully at Friskney in 1969. A pair bred inland in 1980 and reared three young. In 1987 and 1988, a pair reared two young in the Wash and, also in 1988, five young were reared at an inland site. Summering birds have probably bred or attempted to do so on several other occasions.

Early birds may occur in the last week of April but most arrivals are during May and early June. Departures in autumn are usually completed by the end of August, but it has been recorded as late as 11th October.

Goshawk *Accipiter gentilis*

A rare vagrant between autumn and spring. There are 25 records for the county but some of these may refer to escaped birds. The earliest occurrence was of a bird shot at Louth in December 1830 and subsequently preserved in Grantham Museum. One was obtained in the Bratoft area near Skegness about 1840. In 1864 a pair attempted to breed in a larch plantation at Normanby Park, near Scunthorpe. The female was shot and the male eventually left the area. One at Tathwell, near Louth was obtained on 23rd May 1871 and another was shot near Bourne in March 1889. A bird seen catching young Pheasants was trapped near Louth on 29th April 1910. One was seen at Santon Warren, Normanby on 5th October 1919 and one at Miningsby, near Horncastle on 14th September 1935 caught an almost fully grown Pheasant. There was one record in April 1955 and since 1970, there have been a further 15 records mainly on the coast.

Sparrowhawk *Accipiter nisus*

A scarce resident and fairly common passage migrant, chiefly in coastal areas, and a winter visitor in small numbers.

Formerly the Sparrowhawk was a fairly common and widespread breeding species despite heavy persecution by gamekeepers. Migration in autumn was quite pronounced by today's standards, at least until 1927. In 1932, R. May *et al* made an interesting breeding survey of this species and the Kestrel in 13 parishes in the north-east of the county. Sixteen Sparrowhawk nests were located in 12 of the parishes and eight Kestrel nests in six parishes.

By 1950 the species was apparently becoming much less numerous than previously but the real crash came during 1955 to 1957 when the advent of chlorinated hydrocarbon pesticides used in agriculture produced secondary poisoning and wiped out the remaining Lincolnshire breeding population. A gradual increase in the number of sightings of the species began in the late 1960s. A pair bred at Belton Park, near Grantham in 1972 and by the early 1980s birds were present in several areas during the breeding season. Since 1983 there has been a rapid increase in nesting birds with breeding proved at over 50 sites in the county. The first autumn migrants usually appear about mid-September, passage lasting until early November. Return passage usually on a smaller scale is in late March and April.

There are four foreign recoveries of birds ringed on passage at Gibraltar Point. Two autumn migrants were recovered in southern Norway in subsequent summers. A bird ringed in April 1951 was recovered in Denmark one year later and another ringed in October 1952 was found in Belgium in the autumn of 1955. One shot at Holbeach in August 1952 had been ringed on Fair Isle in the previous autumn. One ringed as a nestling in Leicestershire in July 1986 was trapped at Bourne one month later.

Buzzard *Buteo buteo*

A very scarce but regular passage migrant and winter visitor with several recent records of birds in summer. Migrants occur at inland localities as well as on the coast from late August to early November and on return passage between the first week of April and the end of May. It was formerly a not uncommon breeding species in Lincolnshire, nesting in several of the larger woodlands but persistent persecution by gamekeepers resulted in its extinction as a resident during the late nineteenth century. In the Lincoln area the Buzzard nested in the woods at Doddington and Skellingthorpe until about 1850 but in the south of the county one or two pairs persisted until at least 1878. Breeding continued irregularly in the Wragby woodlands until 1888 when the last Lincolnshire nest was found at Gautby. Single pairs were seen near Market Rasen in 1893 and 1900 but there was no proof of breeding. Twelve specimens received by a single taxidermist in Lincoln in 1883 demonstrated the overwhelming persecution waged against the Buzzard during the last century.

Rough-legged Buzzard *Buteo lagopus*

A rare or very scarce coastal passage migrant and winter visitor, chiefly in October and November and occasionally between December and early May. Inland occurrences are not infrequent and mainly in winter, but these birds appear to wander quite at random and seldom remain in one area for any considerable period. In some years it may be absent but influxes are noted at irregular and sometimes long intervals. It was rather more numerous than usual in the autumns of 1839, 1875, 1880, 1891, 1903, 1915, 1962, 1966, 1973, 1974, 1982 and 1985. The biggest arrivals were in 1915 and 1974 when there were about 20 records each year. Three birds together near Caistor between mid-March and mid-April 1975 were observed during the last week of their stay carrying twigs and engaging in tumbling displays.

A nestling ringed in northern Sweden in July 1973 was found dead at Ulceby, near Alford in September 1977.

Golden Eagle *Aquila chrysaetos*

A very rare vagrant that has not been recorded for 60 years. Cordeaux (1899) cited an individual said to have been trapped at Appleby, near Scunthorpe in 1834. One was shot at Normanby Park, near Scunthorpe on 1st November 1881 by R.C. Coulthurst. It was an immature male and had been present nearby at Crosby Warren during the last week of October. Another immature seen at Langton, near Spilsby during the first half of November 1920 was eventually picked up in a dazed condition and sent to London Zoo where its identity was confirmed. One was also seen at Maltby Wood, near Louth on 4th December 1920. An immature frequented Brocklesby Woods from mid-December 1927 to mid-January 1928 when it was shot nearby at Beelsby.

Osprey *Pandion haliaetus*

During the last 20 years the Osprey has become a regular though still rare passage migrant in spring and autumn. Smith and Cornwallis (1955) were aware of only eight or nine records for the county but between 1839 and 1903 at least 28 birds occurred, 20 of these being shot. Single birds also appeared in 1920, 1926 and 1936. Since 1958 it has been reported annually, apart from 1962, with over 140 additional records.

Spring birds occur mainly from mid-April to early June although there are two records in late March. Occasional birds have been seen in summer, with return passage chiefly between the third week of August and the second week of October and occasional stragglers to the end of the month. One was recorded in late November 1920 and a very late bird was shot on 4th December 1868. Numbers are almost equally divided between spring and autumn and the majority of birds have been recorded at inland localities.

Three Swedish-ringed nestlings have been recovered in the county; two were found in autumn and one in spring.

Kestrel *Falco tinnunculus*

A fairly common and widespread breeding species, becoming more common on autumn passage from late July to early November. Return movements between mid-March and mid-May are always on a much smaller scale.

The vast expanses of arable land in Lincolnshire evidently suit the Kestrels' feeding requirements by providing an abundance of voles. It is not known how its present status in the county compares with former times.

The Kestrel nests in most districts but seems to be rather sparsely represented in the Fens, where a lack of suitable nest sites is evident. Following the extensive use of toxic chemicals in the 1950s, the species suffered a serious decline during the period 1958 to 1963 but a decided recovery followed in 1964 and 1965.

Large numbers gather on the coast in the early autumn; many of these birds are juveniles. Smaller numbers are usually seen in early September but passage becomes more marked again in October when a higher proportion of migrants are adult birds. Wintering birds are common and generally distributed.

Nestlings or juveniles ringed in Fife, Cumberland, Westmorland, Yorkshire, Norfolk, Rutland, Buckinghamshire and Warwickshire have been recovered in Lincolnshire in autumn and winter and county-bred birds have been found in Yorkshire, Nottinghamshire, Cambridgeshire, Essex, Norfolk and Shropshire. There is also a recovery in north-west France in January 1953 of a nestling marked at Goxhill in 1947. A nestling ringed in the Netherlands in 1957 was recovered at Spalding in March 1961 and another ringed there in 1972 was found at Tattershall in March 1973.

Red-footed Falcon *Falco vespertinus*

A very rare passage migrant between May and November. There were early records of birds shot in 1864 and 1902 and since 1963 it has occurred on 17 occasions. Ten birds were reported in May and June and one or two in each month between July and November. All but four of the records have been at coastal localities. Most are present only for short periods but birds remained at Gibraltar Point from 8th to 14th October 1967 and from 25th July to 5th August 1969.

Merlin *Falco columbarius*

A scarce but regular passage migrant and a winter visitor. Most records are from the coastal areas between August and May but some occur inland particularly in winter. Its present status appears to have changed little since the last century although there was a temporary decline in numbers in the late 1950s and early 1960s. Like the Peregrine it was taken in nets by the plover catchers on the coast early in the present century and sold to falconers.

A nest containing four eggs was said to have been found on the stump of a felled tree at Branston Booths, near Lincoln about 1860. Eggs were also taken from nests in heather on Manton Common in 1862 and 1875.

One ringed as a nestling in Cumberland in July 1972 was found dead at Scopwick, near Lincoln in February 1973. Another nestling ringed in Shetland in June 1978 was found dead at Lincoln in October 1981.

Hobby *Falco subbuteo*

The Hobby has been a scarce passage migrant and summer visitor since 1964, chiefly from late spring to early autumn. During the last century it was a regular and fairly widespread breeding bird nesting in many of the larger woodlands in the county. Persecution by gamekeepers and egg-collectors resulted in a large scale reduction in numbers especially in the latter half of the century. By the turn of the century it had evidently become quite rare but continued to nest in a few localities. Blathwayt (1915) stated that it still occurred in the county and that a few pairs probably bred. There were no further records until one appeared at Hendale Wood on the Brocklesby Estate on 9th May 1929. Another was recorded from the same wood on 18th April 1932 and one was seen at North Cotes on 9th September 1936. There was one at Cranwell, near Sleaford on 27th August 1960, with about ten records in the next ten years.

Increasing numbers have occurred since the early 1970s, some on passage on the coast though many also inland. These include a few records for late April but most spring birds appear in May and June. An autumn peak occurs in late August with very few recorded after the end of September. One was seen at Covenham Reservoir on 20th January 1987.

Many more birds are now noted in summer and the species appears to be extending its range into the county. Single pairs bred in 1973 and 1979 and two pairs in 1980 and 1987. Six pairs reared at least ten young in 1988. Breeding may also have occurred in several other recent years. A nestling ringed in Buckinghamshire in August 1984 was found dead at Beckingham, south-west of Lincoln in October of the same year.

Gyrfalcon *Falco rusticolus*

A very rare vagrant with no recent records. A bird of the Greenland race *F.r. candicans* was caught in a trap at Twigmoor in 1826. This specimen in the Strickland collection was recorded by Cordeaux (1899). An immature female of the Icelandic race *F.r. islandus* was shot by Dr. Rainbird at Saxilby, near Lincoln in December 1900. This bird is now in the Lincoln museum.

Peregrine *Falco peregrinus*

A rare annual passage migrant and winter visitor that also occurs exceptionally in summer. Autumn migrants occur mainly between the last few days of August and mid-

November with return passage on a smaller scale in April and May. Wintering records are chiefly from localities in the Wash and on the north-east coast.

Formerly the species visited the county less uncommonly. During the nineteenth century several were caught in most autumns by the plover netters in the Humber and the Wash; some of these birds were sold to falconers. Early in the present century Haigh recorded a number of years when autumn passage was particularly good. Several were present at Grainsby in December 1915 exploiting the huge numbers of Woodpigeons there and between 1920 and 1925 he recorded up to nine on the north-east coast in most autumns. Passage on this scale has not been recorded since then.

A bird of the North American race *F.p. anatum* was obtained by J. Stubbs on a plover decoy at Humberston on 28th September 1910. The specimen was verified by Dr. E. Hartert. It was an immature male and only the second British record.

A bird ringed as a nestling in northern Norway in July 1943 was shot at Swaton Fen, near Sleaford in December of the same year.

Black Grouse *Tetrao tetrix*
Formerly a resident in small numbers on the heaths and commons of the north-west, on the unenclosed moors between Lincoln and Nottinghamshire and in the Woodhall Spa area. It is not known when the species became extinct in the county, but it was probably not long after 1935, when the last bird was recorded at Scotton Common.

During the nineteenth century its true status was uncertain. Originally it may have been indigenous to some localities but its numbers were reinforced by introduction prior to 1870. The Black Grouse died out on Whisby Moor in 1842 and on Stapleford Moor in 1883. Birds lingered on in the Woodhall Spa district until about the 1870s and on Brumby Common and Twigmoor Warren until 1900.

In the present century there are records only from Scotton Common. There were still several pairs present in 1920 and 18 birds were flushed together during the 1921/22 winter. Young birds were seen in 1922 and the last two nests were found by keepers in the early 1930s. The final sighting was of a solitary female on 10th June 1935.

Red-legged Partridge *Alectoris rufa*
A numerous and well-distributed species. The initial main introductions in Britain were made in Suffolk in the 1770s but the dates of the earliest colonists in Lincolnshire seem to have gone unrecorded. By 1874 it was quite common in the south and on the coast of the Wash. Some were present in the north at this time, odd ones having been shot on the north-east coast. It began to be common in the north-west around 1882 and by 1889 it was thoroughly established and generally distributed, although ten years later Cordeaux considered that the species was still on the increase.

In many areas it now outnumbers the Grey Partridge but decreases are appararent after summers of high rainfall. Some local movement at least is occasionally recorded. Exhausted birds have been observed arriving from across the Humber on a number of occasions in March, April and September and birds in such a condition have even been found in the centres of Grimsby and Cleethorpes. Many of the birds that breed on the exposed coastal strip are absent during the winter.

Grey Partridge *Perdix perdix*
A numerous, well-distributed species that has decreased noticeably in many areas particuarly in the south of the county during the last 20 years. The decline of the Partridge is a national one and is most likely due to changes in agricultural methods. Many of the hedgerows favoured by the species have been removed in recent years. Additionally ploughing and burning of stubble fields in early autumn and mechanised hay-cutting in summer have also adversely affected the species. Despite these changes there is still a good number of relatively undisturbed areas such as sand dunes, commons and the smaller arable farms where quite high densities remain.

Quail *Coturnix coturnix*
A scarce but annual summer visitor that probably breeds or attemps to do so in most years. Numbers fluctuate considerably from year to year and localities vary but it appears to be most regular on the Wolds and in the south-west. Before extensive drainage and increased cultivation it nested in some numbers in the county. A marked decline was apparent after the 1820s and by the latter half of the century it was mainly a casual visitor nesting irregularly, although it was said to be plentiful in the summers of 1870 and 1893.

Since 1945 there has been a welcome increase in records and in some years, notably 1947, 1958, 1964, 1970, 1972, 1987 and 1988, it was more widespread than usual. Most birds occur during the period May to September but occasional birds have been noted in winter.

Pheasant *Phasianus colchicus*
A numerous and widespread resident. Population levels are extremely high in a number of areas where artificial rearing and releases for shooting take place. There has been a general increase in the numbers of preserved birds in recent years.

In 1899 Cordeaux considered that the old type *P.c. colchicus* was probably extinct in the county and that many birds were hybrids between this race and the more recently introduced Chinese ring-necked race *P.c. torquatus*. At present there are a number of varieties to be found but *torquatus* is dominant in most districts.

The wanderings of the Pheasant appear to be somewhat local although Cordeaux noted several instances of birds crossing the Humber from Yorkshire. At Great Coates where he made these observations, this would involve a river crossing of about three miles.

Water Rail *Rallus aquaticus*
A very scarce but probably regular breeding species and a fairly common passage migrant and winter visitor. Its skulking habits mean that proof of breeding is often difficult to obtain but it appears to nest regularly in the north-west, in pits along the Humber bank and probably also in one or two coastal areas and the Fens. Prior to extensive drainage it was much more widespread though only a locally common nesting bird. Migrants appear on the coast from late August to early November and a good proportion of birds move to suitable areas inland. Return passage occurs in March to early May.

One ringed at Heligoland in November 1958 was found dead at Sloothby, near Alford in October 1959. Another West German bird ringed in August 1981 was recovered at Ancaster two months later. One ringed at Wisbech sewage farm in October 1962 was recovered in Yorkshire in the following April.

Spotted Crake *Porzana porzana*

Formerly a local breeding species but now only a rare though doubtless overlooked vagrant. Prior to the extensive drainage of the eighteenth century it was probably quite generally distributed in suitable habitats but by the latter half of the nineteenth century it nested regularly only at two or three sites in the Fens, at Tetney and North Cotes in the north-east and in the Ashby area, near Scunthorpe. It is uncertain when the species ceased to nest in the county but Blathwayt considered that a few pairs were still breeding as late as 1915.

Until 1900 it was a regular passage migrant in autumn particularly on the north-east coast where Haigh noted arrivals chiefly in September and October. Some measures of its status is shown by his notes of up to six being flushed together from a patch of marsh of less than three acres. There are a number of records of migrants killed against telegraph wires and it was said to be regularly received by the local taxidermists.

Between 1930 and 1952 there were only four records but since 1963 there have been about 32 occurrences. Five of these recent records have been in winter: at Belchford, near Horncastle on 15th December 1963; at Gibraltar Point on 15th January 1967 and 3rd January 1972; at Donna Nook on 22nd December 1976 and at Seacroft on 16th December 1978. Eight spring birds were seen between March and mid-May and the remaining autumn migrants were evenly spread between mid-August and mid-November.

Little Crake *Porzana parva*

A very rare and irregular vagrant. Cordeaux obtained good views of one at Great Coates on 9th October 1869. He was able to watch the bird within a few feet both on the ground and in flight. There seems little reason to doubt his identification although Smith and Cornwallis did not fully accept the record to their list. A female killed by a dog at Spanby, near Sleaford in 1910 is now preserved in Lincoln Museum.

Small crakes thought to have been this species were seen at Tetney in October 1888, 1907 and 1930, at Gibraltar Point on 16th August 1953 and Wrangle, near Boston on 17th August 1978.

Corncrake *Crex crex*

Now only a rare migrant. Vastly increased agricultural mechanisation and earlier hay-making ensured a rapid decline and the ultimate loss of what was formerly a fairly widespread but hardly common summer visitor. Occasional mid-summer records of birds at inland localities indicate that the Corncrake could still nest spasmodically in Lincolnshire.

During the nineteenth century its numbers tended to fluctuate a good deal. It was said to have bred in high numbers between 1864 and 1867 and in 1884 but in some years it

Moorhen

Red-legged Partridge

was particularly scarce. The species was decreasing markedly by the 1890s and regular nesting ceased by about 1920.

Passage migrants on the coast, chiefly in September and October, also became irregular after 1914. Over the last 25 years a few birds have been noted on passage in most years, mainly in April and May and from late August to early October. There are several old records of birds apparently overwintering in the county.

Moorhen *Gallinula chloropus*
A very numerous and widespread species nesting on almost any piece of freshwater from ditches to large lakes as well as on some of the coastal marshes. Some passage migration evidently occurs but high numbers present throughout the year make any movements difficult to detect. Birds sometimes occur on the sea in winter, more especially in the estuaries of the Humber and the Wash. The Moorhen frequently suffers temporary setbacks in numbers following severe winters and in many areas it is a regular victim of road traffic.

Young birds ringed in autumn have been recovered in subsequent winters in Huntingdonshire and Dorset with two in north-west France. One ringed in Nottinghamshire in January 1962 was recovered, probably in its breeding area, in the county in the following May. One ringed at Deeping St. James in January 1979 was found dead in Denmark in June of the same year. Two birds recovered in January had been ringed in Northamptonshire in August and Yorkshire in February.

Coot *Fulica atra*
A common and widespread breeding species occurring mainly on the larger lakes, ponds and ballast pits in the county. As a winter visitor it is much more plentiful, large flocks often being present on reservoirs in addition to the traditional breeding waters. Birds disperse during freezing conditions and may appear on the estuaries of the Humber and Wash.

Migration times are not entirely clear but immigrants probably arrive from Europe from September onwards, followed by influxes later in winter, particularly during severe weather. Some of these birds may be en route to wintering areas further south or west.

There are eight foreign recoveries of birds marked at Deeping St. James. Three ringed in winter were shot in Denmark in subsequent autumns. Two ringed in autumn were shot in France in winter. One ringed in August 1971 was recovered in north-west Spain three months later and another ringed in January 1968 was shot in north Poland in November 1972. One ringed in November 1972 was shot in Italy in February 1980. One ringed in August 1971 was in County Cork three weeks later and one ringed in August 1980 was found in Grampian in January 1981. There are several other recoveries within England.

Crane *Grus grus*
A very rare and irregular vagrant. It was a former breeding bird of the Fens, probably in very small numbers, until about the end of the sixteenth century. Large flocks still visited the county in the middle of the seventeenth century according to Willughby (Ray

1678), but most of these records may have referred to passage migrants as he could find no evidence that they still bred.

There were only two nineteenth century records. One was shot at Hykeham Moor, near Lincoln on 20th July 1869 following a spring of several English occurrences and another was shot at Spalding on 25th October 1881 after being present in the district for several days.

More recently a party of nine was seen at Humberston on 25th October 1953 and single birds appeared at Skegness on 4th November 1966 and at Gibraltar Point on 4th September 1967 and 23rd August 1972. One wintered in the Scotter area, near Scunthorpe from December 1978 until March 1979 and single birds in 1979 were seen at Gibraltar Point on 13th to 14th September, at Anderby on 26th May and at Kirton on 24th November. One occurred at Messingham on 6th September 1984, two flew north-east at Tetney on 7th May 1985 and one flew south over Gibraltar Point on 25th October 1987. In 1988, single birds were seen in April at Tetney on 26th and Huttoft on 30th, then at Gibraltar Point on 1st and 16th May.

Little Bustard *Tetrax tetrax*
A rare vagrant in winter. The first county record was a bird shot on Welbourn Heath, near Lincoln by B.H. Brown on 30th January 1854. A female was shot near Alford in January 1856 and one was seen at Walcot, near Scunthorpe on 22nd January 1913. A bird shot at Addlethorpe, near Skegness on 22nd November 1933 was examined by H.F. Witherby and assigned to the eastern race, *T.t. orientalis*. Another shot at Gosberton Cheal, near Spalding on 30th December 1955 belonged to the western race *T.t. tetrax*.

Houbara Bustard *Chlamydotis undulata*
A very rare vagrant. One shot on a stubble field at Kirton-in-Lindsey by G.F. Hansley on 7th October 1847 was the first British record. It was verified by J. Gould who assigned the bird to the eastern race *C.u. macqueeni* which breeds in Asia.

Great Bustard *Otis tarda*
This magnificent species bred on the Wolds until the early years of the nineteenth century. Extinction became inevitable with increased farming and shooting pressures. There were few records later in the century. One was shot near Louth in 1818 and another is said to have been seen in north-west Lindsey in 1837. A pair is supposed to have been seen at Candlesby, near Alford about 1860. One was seen at Halton Holgate, near Spilsby on 10th April 1866 and a male was shot at Addlethorpe, near Skengess towards the end of the century.

The most recent records were single females shot near Grimsby and at Tetney in December 1902. These may have been genuine immigrants as one was shot in Wales and two in Ireland at the same time, although some were released in Norfolk in 1900 in an attempt at reintroduction.

Oystercatcher *Haematopus ostralegus*
A numerous passage migrant and winter visitor to the coast. It is a fairly common

breeding bird, especially in the Wash and at the mouth of the Humber. In recent years there has been a trend for a significant number of pairs to nest away from traditional sites. In many areas birds breed on coastal arable fields, particularly among potato and pea crops. During the early nineteenth century it bred along the coast in good numbers with a strong concentration of birds at Gibraltar Point. Eggs were constantly plundered by local people and it had become very rare late in the century. Its recovery during the present century has not been documented and may still be in progress.

Early autumn arrivals in July are probably dispersing British birds, followed by immigration of continental birds between late August and early November. Return passage lasts from March until late May or early June. It is scarce inland where records usually refer to birds on spring and autumn passage. Large flocks at high tides are a feature of the Humber and Wash but the huge flocks, sometimes in excess of 15,000 birds, are restricted to the north-west shore of the Wash.

Ringing recoveries show that a fair amount of interchange takes place between the two estuaries. Comprehensive studies by the Wash Wader Ringing Group have resulted in a vast increase in the number of recoveries of this and other species of waders. Over a hundred recoveries involving the coasts of Norway indicate the origin of the bulk of immigrants, with others to or from Iceland, Belgium, France, the Netherlands, Denmark, the Faeroes, Germany, Sweden, Finland and north-west Russia. One bird deserving fuller mention was recovered in Morocco in December after having been ringed at Holbeach in the previous August. Recoveries within Britain involve the Hebrides, Shetland, Orkney, Aberdeenshire, Lancashire, Yorkshire, the Welsh coast, Norfolk, Dorset and Kent.

Black-winged Stilt *Himantopus himantopus*

A very rare vagrant. Two flying south along the shoreline at Gibraltar Point on 26th April 1965 were recorded by J.C. Sillitoe and J.A. Ewan during a spring that produced a widespread influx of the species into England. One was recorded at Grantham sewage farm on the unusual date of 25th December 1968. It was seen again between 2nd and 6th February 1969 after an intervening period of snow. One occurred at Tetney on 19th June 1986 and another in the Barton-on-Humber and Read's Island area in 1987 stayed from 6th to 13th September.

In addition to these occurrences there are several old records which may be genuine but cannot be fully substantiated. One said to have been obtained in Lincolnshire in July 1824 coincided with a bird shot in Norfolk at the same time. An undated specimen in Grantham Museum may have been obtained in the county and one in Lincoln Museum is supposedly from Wainfleet in 1888. One is alleged to have been obtained on Kirton Marsh on 1st September 1889. It is said to have occurred very rarely in the Fens in the eighteenth century but no actual records have been traced.

Avocet *Recurvirostra avosetta*

A scarce passage migrant, chiefly on the coast and most often recorded in spring. There were only five records in the first half of the present century but during the last 25 years or so it has visited the county almost annually. Most of these occurrences refer to one to three birds but parties of up to ten have been seen on a number of occasions. It occurs chiefly between April and early June with a pronounced peak in the second half of May. A few birds have been recorded until August but later autumn records are rather infrequent though there are several records in winter between late December and early March.

Large numbers used to breed near Fosdyke Wash at the mouth of the Welland and possibly in other Fenland areas until the early nineteenth century. Considerable numbers were said to have nested in the Humber estuary at the same time but extinction resulted from the reclamation of breeding sites and heavy exploitation of eggs for food. The last breeding record was on an island at the mouth of the Trent about 1837. Recolonisation as a breeding species in the county seems possible. Parties of spring birds have recently made protracted stays into the summer at one or two localities in the Humber.

Stone-curlew *Burhinus oedicnemus*
Now only a very rare vagrant. Formerly the Stone-curlew nested on the Wolds and the heath districts south of Lincoln and in the north-west. Increased cultivation brought a decline during the nineteenth century and it disappeared from its haunts on the Wolds about 1870. Good numbers were still present on the sandy warrens of the north-west during the latter half of the century but it gradually became scarcer from the 1870s. A measure of its earlier status is illustrated by Cordeaux's (1872) statement that 20 to 30 birds could still be seen during a day's ride across the warrens in the 1860s. It bred on Brumby Common until 1872 and on Scotton Common until 1886 but survived on Crosby Warren for a few more years and on Manton Warren until at least 1904.

After 1910 when one was shot at North Cotes there appear to be no records until 1935 when another was present at North Cotes on 2nd March. Between 1950 and 1968 there were over 20 occurrences, most referring to migrants on the coast between April and early June and in autumn from late July to September. A late bird was seen at Gibraltar Point on 3rd December 1957.

Inland records include one seen and heard at Caistor in early summer 1952 , one at Lincoln in April and three nearby at Beckingham in September 1958. Birds were heard at Biscathorpe, near Louth in July 1964 and at Kirkby Moor in June 1966. Single birds were seen at Sotby, near Wragby and at Cranwell in May 1968. The only recent records were of one at Gibraltar Point on 25th November 1978, another at Saltfleetby on 28th and 29th July 1981, one at North Cotes on 23rd May 1985 and one at Gibraltar Point on 16th July 1988.

Cream-coloured Courser *Cursorius cursor*
A very rare vagrant from North Africa and Asia. An exhausted bird was caught by Reverend J. Mossop on the coast near Marshchapel about 1840.

Collared Pratincole *Glareola pratincola*
One was shot by F. Oats at Branston Hall, near Lincoln on 15th August 1827. There were no further records until one was seen at Gibraltar Point on 21st May 1973 and another flew east at Trent Falls on 11th June 1977. One was seen at Donna Nook on 11th July

1981. A pratincole not assigned to one species flew east at Barrow Haven on 11th August 1980.

Little Ringed Plover *Charadrius dubius*

A scarce breeding bird which has become established at a number of gravel pits, quarries and sugar-beet ponds. The first pair bred at a gravel pit near Woodhall Spa in 1950 and nesting has occurred annually since then. The intial spread was slow but by the 1960s there were at least ten pairs breeding in the county. In 1970 a complete count revealed about 40 pairs at 20 sites, and since then there has been an annual population of at least 30 pairs.

Passage migrants both on the coast and inland have also increased since the early 1950s. Spring migrants chiefly in April and May are rather scarce but it has become fairly common in autumn from late July to September with stragglers into October. Prior to 1950 there is only one somewhat doubtful record from Holbeach Marsh in 1894.

A chick ringed in the south of the county in June 1956 was recovered near Kettering, Northamptonshire in the following October. Another ringed in July 1980 was shot in the Camargue, southern France in October 1981.

Ringed Plover *Charadrius hiaticula*

A fairly common breeding species and a common passage migrant. It is much scarcer between mid-November and early February. In 1973 a national breeding survey of the species was organised by the British Trust for Ornithology. A complete census of the county revealed a total of 152 pairs. Eleven of these pairs were at six inland sites where nesting has been known only since 1963.

Another census in 1984 resulted in 242 pairs of which 36 were nesting inland. Much of this increase has occurred in the Humber and inland in the north-west. There are good concentrations between Tetney and Saltfleetby and in the Skegness and Gibraltar Point area. In some areas disturbance by holidaymakers has had an adverse effect on the breeding population.

Passage birds occur on the coast between early April and early June. Return movements last from late July to mid-October with stragglers until mid-November. Smaller numbers are seen on inland passage, mainly in autumn. Most birds belong belong to the nominate race *C.h. hiaticula* but the smaller Arctic race *C.h. tundrae* appears to be fairly regular in variable numbers in May and early June and in August and September.

One ringed as a nestling on Heligoland, Germany in June 1963 was recovered on passage in the county two months later. Birds ringed in Lincolnshire in August and September have been recovered in subsequent autumns in France, Spain, Morocco, Norway and the Murmansk coast of Russia. One ringed at Gibraltar Point in September 1982 was recovered in Ghana in December 1982.

A nestling ringed at Skegness in July 1961 was in County Mayo in November 1963, and one from Gibraltar Point in July 1984 was trapped in West Germany in May 1986. Three birds ringed in the county in July and August have been recovered in Lancashire in spring.

Grey Plover

Ringed Plover

Kentish Plover *Charadrius alexandrinus*

A rare vagrant which has been noted on 22 occasions. It has also bred once. There is an old record of an immature bird shot near Friskney on 8th October 1881. Three birds arrived together at Gibraltar Point on 13th April 1950, one bird remaining until the following day. Later records, all since 1959, have involved mainly single birds. Most of these were seen in May and June with one or two in July and August.

A pair hatched two young at a coastal site in 1979. The species is alleged to have bred annually at Humberston between 1902 and 1905 but the evidence is not convincing.

Greater Sand Plover *Charadrius leschenaultii*

One seen by H. Bunn and J. Leece at North Cotes on 7th August 1981 was presumably the bird previously present at Spurn Point. This was the fifth British record of this rare vagrant from southern central Asia.

Dotterel *Charadrius morinellus*

A scarce passage migrant chiefly in spring but also in autumn. Since 1970 it has been recorded almost annually. In the early part of the nineteenth century it was a regular migrant, often in some numbers in late April and May. Flocks frequently occurred at traditional localities, more particularly on the north-east coast, the Wolds, the heath district south of Lincoln and in the Fens. Dotterel shoots were a regular feature in May in several areas. Autumn birds were much scarcer and were usually recorded in late August and September. Numbers decreased in the second half of the nineteenth century, but it continued to be a regular migrant until the early years of the present century. Several large flocks were occasionally recorded especially during the 1890s, when for example, there was a flock of 200 at Stallingborough on the north-east coast in May 1891.

After 1924 there were very few records anywhere in the county but since 1958 small numbers have returned to traditional sites. Most of these recent trips have involved fewer than ten birds but a party of 47 occurred near the Nene mouth on 20th August 1959. Since 1977 there have been several spring parties of up to 26 on the north-east coast and in the Fens near Bourne. Migrants are usually on arable or pasture fields and in autumn may consort with Golden Plovers.

There are several late records. Two were shot at Tetney on 7th November 1921 and three more were shot at North Cotes on 24th November of the same year. Five were seen at Frampton on 29th November 1959.

American Golden Plover *Pluvialis dominica*

There are four records of this vagrant from North America. The first was seen by J.A.W. Moyes at Wisbech sewage farm on 10th August 1974. One was at North Killingholme on 24th July 1982; one occurred at Saltfleetby on 16th July 1983 and another was at Tetney on 27th July 1986. All were adult birds.

Pacific Golden Plover *Pluvialis fulva*

An adult of this vagrant from north and north-east Asia was present at Tetney and North

Cotes from 21st July to 19th August 1986. It was seen by A. Baker, R.S. Slack and I.G. Shepherd and subsequently by many other observers. This was the fifth British record.

Golden Plover *Pluvialis apricaria*
A numerous and well-distributed passage migrant and winter visitor, both on the coast and inland. Immigration in autumn occurs chiefly from early July until early November. Birds remaining to winter are sometimes in very large flocks of 1,000 or more and often associate with Lapwings. Severe weather may produce considerable movements and during prolonged periods of snow and frost the the species practically deserts the county.

Spring passage usually on a smaller scale takes place from late February to the end of May. At this time many of the migrants are in full breeding plumage and are racially identifiable. The northern race *P.a. altifrons* often outnumbers the southern race *P.a. apricaria* but the numbers of both races may fluctuate. A few birds remain during the summer.

One ringed in the Wash in February 1954 was found dead in Denmark in April 1965. A bird ringed in the Netherlands in March 1956 was found dead at North Cotes in October 1959 and one shot at Crowland in January 1976 had been ringed in southern Norway in August 1972.

Grey Plover *Pluvialis squatarola*
A common passage migrant and winter visitor to the coast which congregates in large flocks of 1,000 or so on the highest tides in the Humber and the Wash. Autumn immigration begins in early July and lasts until early November. Return passage occurs between late March and early June, peak numbers passing during May. A few birds are present during the summer. It is only a rare visitor to inland waters.

Birds ringed on passage and as winter visitors have been subsequently recovered on migration in Denmark, West Germany, France and Morocco. One ringed as an adult at Dawsmere in the Wash in September 1963 was shot on the Barents Sea coast of Russia in June 1967.

Lapwing *Vanellus vanellus*
A common well-distributed breeding species and an abundant passage migrant and winter visitor. As a breeding bird it has decreased during recent years, the decline being quite marked in some areas. The conversion of permanent pasture to arable land, the increase in agricultural mechanisation and improved drainage of remaining pastures have all contributed to the Lapwing's decrease. Before the final reclamation of the Fens at the start of the nineteenth century it nested very plentifully. A widespread decrease was accelerated by intensive netting by the plover-catchers of the Marsh district. Huge numbers were trapped and sent to the London markets prior to the passing of the Lapwing Protection Bill in 1926, which forbade the use of live decoy birds. Smaller numbers continued to be netted until 1946 when the species gained full protection.

Visible movements are frequently recorded in every month of the year. Migration often takes place on very broad fronts inland and along the coast. The earliest immigrants arrive usually in small numbers in the second half of June but the largest influxes sometimes numbering many thousands occur between September and mid-November. Huge flocks are present during the winter, especially on the Wolds and along the coastal belt. Weather movements occur particularly during periods of snow and frost and in very severe winters there may be a virtual desertion of the county. Emigration to the east begins in late February and lasts until mid-April, with stragglers until late May. Much of this passage occurs at considerable height and many must leave undetected but large numbers are observed in some springs.

Birds ringed as chicks and recovered in the county have originated in Germany, Hungary and Lithuania, with several from Norway, Sweden, Denmark and the Netherlands. Several chicks ringed in the county have been recovered in Ireland, France, Spain and Portugal and birds ringed as fully-grown have reached Russia and Morocco.

Knot *Calidris canutus*

An abundant passage migrant and winter visitor to the coastal sand and mudflats. Vast flocks of many thousands frequent the extensive shores of the Humber and the Wash on migration and during the winter, and smaller numbers are regularly present on the more open coast.

Early adult birds begin to arrive in the first half of July but no large numbers occur until mid-August when the first juveniles appear. Immigration and passage continues on a large scale until the end of November. Spring emigration extends from mid-March to early June. During migration single birds or very small numbers are regularly recorded at several inland waters. A few birds are also present on the coast during the summer. In the severe frosts of January and February 1926, Haigh recorded much larger numbers than usual at North Cotes. He described a mile-long flock which may have numbered hundreds of thousands. Haigh was by no means given to exaggeration and this flock was noted by him as the ornithological highlight of that year.

Large numbers were regularly taken in nets by the bird-netters of the Wash in the eighteenth and early nineteenth centuries. The traditional catching season was between August and November and birds were kept alive and fattened for market, being esteemed as a delicacy equal to Ruffs.

Large catches of birds by the Wash Wader Ringing Group have produced some spectacular recoveries. There are recoveries to, or from, all the western maritime countries of Europe as well as Iceland, Sweden and Poland. Six birds ringed in autumn have been recovered in Greenland in June and one, probably of the Siberian-breeding population, was recovered on board a ship in the Barents Sea in July. One ringed in September 1963 was controlled on Ellesmere Island, Canada in June 1974 and another ringed on Ellesmere Island in June 1974 was controlled in the Wash only two months later. Further rapid long-distance recoveries are shown by a bird ringed in September 1963 and recovered in Liberia after only eight days and five birds, ringed at the same time, all recovered on the coast of Senegal between three and five weeks later.

Sanderling *Calidris alba*

A common passage migrant on the coast and a winter visitor in smaller numbers. It occurs chiefly on sand flats and along the tide edge but a few occur quite regularly on

Little Stint

Pectoral Sandpiper

116

sewage farms, reservoirs and the muddy edges of other inland waters on spring and autumn migration.

Some migrants arrive in early July, larger flocks occurring from mid-August when the first juveniles appear. Passage continues until early November. Nowhere are wintering flocks large but the Sanderling occurs along all suitable stretches of coastline, often in flocks of 20 to 50 birds and frequently amongst parties of Dunlin and other waders. It is rather scarce on the salt marshes of the Wash. Return passage lasts from March to early June and is often on a greater scale than in the autumn. The largest flocks are generally in the second half of May and are sometimes in excess of 1,000 birds. A few birds are invariably present during the summer.

Two birds ringed on passage in southern Norway in September 1959 were recovered at Tetney in May 1960 and at Cleethorpes in September 1963. One ringed in Lancashire in May 1969 was controlled at Gibraltar Point in September 1972.

Semipalmated Sandpiper *Calidris pusilla*
One present at Wisbech sewage farm from 12th November to the end of December 1966 was trapped on 13th November. It was recorded by J. Hardman, C.D.T. Minton, J.A.W. Moyes and other observers. The species breeds in northern North America and is a very rare vagrant to Britain.

Little Stint *Calidris minuta*
A fairly common autumn passage migrant which occurs in fluctuating numbers. It is now annual in small numbers in spring whereas there were no spring records prior to 1953. It occurs frequently on the coast but is also regular on inland reservoirs, flooded pits and sewage farms. In good years it may be recorded in small parties of up to about 20 birds but, exceptionally, 80 were present at Wisbech sewage farm in late September 1973 and 130 in mid-September 1978. Odd birds sometimes arrive in late July but the main passage lasts from August to late October or even early November. Spring birds appear between late April and early June. There have been occasional records of single birds in winter at Covenham Reservoir, Wisbech sewage farm and Trent Falls.

Temminck's Stint *Calidris temminckii*
A rare but annual passage migrant in spring and autumn. There were only five reports before 1954 but regular observations at certain localities have improved the total to about 140 records. About a third of these birds were noted in spring. Many of these occurrences have been at Wisbech sewage farm and it is also seen quite regularly at Bardney and Donna Nook. Spring passage is almost exclusively during the second half of May though there are records in June. Autumn birds appear between early July and the end of September with occasional late birds present until early November.

White-rumped Sandpiper *Calidris fuscicollis*
A rare vagrant noted on eight occasions. One trapped by C.D.T. Minton at Wisbech sewage farm during its stay between 13th and 17th November 1955 was also seen by several other observers. Since then single birds have been identified at the same locality

from 24th October to 7th November 1964, 10th to 19th August 1970, 7th to 19th August 1971 and 28th July to 10th August 1973. Others occurred at Frampton Marsh on 16th September 1973, at Killingholme on 26th and 27th July 1976 and at Holbeach Marsh on 25th August 1985. The species breeds in northern North America.

Baird's Sandpiper *Calidris bairdii*
There are three records of this rare vagrant which breeds in the extreme north-east of Siberia and across northern North America to north-west Greenland. One at Wisbech sewage farm from 22nd July to 6th August 1963 was recorded by J.S. Clark, G.M.S. Easy, C.A.E. Kirtland and other observers. It was the ninth British record. One present at Bardney between 1st and 8th September 1966 was seen by K. Atkin, R. May, K. Wood and other observers and one at Killingholme on 19th and 20th September 1979 was recorded by G.P. Catley and D.A. Robinson.

Pectoral Sandpiper *Calidris melanotos*
There are about 75 records of this rare North American visitor which was unrecorded in the county before 1948. It has occurred annually since 1960 apart from 1965 and 1986 and has been identified most regularly at Wisbech sewage farm where about 30 birds have been noted. There have been two records in June, otherwise all arrivals have been between early July and late October with a peak in late August and September. Most birds remain off-passage for several days or sometimes longer periods and two birds stayed until the second week of November. This species is the most frequently recorded of the transatlantic waders though some east coast birds may originate in eastern Siberia.

Sharp-tailed Sandpiper *Calidris acuminata*
A very rare vagrant from north-east Siberia. One at North Killingholme between 18th and 20th September 1982 was seen by G.P. Catley and many other observers. Another at Holbeach Marsh was seen by P. Clement on 24th August 1985. These were the sixteenth and nineteenth British records.

Curlew Sandpiper *Calidris ferruginea.*
A passage migrant in fluctuating numbers. It is fairly common in most autumns with large influxes in some years. Very small numbers are recorded in spring. Occasional single birds have been recorded in winter between December and March. It inhabits the seashore and tidal creeks as well as reservoirs, sewage farms and other suitable inland waters.
  In favourable autumns, usually following a successful breeding season and easterly winds, there may be considerable arrivals of the species. Particular invasion years were 1873, 1881, 1887, 1890, 1892, 1912, 1946, 1950, 1953, 1954, 1959, 1969, 1971, 1978, 1985 and 1988. Easily the largest of these occured in 1969. During the last week of August record numbers were reported at several localities. Peak counts included 400 at Wisbech sewage farm, 265 at Donna Nook, 45 at Gibraltar Point, 44 at Saltfleet and 40 at Frampton Marsh.
  Early autumn birds arrive in July and passage extends until mid-October with

maximum numbers in August and September. Birds from late August onwards are almost invariably juveniles. Spring birds are present between late April and early June and one in winter plumage was at Frampton Marsh on 23rd and 24th June 1979.

One ringed in the Wash in October 1964 was shot in north-west Russia in August 1967. Two ringed in early September 1969 were shot near the Black Sea in August 1972 and another ringed in late August 1969 was also shot on the Black Sea coast in August 1971. One ringed in October 1963 was controlled on the east coast of Tunisia in May 1968 and another ringed in August 1971 was caught in southern Finland a year later. One ringed in September 1969 was controlled in Poland in July 1974 and one ringed in September 1975 was recovered in Senegal one month later.

Purple Sandpiper *Calidris maritima*
A scarce but regular passage migrant and winter visitor on the coast. In recent years it has been recorded more frequently than in the past. Wintering birds, chiefly singly and seldom more than two or three together, may occur anywhere on the coast but only with any degree of regularity on the stony bank at the mouth of the Witham and on concrete groynes at Trusthorpe, near Mablethorpe and at Grimsby Docks. Most records however merely refer to autumn migrants which occur from early August until early November. Spring birds are rare and are generally noted in April and early May. It has visited Covenham Reservoir fairly regularly in autumn since 1971 but the only other recent inland records were of single birds at Spalding on 22nd September 1961 and at Cadney Reservoir from 21st to 25th September 1978.

One ringed at Donna Nook in October 1983 was controlled in Sweden in May of the following year.

Dunlin *Calidris alpina*
A numerous passage migrant and winter visitor on the coast, particularly in the Humber and the Wash. It occurs regularly on passage at inland waters, sometimes in fair-sized flocks in the autumn. Both Blathwayt (1915) and Haigh in the early 1930s recorded decreases on the coast, probably due to intensive shooting. Until the early years of the present century one or two pairs used to breed on Scotton Common. A single pair nested on Read's Island in 1958 and two were in song at Trent Falls in late June 1974.

Autumn immigration begins in early July, reaching a peak in August and September and lasts until early November. Return passage extends from mid-March to early June. The northern race *C.a. alpina* and the southern race *C.a. schinzii* both occur in considerable numbers on passage but *alpina* clearly predominates in winter. Small parties of non-breeding birds remain during the summer, chiefly in the estuaries.

There are many ringing recoveries of Dunlin, mainly ringed or controlled on passage in the Wash. Over 200 recoveries are of birds found in Norway, Sweden and Finland or of birds ringed usually on passage through these countries and subsequently recovered in Lincolnshire. There are several recoveries involving Greenland, Iceland, the Netherlands, Denmark, Germany, Poland and Russia.

Many of our passage birds winter farther south as shown by recoveries in the Channel Islands, France, Spain, Portugal, Sicily and Morocco. One bird was recovered in the

Dunlin

Jack Snipe

Canaries and another in Mauritania. Other migrants ringed in the county have been recovered wintering on the west coast of Britain and in Ireland.

Broad-billed Sandpiper *Limicola falcinellus*
A rare vagrant recorded four times in spring. One was seen by J.M.S. Arnott at Wisbech sewage farm on 18th and 19th May 1959. One at Saltfleetby on 26th May 1982 was followed by another at the same place on 19th May 1984 and one at North Cotes on 29th May 1984.

Stilt Sandpiper *Micropalama himantopus*
A very rare vagrant. An adult still largely in summer plumage was trapped at Wisbech sewage farm by G. Gould, J.A. Hardman, C.D.T. Minton and others on 19th July 1963 and was last seen on 7th August. Another at the same locality between 12th and 19th August 1965 was seen by J.A.W. Moyes and several other observers. These were the third and fifth British records of this North American species.

Buff-breasted Sandpiper *Tryngites subruficollis*
There are four records of this rare vagrant from North America. One was shot by Haigh on the fitties at North Cotes on 20th September 1906. Others were seen at the Witham mouth on 13th September 1975, at Alkborough from 3rd to 14th September 1981 and at Saltfleetby from 11th to 16th August 1982.

Ruff *Philomachus pugnax*
A fairly common passage migrant on the coast and inland. Since the 1930s increasing numbers have wintered in the county as part of a national trend. Increases have also been noted in the numbers of passage migrants in spring and autumn.

Spring parties tend to be small, mainly between late March and early June, and some birds present in early summer indulge in courtship display — but there has been no evidence of breeding in recent years. Autumn counts of migrants between early July and October may be variable but quite large flocks are now no longer unusual. At this season it is fairly widespread occuring on ploughed and stubble fields as well as more typical flooded fields, sewage farms, reservoirs and coastal marshes. Some of the larger autumn flocks tend to comprise moulting adult birds and adults also preponderate in wintering parties. Peak passage numbers have usually been recorded at Wisbech sewage farm where up to 200 birds used to be present in autumn.

Before drainage of the Fens the Ruff was a common breeding species. It also bred on low ground in the Marsh district between Louth and the coast and in the north-west of the county. By the early nineteenth century, nesting birds were much reduced but were still to be found regularly on a number of washes and small fens near Spalding, Boston, Spilsby and Crowland. A few pairs also lingered on in the heaths in the north-west but it was practically extinct by the middle of the century. In 1882 a pair nested on Scotton Common but the female was shot and the eggs taken. Even after drainage of the large tracts of fenland it might have survived as a breeding bird in suitable areas had it not been in such great demand as a table bird.

There are a number of recoveries of birds ringed on autumn passage in the Wash. Five birds have been recovered in Italy betweeen September and April, three in Spain during November, one in Portugal in March and single birds in France in December and July. Others have been found in the Pechora Valley in Russia in July, Poland in June, Germany in August and Mali in January. One bird was wintering in Kent three years later and another individual ringed in August 1969 was controlled in Flintshire in March 1971 and eventually found dead in Norfolk in January 1974.

Jack Snipe *Lymnocryptes minimus*
An unobtrusive species whose status is somewhat difficult to assess. It is a fairly common autumn immigrant most years but numbers may be quite variable. Some birds remain in winter and there is a regular spring passage.

Early birds may sometimes be seen in August and September but the main arrivals take place from October to mid-November. Wintering birds are quite widespread but numbers tend to be small. During severe weather some movement is evident and birds will sometimes feed on the shore amongst debris along the high water mark. Return passage is on a small scale and extends from late March to the first week of May.

One ringed at Wisbech sewage farm in October 1957 was recovered in southern France seven weeks later.

Snipe *Gallinago gallinago*
A fairly common and widespread breeding species, nesting on marshy ground through-out the county. It is numerous on autumn passage when immigration takes place from the Continent and common in winter and on spring migration. There was a considerable decrease in breeding numbers during the early part of the last century attributed to the extensive spread of improved drainage and increased cultivation of land. A further decrease has occurred during the last ten years.

Autumn migration extends from mid-August to late November with a distinct peak in October when small parties can often be observed arriving off the sea. Many of these immigrants pass through the county to winter in other areas. Wintering numbers fluctuate a good deal according to the severity of the weather and movements are a frequent feature during periods of snow and frost. Return passage in spring is usually much less pronounced than in autumn and lasts from mid-March until early May.

Over 20 birds ringed on passage in the county have been recovered still on passage or wintering in France, Spain, Portugal and Morocco. One ringed in September 1964 was recovered in Sardinia six weeks later and one ringed in October 1964 was recovered in Russia a year later. One ringed in East Germany in September 1976 was found dead in the county in September 1981.

A number of passage migrants ringed in Lincolnshire have been recovered in wintering areas farther west in England, Wales and Ireland.

Great Snipe *Gallinago media*
A very rare autumn vagrant with one spring record. During the last century it was recorded more regularly than at present. Between 1826 and 1901 there were 15 records

of birds shot in the county, all in September and October. In addition to these there were a number of sight records but some of these are not reliable. During the last 50 years there have been at least eight records. Birds were shot at Grantham sewage farm on 12th September 1938, Tetney on 20th September 1939, and at Rothwell, near Caistor in September 1947 and on 3rd October 1952. One was present at Wisbech sewage farm from 21st to 23rd August 1969 and another at Saltfleetby from 8th to 15th October 1978 was trapped and ringed. One was seen at Barton-on-Humber on 23rd and 24th March 1983, then there was one at Saltfleetby on 24th August 1984 with probably a different individual present from 15th to 18th September.

Long-billed Dowitcher *Limnodromus scolopaceus*
A rare vagrant from North America. One at Wisbech sewage farm from 28th September to 6th October 1963 was recorded by P. Carah and seen by several other observers. One found by K. Atkin at Bardney Ponds on 28th September 1971 was also seen by a number of observers during its stay until 10th October. An adult seen at Holbeach St. Marks by P. Clement and other observers between 19th and 24th July 1986 was relocated at Moulton Marsh from 3rd to 14th August. There is an old record of a dowitcher shot at Humberston on 15th August 1882. At that time the two dowitchers were considered to be races of the same species. The specimen was examined by Cordeaux and recorded as an adult still partly in summer plumage but unfortunately the fate of the skin is unknown.

Woodcock *Scolopax rusticola*
A fairly common breeding species and a common widespread passage migrant and winter visitor. Breeding birds inhabit many woodlands, the main population being in western and central areas of the county. In the north-east, along the coast and in the Fens nesting is rare and irregular. In recent years it has increased in some areas, particularly where there are new conifer plantations.

There is considerable immigration from the continent between the end of September and late November, the majority usually arriving in late October and early November. Many of these birds winter farther west in Britain but good numbers are distributed throughout the county, including some in the coastal dunes. During severe winters mortality may be high and birds will even resort to feeding in ice-free areas along the seashore. Return passage lasts from late March until the first week of May but numbers observed on the coast at this season are usually very small.

One ringed on passage at Gibraltar Point in March 1950 was wintering in north Wales in January 1952. A Norwegian-ringed chick marked in June 1959 was recovered in the Fens in the following January and one ringed in Germany in April 1960 was recovered in the north of the county in the following December.

Black-tailed Godwit *Limosa limosa*
A fairly common passage migrant, mainly on the coast, that has increased during recent years. Some are present in the summer and there are occasional records of breeding and territory holding. Prior to drainage of the Fens it bred in some numbers. Regular

Woodcock

Bar-tailed Godwits

breeding ceased about 1829 and several potential nesting pairs were shot during the next few years. As a migrant it became rare and irregular from the middle of the nineteenth century. A nest containing eggs is said to have been found near Wainfleet in 1885. Occurrences began to be more frequent from the 1920s, the increase being more striking by the 1940s. A pair bred at Cowbit in the Fens between 1940 and 1942 and successful nesting was also recorded nearby at Crowland Wash in 1951. Single pairs nested in the Humber in 1974 and 1979 and other pairs have attempted to breed or held territories in the Humber and the Wash during the 1970s and 1980s. Small parties have summered especially in the Wash in recent years. With a colony firmly established on the Ouse Washes in Cambridgeshire since 1952, it seems likely that occasional breeding attempts will continue where suitable conditions exist in the county.

Spring migrants are noted chiefly in April and May. Larger numbers return between July and September with stragglers to the end of October. Some birds have remained to winter particularly in the Wash during recent years. Some of these birds may belong to the Icelandic race *L.l. islandica*. A specimen of this race was shot at Tetney on 27th November 1943. Most birds occurring in the county probably belong to the race *L.l. limosa* which breeds in Continental Europe.

Hudsonian Godwit *Limosa haemastica*
A very rare vagrant from North America. One at Blacktoft, Yorkshire in September and October 1981 regularly crossed the Trent and was seen feeding on Alkborough Flats by G.P. Catley on 15th September. This was the first British record.

Bar-tailed Godwit *Limosa lapponica*
A numerous passage migrant and winter visitor on the coast. It is present in much greater numbers in the Wash than in the Humber and occasionally flocks of up to 10,000 birds are recorded. Parties on the more exposed coastline are comparatively small.

Passage birds begin to arrive in early July, reaching a peak in late August and September and continuing until early November. Wintering birds begin to leave at the end of February, spring passage extending until late May or sometimes early June. Very small numbers are present during the summer. There is a regular westerly passage up the Humber between April and September and a few not infrequently depart south-west inland in autumn, sometimes in association with flocks of Curlew and Whimbrels.

Ringing recoveries in the county have included two birds from Norway, two from the Netherlands and one from Denmark. Two birds ringed in the Wash have been recovered in the Netherlands and three were found in West Germany. Another ringed at Wrangle in September 1983 was found dead in Mauritania in November of the same year.

Whimbrel *Numenius phaeopus*
A common passage migrant in spring and autumn. Good numbers occur on the coast between mid-April and mid-May. Early migrants sometimes arrive in late March and stragglers may continue until early June with odd birds sometimes frequenting the coastal marshes during the summer. Autumn passage extends from early July to October

with a few remaining to early November. Many of the autumn birds pass high over the coast and continue inland to the south-west. There are occasional records of birds seen during the winter.

Curlew *Numenius arquata*

A scarce breeding species. It is a common passage migrant inland as well as on the coast with smaller numbers remaining to winter, chiefly in the Humber and the Wash. Nesting birds have recently been confined to marshy fields and heaths in the west and north-west of the county. A number of birds are present in other districts during the summer but the only authentic breeding records away from traditional nesting areas were single instances on the coast at Tetney, Mablethorpe and Wainfleet in the 1850s.

Autumn migration is quite prolonged extending from late June until mid-November, peak numbers usually occurring in late August. Some of the birds which winter on the coast flight inland to feed at dawn and return to the shore in the evening. Spring movements between late March and early June are generally much less marked than those in autumn.

Many immigrants are evidently of Scandinavian origin. Eleven chicks ringed in Finland have been recovered in the county in adddition to six from Sweden and one from Norway. One Dutch-ringed chick has also been found in the county. Birds caught in the Wash in autumn have been subsequently recovered in Denmark, Sweden, Finland and Russia.

Spotted Redshank *Tringa erythropus*

A fairly common autumn passage migrant and regular in small numbers in spring. It has certainly increased in recent years when flocks have been recorded in the Wash during the summer and odd birds have wintered almost annually. It occurs chiefly on the coast but is regular inland in small numbers particularly at sewage farms, reservoirs, lakes and gravel pits.

Spring birds usually occur betweeen late April and the first week of June. Return passage lasts from early July to about early November but main numbers occur in August and September. Both Cordeaux (1899) and Blathwayt (1915) considered it to be a scarce annual autumn migrant although Stubbs (1929) recorded regular numbers caught at the plover decoys of the north-east coast in the late nineteenth and early twentieth centuries.

One ringed in the Netherlands in September 1964 was found dead at North Cotes in January 1969.

Redshank *Tringa totanus*

The Redshank has increased considerably during the present century. It is now a common breeding species with nesting numbers concentrated on the marshes of the Humber and Wash. Relatively few nest inland and are found chiefly in the north-west and west of the county. It is numerous on passage, particularly in the autumn and is a common winter visitor. Large numbers bred in the Fens prior to drainage but numbers were much diminished after the early part of the nineteenth century. A few pairs nested on the north-east coast and probably also in the Wash in the ensuing years and by the end of the century Cordeaux (1899) noted an increase and spread in breeding range particularly in the north of the county. Nesting numbers were also improving in the Wash at about the same time and there was a steady increase in both areas until about the 1940s. The species suffered heavy mortality in the severe winter of 1962/63 but numbers recovered within a few years.

Migration times are somewhat complex as different populations are involved. Breeding birds disperse into non-breeding areas in late June and early July. These birds belong to the race *T.t. britannica* but immigrants belong to the continental race *T.t. totanus* and the Icelandic race *T.t. robusta*. Birds of the Icelandic race have been shot and trapped regularly in the county on passage and in winter and European birds, which are indistinguishable from British stock in winter plumage, are almost certainly regular winter visitors. The main immigration of these last two races is probably between late August and early November when coastal numbers reach their peak. Return passage along the coast extends from mid-March to the end of May.

Birds ringed in the Wash in autumn have been recovered in a number of east coast counties of England and Scotland as well as in Lancashire, Dorset and Hampshire. One ringed in the Western Isles has also been recovered in the county. Eight birds ringed in autumn were shot in France in later winters and a chick ringed near Grantham in June 1960 was recovered in France two months later. One ringed in France in August 1985 was found dead at Grainthorpe in the following March. One ringed in September 1975 was found in the Netherlands in February 1976 and another ringed in July 1962 was recovered in Portugal in September of the same year. One ringed in autumn 1961 was recovered in Denmark in July 1964. A juvenile ringed in August 1966 was shot on the north-west coast of Morocco two months later and one ringed in January 1983 was shot in Spain in November 1984. Three birds ringed in the Wash have been recovered in Iceland in June and July and another was found dead in the Faeroes in March.

Marsh Sandpiper *Tringa stagnatilis*
A very rare vagrant. One was watched feeding on the mud of the Welland estuary near Holbeach St. Mark's by I.C.T. Nisbet and other observers on 8th August 1954. This was the sixth British record. One was seen at the Witham Mouth from 8th to 15th August 1987 by C.R. Casey, S. Keightley and other observers.

Greenshank *Tringa nebularia*
A fairly common autumn passage migrant also occurring in small numbers in spring. Most movement takes place on the coast but it is recorded frequently on inland waters and coastal birds may often be seen heading inland.

Spring passage extends from mid-April to early June with the return movement in autumn from mid-July to the end of October, peak numbers being in August and early September. Exceptionally, early migrants may occasionally be recorded in late March and there are a number of November records. Cordeaux (1899) stated that it occurred exceptionally in winter and there have been a few recent records between December and February. Brogden writing in the 1890s considered that passage numbers in the south of the county were decreasing, a statement echoed by Haigh referring to the north-east coast 30 years later. It is probable that these were only short term decreases.

One ringed at Wisbech sewage farm in August 1965 was shot on the north coast of France in August 1969.

Lesser Yellowlegs *Tringa flavipes*

There are seven records of this North American vagrant. The first was shot at Tetney by J.H. Stubbs on 15th September 1932. Since then it has been recorded at Wisbech sewage farm on 17th September 1966, North Killingholme from 3rd to 30th October 1970, Wisbech sewage farm on 11th October 1973, Huttoft Pit from 25th July to 4th August 1976, Humberston on 24th September 1978 and at Covenham Reservoir on 20th May 1984.

Solitary Sandpiper *Tringa solitaria*

A very rare vagrant. One was observed for long periods during its stay at Bardney Ponds from 10th to 12th August 1963. It was seen by A.D. Townsend, G.F. Leachman and R. May and subsequently by several other observers. This was the eighth British record of this North American species.

Green Sandpiper *Tringa ochropus*

A rather scarce spring passage migrant although it is fairly common in autumn with a few staying to winter. It is often seen on the coastal marshes but occurs regularly at inland waters, sewage farms and along rivers and dykes.

Spring birds usually occur in very small numbers during late April and early May and occasionally to early June. Forerunners of the autumn movement may arrive in late June but the main passage, often involving small parties, extends from mid-July to the end of September with a few later migrants during October. There has been some decline in numbers in recent years. A few birds are annual in winter when it is usually found on inland waters. Exceptional numbers were recorded in the north-east of the county in the winter of 1885/86.

One ringed at Wisbech sewage farm in October 1963 was shot in south-west France in the following February.

Wood Sandpiper *Tringa glareola*

A scarce autumn passage migrant and rather rarer in spring. Like the Green Sandpiper it is usually found by dykes, ponds, sewage farms and on marshy areas both on the coast and inland. A record of breeding on Scotton Common in 1871 quoted by Cordeaux (1899) is not convincing. Early birds are sometimes seen in late April but most migrants pass in May. Prior to 1953 there were only two spring records but since then it has been noted regularly each spring.

Autumn passage lasts from late July to the end of September with occasional stragglers into October. In most years migrants appear singly or in very small parties but in the autumns of 1952 and 1963 there were large influxes of birds into Britain and much higher numbers than usual were seen in Lincolnshire. In some years concentrations at Wisbech sewage farm in autumn have been more pronounced than elsewhere in the county. Flocks were not infrequently in double figures and a maximum of 37 birds was counted on 13th August 1969.

One ringed at Tetney in August 1960 was controlled at Wisbech sewage farm ten days later.

Common Sandpiper *Actitis hypoleucos*

A common passage migrant in autumn and in smaller numbers in spring. In recent years single birds have been occasionally recorded in winter. It is regularly recorded on most inland streams, ponds, lakes and reservoirs as well as in the coastal marshes. Two pairs were said to have nested at Saltfleet in 1893 but close examination of this record suggests that the birds involved were Ringed Plovers. Brogden (1900) stated that it also nested occasionally in the Spalding area. These records can only be regarded as doubtful, especially as spring migrants will sometimes indulge in song and display, although a pair did breed at Scunthorpe in 1979.

Spring migration lasts from mid-April to early June and return passage extends from late June to the second week of October with peak numbers in August. Autumn birds are often in small parties.

Five birds ringed in Lincolnshire in August have been recovered in France in subsequent autumns and another was recovered there in January. One ringed in September 1966 was recovered in Spain in December 1968 and another ringed at Bardney in August 1957 was in Portugal only six days later. One ringed at Gibraltar Point in August 1963 was found, possibly in its breeding area, in south-west Norway in early June 1970. One ringed in Essex in July 1952 was recovered in the county in August 1954 and another ringed in Essex in July 1961 showed reverse migration when it was controlled at Tetney ten days later.

Spotted Sandpiper *Actitis macularia*

There are two or three records of this rare vagrant from North America. One was seen by J.A.W. Moyes at Wisbech sewage farm between 9th November and 19th December 1970. Another was seen by the same observer at the same locality on 13th June 1971. What was perhaps the same bird was also recorded on 29th July and 30th August.

Turnstone *Arenaria interpres*

A common passage migrant on the coast and a winter visitor in smaller numbers, chiefly in the Humber and the Wash. Very small numbers are regular inland on migration.

Autumn immigration lasts from mid-July to late October, most birds moving through during late August and early September. Wintering flocks in the estuaries may occasionally be several hundred strong especially on the more extensive mussel beds. Very few are present on the open coast at this time. Return passage on a smaller scale begins in April, numbers reaching a peak in the second half of May and early June. A few birds are present during the summer.

One bird ringed as a chick in Finland in July 1969 was controlled at Wisbech sewage farm two months later and two from Norway have been recovered in the Wash. There are several long distance recoveries of birds ringed in the Wash. One ringed in August

Red-necked Phalarope

Greenshank

1966 was recovered in Finland in May 1969. One ringed in August 1967 was shot on its nest in Peary Land, Greenland in July 1973 at 82N — this is the most northerly piece of land in the world. Another bird ringed in September 1975 was recovered in Ghana in the following December and one ringed in August 1977 was found dead in Morocco in December of the same year. One ringed in August 1983 was controlled in Guinea Bissau in January 1987. Two birds ringed in August 1974 were both shot in Spain in May 1984.

Wilson's Phalarope *Phalaropus tricolor*
A rare vagrant from western central North America. One arrived at Wisbech sewage farm on 28th September 1967 to be joined by a second bird on the following day. Both birds remained to 16th October and one was still present on 2nd November. Many observers, including R.P. Bagnall-Oakeley, J.A.W. Moyes and S. Greenwood saw these birds which occurred in an autumn that produced seven other individuals in Britain and Ireland. A male occurred at the same locality from 7th to 11th June 1975 and two birds were present on 29th August 1979. In 1984 single first winter birds were seen at Gibraltar Point from 11th September to 5th October and at Anderby Creek on 3rd October. A juvenile was seen at Covenham Reservoir between 19th and 22nd August 1985 and a female was at Gibraltar Point on 8th June 1987.

Red-necked Phalarope *Phalaropus lobatus*
A rare but almost annual autumn passage migrant to the coast and inland waters occasionally seen in spring. It occurs inland more often than the Grey Phalarope and migration is generally earlier than that species.

Between 1850 and 1934 there were 18 records, mainly on the north-east coast in September and October. There were no further records until 1956 but since then there have been about 50 occurrences. A few have been seen during May and early June. Early autumn migrants have sometimes been seen from late June onwards but most records are in August and September with a few in October. A very late bird was recorded at Donna Nook on 19th November 1966.

Grey Phalarope *Phalaropus fulicarius*
A rare autumn and exceptional winter visitor, chiefly on the coast but occasionally on inland waters. It was formerly regarded as irregular but probably due to increased observations it has been noted almost annually in recent years. Most records in early autumn coincide with south-west or westerly gales and November occurrences frequently follow north-west or northerly gales.

There were about 20 records in the second half of the nineteenth century, mainly of birds shot in October and November with three in December. Only nine birds were recorded in the first half of the present century but over 60 have been noted since 1954. October and November produced the bulk of these records although there have been several during July to September. A few have occurred in winter between December and March. Most records refer to single birds but sometimes two or three are seen together and a party of seven occurred at Donna Nook on 24th October 1970.

Arctic Skua

Long-tailed Skua

Pomarine Skua *Stercorarius pomarinus*
A scarce or sometimes fairly common passage migrant on the coast in autumn. It is very rare in winter and spring. Passage occurs between late July and December with most birds in September and October. Movements are often associated with other skua species and small numbers in a day are normal, although 1985 and 1988 produced exceptional passages with between 50 and 100 on several dates and about 300 birds reported in each year. There are occasional records of birds in January and February and also in April and May. Single birds at Covenham Reservoir on 2nd October 1974 and 10th November 1985 are the only inland records.

Its former status seems to have been similar to the present day, and it was stated to be more plentiful than usual in the autumns of 1879 and 1881. There were no records of the species between 1936 and 1957 but as Smith and Cornwallis (1955) pointed out this must have been caused by a lack of sea-watching during that period.

Arctic Skua *Stercorarius parasiticus*
A common autumn passage migrant on the coast, being much more plentiful in some years than others. It is rare in winter and spring. There are several inland records and not infrequently parties of birds are seen passing inland, chiefly over the north-east and Wash coasts.

One was shot in May 1859 and there have been about 60 birds between late April and early June since 1971. One or two have been recorded in late June but passage is mainly from early July to the end of October, with peak movements in August and September. Large southerly movements of several hundreds sometimes occur at these times, especially during gales from between the north-west and north-east. A few birds may be seen in November and there are several recent records in winter.

One ringed as a nestling in Shetland in July 1962 was found dead at Tetney in the following October.

Long-tailed Skua *Stercorarius longicaudus*
A rare autumn passage migrant on the coast but exceptionally there are good years as in 1879, 1895, 1912, 1976, 1985 and 1988.

It occurs between late July and November with the majority of records from September to mid-October. It was described by Cordeaux as being common in mid-October 1879 and in 1895, although he mentioned no actual numbers. Between 10th September and 1st October 1912 seven were shot at North Cotes and Donna Nook, one was found dead at Tetney and four were seen at Grainthorpe. There were no further records until one was found dead at Tetney in August 1948 and another was found dead at Blyborough, near Gainsborough on 15th November 1949. It has been recorded more regularly since 1961 and up to nine birds have been seen annually since 1966, apart from 12 in 1976, 14 in 1985 and about 70 in 1988. The last total included 17 at Huttoft on 24th September.

In addition to the 1949 record above it has been recorded inland at Spalding on 7th October 1961 and one was found dead at Wisbech sewage farm on 3rd October 1973.

Great Skua *Stercorarius skua*
A fairly common passage migrant along the coast in autumn and also noted occasionally in winter and spring. It was formerly rare and irregular. There are only two records for the nineteenth century — in 1865 and 1874 — and 13 for the first half of the present century. Since then, however, there has been a very marked increase in sightings directly attributable to full protection and a huge population rise on its Scottish breeding grounds.

Early migrants sometimes occur in late July and August but the main passage occurs from September to November with the largest numbers occurring during gales. Single birds are occasionally noted in winter between December and March and there are a few recent records in spring. Exceptionally birds have been recorded heading inland mainly on the Wash coast and there are a number of records from Covenham Reservoir and in the Humber as far as Trent Falls.

Three ringed as nestlings in Shetland in July have been recovered in the county in September.

Mediterranean Gull *Larus melanocephalus*
A very scarce visitor, chiefly in autumn, but also recorded at all other times of the year. It is noted mainly on the coast although there are several inland occurrences particularly at Covenham Reservoir and in the Lincoln area.

There were no records in Lincolnshire until one at Gibraltar Point on 6th and 7th August 1950. No more were forthcoming until 1965 but since then there has been a steady increase with about 150 records. Birds of all ages have occurred although the easier identification of adults is probably the reason for immatures to be slightly in the minority of records.

Laughing Gull *Larus atricilla*
A rare vagrant from North America recorded on four occasions. One was seen by S. Lorand at Donna Nook on 24th February 1979 and another was recorded at Huttoft on 6th October 1979. In 1984 one was at Thorpe Pits, near Lincoln on 23rd May and another was present at Barton-on-Humber on 28th December. All the records were of immature birds.

Little Gull *Larus minutus*
A fairly common visitor, chiefly to the coast, that has increased considerably since the 1960s. During recent years sightings have averaged more than 100 birds annually and most are immatures. Early records mainly refer to autumn passage migrants and wintering birds and although small numbers still occur in winter the vast majority of recent appearances have been between May and November. Second year birds and adults sometimes make protracted stays in summer at certain localities and one or two have been observed amongst colonies of Black-headed Gulls in recent years. It occurs quite regularly on inland reservoirs, gravel pits, lakes and sewage farms. Small parties at sea are sometimes associated with heavy Kittiwake passage from November to February.

One ringed near Louth in February 1915 was recovered in Denmark a year later and a nestling ringed in southern Sweden in July 1937 was found in the county in the following November.

Sabine's Gull *Larus sabini*
A rare autumn migrant, chiefly on the coast. About 50 birds have been recorded, all but six of these since 1964. Most occurrences have been between late August and October although there are two records in July. There were more sightings than usual in 1971 when five were recorded, in 1977 when seven were recorded and in 1985 when five were seen. The only inland records were at Bardney Ponds from 10th to 28th September 1974 and at Baston Fen on 16th October 1987. Adult and immature birds have been recorded in about equal numbers.

Bonaparte's Gull *Larus philadelphia*
A very rare vagrant from North America. An immature bird was seen by G.P. Catley and M. Mellor at Grimsby Docks on 17th March 1979.

Black-headed Gull *Larus ridibundus*
A numerous breeding species and an abundant passage migrant and winter visitor. There has been considerable variation in breeding numbers and movement of colonies.

Prior to drainage of the Fens vast numbers frequented these areas where their eggs were harvested in huge quantities for the London markets. By the middle of the nineteenth century breeding was apparently confined to the heath district of the north-west and on the salt marsh at North Cotes. The latter colony was probably of little significance and became extinct about 1855, but the gull ponds at Twigmoor and Scotton Common were occupied by large numbers. Between 5,000 and 10,000 pairs were present at Twigmoor alone in the 1840s and 5,000 pairs were estimated there in 1909. Smaller colonies existed on Bottesford Moor, Crosby and Manton Warrens but these were deserted and merged into the two larger colonies in the early years of the present century. In 1938, a census revealed 6,000 pairs in the county. Most of these were still concentrated at Twigmoor and Scotton, but by 1958 there were less than 2,000 pairs about equally divided between coastal and inland localities. A small colony on the salt marshes at Kirton and Frampton increased rapidly in the 1960s and reached a peak of 22,000 pairs in 1974, but this has declined considerably in recent years. Several colonies in the Wash have been destroyed by reclamation and others at Grainthorpe Marsh and several inland sites have decreased and are small by comparison to the Kirton and Frampton congregation.

Outside the breeding season the Black-headed Gull is widespread all along the coast and inland. It often travels up the rivers to visit lakes, reservoirs, sewage farms and other inland waters as well as rubbish tips, open fields, parks and even gardens. Large roosts on the coast are largely deserted each morning as most birds flight inland to feed. Inland roosts are regular at some waters, those at North Hykeham gravel pit and Covenham Reservoir being the most significant.

The ringing of Lincolnshire nestlings has produced many recoveries demonstrating a largely south-westerly dispersal to midland counties, Wales and Ireland with a few to Durham, Yorkshire and Lancashire. Others, however, have been recovered in Spain, Portugal and Tunisia.

Birds ringed as fully grown in the county have been recovered in Russia, Poland, Finland, Norway, Sweden, Denmark, Belgium, the Netherlands, Germany, Czechoslovakia and Spain. The origins of some passage migrants and winter visitors is shown by recoveries of birds ringed as nestlings in Norway, Sweden, Finland, Russia, the Netherlands, Denmark, Germany, Poland, Austria, Czechoslovakia and France and a fully grown bird from Italy.

Movements of these migrants are often masked by the presence of the local population. Immigration is usually between late July and the end of October with return movements sometimes in February but often from early March to the end of May. The breeding colonies are generally occupied in late February or early March and abandoned by about the end of July.

Ring-billed Gull *Larus delawarensis*
A rare vagrant from North Amercia. An immature at Bagmoor, near Scunthorpe, from 24th July to 3rd August 1988 was seen by G.P. Catley, A.C. Sims and several other observers.

Common Gull *Larus canus*
An abundant and widespread passage migrant and winter visitor. There are very large roosts of many thousands at several sites on the coast, chiefly in the Humber and the Wash and on some inland waters, especially at Covenham Reservoir and North Hykeham and Tallington gravel pits. The majority of birds at the coastal roosts head inland at dawn to feed in large open fields, on rubbish tips and in towns. Returning flight-lines in the evening may be quite spectacular as thousands in the company of Black-headed Gulls move to the sandflats in 'V' formation.

Early immigrants arrive in July but the main passage occurs between early August and the end of October. Return passage often on a larger scale than in autumn is from early March to mid-May with a distinct peak during April. Inland passage is concentrated along rivers. Immature birds are present in small numbers during the summer.

There are a number of recoveries of birds ringed as nestlings in Russia, Norway, Sweden, Finland and Denmark and found in Lincolnshire between autumn and spring. Birds ringed in the county have also been recovered in those countries as well as in Germany and the Netherlands.

Lesser Black-backed Gull *Larus fuscus*
A fairly common or perhaps common passage migrant in spring and autumn. In Lincolnshire it occurs least commonly of the regular British breeding gulls.

Summering birds, mostly immature, are present at some of the larger gravel pits and other inland waters sometimes in good-sized flocks, and odd non-breeding adults and sub-adults not infrequently attend Black-headed Gull colonies. Both the British race *L.f. graellsii* and the Scandinavian race *L.f. fuscus* are recorded regularly on passage. In

Sabine's Gull

Little Gull

Herring Gull

spring when passage is often observed inland as well as on the coast, *fuscus* usually moves through the county between early March and early May and *graellsii* from late March to early June. *Graellsii* returns in autumn chiefly between early July and mid-October but only very small numbers of *fuscus* occur from August to November. Wintering birds are scarce but most belong to *fuscus*. In recent years there have been some records of *L.f. intermedius* which breeds in southern Norway, western Sweden and Denmark. It seems likely that some records of *fuscus* may refer to this race.

A nestling ringed in Sweden in July 1951 was recovered at Grimsby in May 1952 and one ringed in Norway in June 1954 was recovered on the Humber Bank at Winteringham in April 1955. Another nestling ringed in Lancashire in July 1934 was recovered at Grimsby in February 1935.

Herring Gull *Larus argentatus*
A numerous passage migrant and winter visitor. In 1947 a pair nested unsuccessfuly on the wreck of a destroyer on the sandflats at North Cotes. Summering birds which are chiefly immature are present in small numbers. Huge increases in the breeding colonies elsewhere during recent years have resulted in similar rises in the wintering population which is concentrated all along the coast with particular congregations at refuse tips and fish docks. It is widespread inland though numbers tend to be small in most areas. Northerly movements offshore begin in January and passage lasts until May. Flocks start to build up again in early July, migration continuing until early November.

There are several recoveries in the county in autumn and winter of birds ringed as nestlings in Cleveland, Durham, Northumberland, eastern Scotland and Shetland. Two nestlings ringed in the Netherlands and one from Norway have also been found in the county in winter. Birds of the yellow-legged race, *L.a. omissus* ringed on the Murmansk coast of Russia have been recovered in their first winter at Saltfleet in February 1942 and Grimsby in January 1972. *Omissus* probably only occurs as a vagrant. Adult birds with yellow legs have been seen on several occasions in winter but the occurrence of the similar Mediterranean race *L.a. michahellis* has also been proved by a ringing recovery. This bird marked as a nestling in Italy in May 1982 was found dead at Holbeach Marsh in June 1983.

Iceland Gull *Larus glaucoides*
A rare passage migrant in spring and autumn and also occasionally recorded in winter. There are 55 records and all but five have been seen since 1968. Early records were in 1872 and 1891. Seventeen birds have occurred in autumn between August and December and 24 in spring from March to early May. Fourteen were in January and February. Most sightings have referred to birds on the coast but it has been noted inland on a few occasions. Almost all the records are of birds in immature plumage.

Glaucous Gull *Larus hyperboreus*
A scarce but regular visitor to the coast occurring inland only rarely. It tends to feed along the tide-edge and particularly favours fish docks, rubbish tips and the Donna Nook seal colony. Odd birds sometimes arrive during October but the bulk of records are between

November and March. Sightings in April and May are not infrequent and there are a number of recent records during the summer months. An increase in the last 20 years is probably due to more intensive observations on the coast. Most birds occur singly, two or three together being encountered more rarely. One exceptional total was that of 14 passing south at Huttoft on 26th December 1985. Immature birds especially in first-winter plumage form the vast majority of records.

Great Black-backed Gull *Larus marinus*
A numerous passage migrant and winter visitor on the coast with smaller numbers inland. It has increased considerably during the present century. The main causes of this increase include the exploitation in winter of the edible refuse to be found at fish docks, rubbish tips and coastal sewage outfalls, as well as a reduction in persecution. Very large numbers frequent the fish docks at Grimsby and many of the larger rubbish tips including some well inland. Coastal birds are most numerous on the extensive sandflats of the Humber and Wash where roosts of many thousands occur. Large flocks are frequently observed resting on the shore all day, numbers being largely dependent on the activity of fishing fleets.

Passage in autumn extends from July to early November with return movements from March to early May. Many immature birds are present throughout the summer.

Eight birds ringed as nestlings on the coast of Norway have been recovered in Lincolnshire during their first winter. A nestling ringed on the Murmansk coast of Russia in June 1960 was recovered in the county in January 1963 and another from the same area was recovered in its first winter in December 1967. A first year bird ringed at Tetney in August 1968 was found dead in Durham in the following January.

Kittiwake *Rissa tridactyla*
A numerous passage migrant on the coast and a scarce visitor to inland waters. Very large increases at British breeding colonies during the present century have been paralleled by much greater numbers occurring in Lincolnshire in recent years. Birds on spring passage between late February and late April are generally seen in only small numbers. Flocks on the shore begin to build up in late May and June but larger flocks of several hundreds are more usual from July to September when it is often in the company of Sandwich Terns. Visible passage involves fluctuating numbers and on some days several thousands may move south. These occasional large movements are more usual between late October and early January. It is abundant in the North Sea in winter but is seldom seen from the shore except during stormy weather when dead birds are often washed ashore. Small parties occur in the Humber as far as Trent Falls but it appears at inland waters only rarely. Exceptionally 242 were counted heading inland at Holbeach on 5th December 1954 and a flock of 41 was present at Messingham on 24th May 1986.

Four birds ringed on the Farne Islands, Northumberland were recovered in the county between April and July and a nestling from the Isle of May, Fife was found dead at Covenham Reservoir in August 1987, one month after being ringed.

One nestling ringed on the Murmansk coast of Russia in July 1956 was recovered at Gibraltar Point in the following February; another from the same region in July 1957 was recovered at Donna Nook in April 1958.

Gull-billed Tern *Gelochelidon nilotica*
A rare autumn vagrant noted on five occasions. The first record was of one seen by M.L. Chalmers and D. Elias at Gibraltar Point on 30th August 1967. One flew south at Donna Nook on 4th August 1969. The only immature recorded made a lengthy stay at Covenham Reservoir from 16th September to 14th October 1972. One was present at the mouth of the Witham on 7th September 1975 and another was seen at Trusthorpe on 3rd September 1978.

Caspian Tern *Sterna caspia*
A very rare vagrant. One was shot at Caythorpe, near Grantham by W.F. Foottit on 17th May 1853. One was seen at Gibraltar Point on 5th September 1971 and in 1979 there were single birds at Messingham on 4th July and Donna Nook on 14th July. One at Messingham on 14th June 1981 was also seen nearby at South Ferriby on 15th and 16th. In May 1988, one was seen at Spalding on 5th and perhaps the same bird at Apex Pit, near Lincoln, on 8th.

Sandwich Tern *Sterna sandvicensis*
A coastal migrant in small numbers in spring but numerous in autumn when it is the commonest tern. Passage birds are noted inland only occasionally. It was a common migrant in the mid-nineteenth century but decreased considerably at some time before the turn of the century. It began to increase in the county again following the colonisation of large numbers on the Norfolk coast in the 1920s. Autumn flocks continued to increase and since the 1960s congregations sometimes of several thousands have been recorded on the north-east coast and more especially at Gibraltar Point.

Spring migrants arrive in April and May though eight very early birds were at Gibraltar Point on 26th March 1982. Non-breeding birds are present on the coast throughout the summer in very small numbers and isolated pairs are occasionally present in the vicinity of colonies of Common and Little Terns. Breeding has been confirmed on only one occasion in 1950 when six pairs nested unsuccessfully amongst Common Terns at Friskney. Flocks begin to gather in early July and usually attain peak numbers by the end of the month and in early August. Passage continues on a decreasing scale until early October with stragglers to the end of the month. One very late bird was recorded at the Witham mouth on 8th December 1959.

There are several autumn recoveries in the county of young birds from east coast colonies in Aberdeenshire, Northumberland and Norfolk. One ringed in Germany in June 1964 was in the Wash by early September of the same year and a nestling from County Down in July 1972 was found dead at Grimsby in June 1983. One ringed in the Wash in August 1980 was found dead in France in April 1986 and another ringed in the same area in August 1984 was picked up dead in Kent one month later.

Roseate Tern *Sterna dougallii*
A rare and irregular passage migrant recorded only during the last 25 years. Two were

Sandwich Tern

Whiskered Tern

seen at Gibraltar Point on 30th May 1964, with four on 1st September of the same year. Single birds were recorded at the same locality on 11th July 1965 and 31st August 1967 and a party of 15 was seen there on 15th September 1968. There was one at Donna Nook on 16th August 1974. One was recorded at Tetney on 27th June 1976 with another on 11th May 1977 followed by five on 31st July. In 1978 there were two at Donna Nook on 24th May, one at Killingholme in early June and two at Huttoft on 17th August. One occurred at Tetney on 25th July 1979, then none until one at the Inner Dowsing on 21st August 1985, two at Tetney on 15th May 1986 and one at Huttoft on 16th and 18th October 1987.

Common Tern *Sterna hirundo*

A fairly common summer visitor and a common passage migrant. Breeding colonies are only very small. It has increased in recent years and by 1973 there were about 120 pairs in the county. Of these, 75 pairs were on the coast, chiefly in the Wash, and 45 pairs were at eight inland localities. Inland numbers fluctuate a good deal as most birds nest at gravel pits where conditions may vary from year to year. The coastal population seems very low despite large stretches of apparently suitable breeding habitat. It was said to have nested commonly on the Lincolnshire coast in the early nineteenth century but it was reduced to only a few pairs in the latter half of the century. The taking of eggs and persecution by shooting are attributable to this decrease.

On passage it occurs regularly at inland waters but in much smaller parties than on the coast. The main spring arrival is from late April to early June. An early bird was seen in the Wash on 19th March 1950. Autumn movements are much more marked between mid-July and early October. Peak numbers are usually during August when large flocks occur especially in the Humber and Wash.

Chicks ringed at inland sites have been recovered in Ghana and Liberia in the following spring, and three young birds ringed in Germany and one from Estonia have been found on the coast in autumn. Two from the Norfolk coast have been recovered on the Lincolnshire side of the Wash in later years.

Arctic Tern *Sterna paradisaea*

A common passage migrant mainly on the coast. It is usually quite scarce at most inland waters although it appears regularly in spring, especially at Covenham Reservoir. Breeding occurs only spasmodically. A pair and young were obtained at Gibraltar Point in 1843. Four pairs bred at North Cotes in 1872 and there were small colonies at Friskney in 1883 and 1884 and at Wrangle in 1912. A pair nested at Gibraltar Point annually from 1951 to 1954 and again in 1956, and one pair bred at Frampton in 1980.

Numbers on spring passage between late April and early June are usually rather small. In autumn, when it occurs from mid-July to early October, it is sometimes more numerous than the Common Tern but proportions of both species are highly variable. In 1982 a huge flock of 3,500 was roosting at Noth Cotes on 20th August. In the late nineteenth century and early years of the present century it was said to be far more frequent than the Common Tern in autumn.

A chick ringed on the Farne Islands, Northumberland in July 1936 was recovered in the county one month later.

Little Tern *Sterna albifrons*
A fairly common summer visitor on the coast that has increased during recent years. It occurs inland exceptionally on passage in spring and autumn although it is regularly seen at Covenham Reservoir. Its status in the nineteenth century appears to have been rather precarious. Small numbers nested regularly at Gibraltar Point but colonies on the north-east coast were subject to a great deal of fluctuation probably due to persecution. The population remained fairly low in the first half of the present century but an increase began in the 1950s. This increase was initially rather slow but has escalated during the last few years as good protection measures through wardening have greatly assisted the species. Well-established colonies are present at Tetney, Skidbrooke North End, Saltfleet, Saltfleetby, Skegness and Gibraltar Point. A few pairs bred at the Witham Mouth in the early 1980s. By 1977 there was a record total of 205 pairs, over half of these nesting at the Tetney colony. Despite increased protection, colonies still face several hazards particularly from high spring tides and mammalian predators. These may result in the rearing of hardly any young birds in some seasons.

The first birds arrive at the colonies in the second half of April, immigration continuing during May. Breeding sites are forsaken by late July and passage migrants are noted usually in small numbers until late August or early September. Occasionally birds have been seen as late as the third week of October.

There are four recoveries of chicks ringed at the Tetney colony. One ringed in June 1967 was shot in France in the following September and another ringed in June 1973 was shot in Morocco in the following September. One ringed in July 1970 was breeding on the Cumberland coast in July 1974 and another ringed in June 1974 was nesting in Angus three years later.

Whiskered Tern *Chlidonias hybridus*
A very rare vagrant. One probably in its first summer was present at Covenham Reservoir between 10th and 15th June 1987 and seen by by S. Lancaster, K.E. Wilson and other observers.

Black Tern *Chlidonias niger*
A fairly common passage migrant recorded more frequently in autumn than in spring. It occurs regularly on inland waters as well as on the coast. The largest numbers usually occur in the Wash. Displaying birds have sometimes been seen in spring and in 1961 a pair actually built a nest at Bardney Ponds. Vast numbers used to breed before drainage was completed in the Fens. Pennant who visited the East Fen in 1769 wrote that 'the Black Terns almost deafened one with their clamours'. The extinction of nesting birds was also assisted by the extensive taking of eggs. Very few are likely to have survived beyond the early years of the nineteenth century although eggs were taken from Crowland Wash just prior to 1845.

Early birds appear rarely in late April, the main movement lasting from early May to early June. There are a number of mid-summer records. Autumn passage begins in mid-

July but the main migration occurs in August and September with stragglers into October or, exceptionally, November. Immature birds form the majority of autumn migrants.

White-winged Black Tern *Chlidonias leucopterus*
A very rare passage migrant, chiefly in autumn but also occasionally in spring. There are 21 records, all of which have been since 1957. Birds on inland waters form half of the total and most of the autumn occurrences involve immature birds. In spring it has been seen at Grantham sewage farm on 3rd June 1959, at Anderby Creek from 15th to 17th May 1970, and two together were at Gibraltar Point on 24th May 1973. Autumn appearances are chiefly in August, with only four arriving in September. Several birds have remained off-passage for up to two weeks and one at Wisbech sewage farm in September 1958 remained until 7th October.

Guillemot *Uria aalge*
A fairly common passage migrant and winter visitor to coastal waters. It is seen most frequently from late July to the end of October with a scattering of records in winter and spring. It is usually the commonest of the auks occurring in the county. Following severe weather dead birds are washed ashore sometimes in large numbers and oiled birds are frequently found. Occasional birds may be storm-driven inland in autumn and winter. Both the northern race *U.a. aalge* and the southern race *U.a. albionis* occur regularly.
A nestling ringed in Anglesey in June 1962 was recovered at Chapel St. Leonards in January 1963 and another nestling ringed on Heligoland, Germany in July 1963 was picked up oiled at Anderby Creek in January 1966. A nestling from Shetland was found dead in the county in February 1983 and at the same time as one which had been ringed in Norway in July 1981.

Razorbill *Alca torda*
A scarce visitor to coastal waters, chiefly in autumn but also at all other times of the year. As most sightings of auks refer to birds passing at some distance from the shore when specific identification is often impossible, this species, the Guillemot and Puffin are probably very much under-recorded.
Parties seen on the sea in late July and August often include juvenile birds not fully grown which are presumably from the Yorkshire cliffs. Storm-driven and oiled birds are regularly washed ashore, sometimes in large numbers, especially in February and March. Occasionally birds have been picked up inland.
Single birds ringed at west coast colonies on the Isle of Man and in Pembrokeshire have been recovered in Lincolnshire in autumn. A nestling of the race *A.t. torda* ringed in southern Finland in July 1974 was found dead at Immingham Docks in February 1976 and another ringed in Norway in July 1980 was found dead on Freiston Shore in February 1983. One ringed in Iceland in July 1981 was found dead at Huttoft in February 1983 and during the same period there were six recoveries of birds ringed in the Western Isles. British birds belong to the race *A.t. islandica*.

Black Guillemot *Cepphus grylle*
A rare vagrant recorded on eleven occasions. One in Lincoln Museum was said to have been shot at Washingborough, near Lincoln on 21st January 1899. More recently it has appeared at Chapel Point in the third week of September 1963, Gibraltar Point on 13th November 1965 and 15th January 1966 and at Donna Nook on 30th August 1967. One was found dead at Gibraltar Point on 16th November 1968 and another was present at the Witham mouth from 29th December 1977 to 3rd January 1978. In 1980 there was one at Donna Nook on 5th November and one was found dead at North Cotes on 23rd November. One was recorded at Huttoft on 13th February 1983 and another flew south there on 2nd November 1985.

Little Auk *Alle alle*
A fairly regular autumn and winter visitor in widely fluctuating numbers. Following strong gales especially from the north sizeable flocks occur close inshore and some may be driven considerable distances inland. As storms abate small parties head north along the tide-line and some penetrate the Humber.

In most years only small numbers are recorded but from time to time there have been large movements and wrecks of the species with several hundred birds involved. The most notable of these were in December 1894 and January 1895, February and March 1900, January and February 1912, November 1948, November 1957, November 1969, late October 1974, November 1975 and February and October 1983. The largest movement was in 1986 when at least 1,000 flew north along the coast on 2nd November.

It is seldom seen before the last week of October. The majority of sightings are during November with rather fewer until about mid-March. One was seen at Donna Nook on 2nd May 1981. There are two midsummer records. One flew aboard a boat in the Wash on 16th July 1872 and more recently one in summer plumage was seen at the tide-edge at Donna Nook on 31st July 1975.

Puffin *Fratercula arctica*
A scarce visitor to coastal waters, chiefly between late August and November and more rarely in winter, spring and summer. As with the other auks, occasionally storm-driven birds may appear inland. It is usually recorded far less regularly than the Guillemot and Razorbill and is seldom found washed ashore in any numbers although at least 50 were found dead on the coast in February and March 1969 and almost 300 were found dead in February 1983. In the late nineteenth century it was noted more commonly along the coast and Cordeaux (1899) recorded that it was sometimes plentiful in the Humber in winter during prolonged storms. Since then there has been a very marked decline in the British breeding population and most recent records refer to single birds or very small parties.

The only ringing recoveries were all found dead on the coast in February 1983. These were five from the Farne Islands, two from the Isle of May, three from East Lothian and one from Sule Skerry.

Pallas's Sandgrouse *Syrrhaptes paradoxus*

An Asiatic species that has not been recorded in Lincolnshire since the great irruptions of the late nineteenth century. As all of the records were during the five years, 1863, 1888, 1889, 1890 and 1899, all those traced are listed below in an attempt to illustrate the extent of such spectacular invasions of this exciting rarity.

The first birds to arrive in 1863 were a flock of 40 to 50 at Saltfleetby at the end of April. At least 24 of these were shot but the survivors remained until July. One was found dead near Grimsby in the second week of May and two were shot from a party of 20 at Leake, near Boston on 25th May. Others were shot at about this time in the areas around Louth and Alford and sold on the markets without their rarity being realised. In early August two were shot from a flock of 20 arriving from the east at Huttoft.

The second invasion in 1888 was of much greater magnitude than the earlier one. The forerunners arrived in late May in the north of the county. Ten to 12 birds were seen at Irby, near Grimsby on 18th May, followed by four nearby at Swallow on 22nd and five at Epworth in the Isle of Axholme on 23rd. Two arrived at Tetney on 25th May and two were shot at Cawkwell, near Louth on 28th.

By the end of the month, 26 birds were present at Tetney. The 2nd June was evidently a good day as five were seen near Lincoln, one was shot at High Toynton, near Horncastle, one was found dead under telegraph wires along the Bourne to Spalding railway line and eight were found poisoned in a field at Fulstow. One was seen at Cabourne Wold, near Caistor on 4th June and a flock of 20 to 30 birds frequented the Asserby area, near Alford for several days until 9th June. A flock of 21 was at Horkstow, near Barton on 14th June and on the following day seven reached Brumby Common, where parties totalling 14 birds were present from 17th June to 9th July. Twenty at Humberston stayed from 18th June to the end of the month, when there were also 15 at Tetney.

Several small parties were reported at Authorpe, near Louth on 8th July but the only others during the month were two shot at Holbeach just prior to 20th, followed by two more at the same locality on 28th July. Five were present at Cuxwold, near Caistor during mid-August and on 30th a flock of 40 was seen at Mablethorpe. At North Cotes there were 20 birds on 13th September and five arrived at Tetney from the direction of Spurn on 3rd October. Six more birds were seen at North Cotes on 10th October, when two were also shot at North Somercotes. A flock of 20 at Goxhill on 23rd October was said to have been present from some days previously. Forty were recorded at Grainthorpe on 11th November but even this flock was eclipsed by one of 100 birds which wandered the sand dunes between North Somercotes and Saltfleetby from the last week of January to the end of March 1889. There were also 30 on the north Wolds and three at Ingoldmells in late January. The only other records in 1889 were of five near Brigg on 4th May and ten at the same place on 27th July.

It was much scarcer in the influx of 1890 and appeared to be less well documented. There were eight birds at South Killingholme on 24th May. A flock of 30 occurred on the marshes of the Humber and a few others were seen and shot but no dates were recorded.

In 1899 a flock of 30 was recorded on the north Wolds from the end of February to

25th March and a solitary bird was seen there on 19th May. Two were shot from a flock of 13 birds at Holbeach on 16th March.

Feral Pigeon *Columba livia*
A common and widespread resident. Feral Pigeons showing many plumage types have originated from both dove-cote and racing stock and may be encountered almost anywhere except in well-wooded areas. The main breeding concentrations are in the larger towns but birds are quite widely distributed in rural areas, particularly in churches, old farm buildings, under bridges and other sites which offer nest-holes.

Stock Dove *Columba oenas*
A common and well-distributed breeding species. In the nineteenth century it was largely confined to old woodlands in the north-west, with isolated instances of nesting elsewhere. An increase and spread began in the later years of the century, continuing until about the 1930s when it was breeding in all parts of the county. It is now a typical bird of farmland as well as old woods and parklands and uses a wide range of breeding sites. It particularly favours hollow trees, old buildings, haystacks and the old nests of other species, and on the coast and sandy warrens in the north-west it regularly nests in rabbit burrows. There was a sudden sharp decline in numbers in eastern agricultural areas of England in the late 1950s and early 1960s that was attributed to the use of organochlorine seed dressings but the species seems to have rapidly recovered to its former status.

There is evidence of some passage on the coast. Birds are often present in small numbers in the large flocks of migrating Woodpigeons and fair-sized parties occur between late autumn and spring. Ringing recoveries have so far indicated only local movements.

Woodpigeon *Columba palumbus*
An abundant and widespread breeding species, passage migrant and winter visitor. It increased enormously during the last century when there was a spread in the cultivation of green crops, particularly clover, thus providing good winter feeding areas. The highly intensive cultivated districts of Lincolnshire with sufficient woods, copses, plantations and hedgerows for nesting and roosting purposes provide the Woodpigeon with ideal habitat.

Immigration of fluctutating numbers extends from late October to mid-December, sometimes followed by more birds later in the winter when the weather is severe. The largest flocks, sometimes of many thousands, usually occur in early December. There is no evidence of regular immigration from the continent although it was formerly considered that most wintering birds originated from abroad. It is probable that many of the coastal migrants are from northern Britain. In some of the larger woodlands where there is little persecution there are huge winter roosts, sometimes totalling tens of thousands. Movements in spring are usually light and somewhat irregular, mainly in March and early April. Spasmodic passage up and down the coast in May and June is probably only local movement. Flocks of several hundreds are quite usual in the early summer.

Three birds ringed as nestlings in Yorkshire have been recovered in the county in winter and spring and three birds ringed as fully grown in Northamptonshire in autumn have been found in Lincolnshire later in the winter. Nestlings ringed in the county have been recovered in their first winters in Yorkshire and Norfolk and one ringed at Friskney in August 1959 was recovered in Brittany, France in January 1960. One ringed as fully-grown at Deeping St. Nicholas in August 1984 was found dead in Suffolk in May 1986.

Collared Dove *Streptopelia decaocto*

A numerous breeding species concentrated chiefly in urban and suburban areas. It is often associated with flour mills, granaries and farms, in addition to parks, churchyards and gardens. It is now widespread in the county although there are still several areas, particularly on the coast and in more rural districts, where it is local as a breeding bird. In autumn and winter quite large flocks of up to 500 birds occur and there are a number of communal roosts. On the coast there is some evidence of light passage chiefly between mid-April and early June and in autumn from late August to early November. Several have been reported in recent years at the Inner Dowsing during May to July.

The spread of the Collared Dove north-west across Europe since about 1930 has been well documented (Hudson 1965 and 1972). The first bird recorded in Lincolnshire was a singing male at Manton, near Scunthorpe holding territory for at least six years from May 1952. It was also the first British record but has not been officially accepted as such as some were known to have been imported for aviculture from 1947. However, the territorial behaviour seems more typical of an early colonist, rather than an escape from captivity. In 1957 a pair bred at Manton where the original bird was still present. Four birds were present at Manton in 1958 with three in the following years when a pair also bred at Skegness. One was shot at Lincoln on 1st June 1959 and another was heard at North Hykeham, near Lincoln later in the same month. Single pairs became established in Cleethorpes and Holbeach in 1960 and also in Grimsby and probably Boston by 1961. Colonisation of towns and villages increased rapidly over the next few years until it was well established, though the rate of spread slowed down by about 1970.

One ringed in Belgium in November 1969 had reached Heckington, near Sleaford in May 1970. One ringed at Cleethorpes in April 1967 was found dead in Lancashire two months later and another ringed at Gibraltar Point in November 1970 was recovered in Northumberland in July 1976. One ringed at Spurn in May 1960 was controlled at Skegness in January 1961.

Turtle Dove *Streptopelia turtur*

A numerous summer visitor and passage migrant. It was restricted to southern England in the early nineteenth century but increased and spread northwards to reach southern Lincolnshire by the 1860s, becoming more generally distributed in northern districts by the 1880s and 1890s. Turtle Doves are inhabitants of open country so long as trees, shrubs and hedgerows are readily available for nesting. There has been considerable removal of the large hedgerows typically favoured by the species in the county but ample compensation in the form of new forestry plantations and pheasant-rearing coverts has

Short-eared Owl

Collared Dove

produced an increase during the last few years.

It has also recently increased as a passage migrant on the coast in spring. Movements last from about the third week of April until the second week of June, with the largest numbers usually occurring in late May. Spring passage is also quite conspicuous inland. Flocks sometimes of a hundred or more birds occur at several localities, particularly on the coast, in the late spring and early summer, and may be present well after local birds have settled down to breed. Autumn migration is much less pronounced on the coast, many birds leaving on a broad front inland. Most birds at this season are in very small parties, chiefly between late August and the end of September with occasional stragglers to the third week of October. Late birds were recorded on 11th November 1974 and 26th November 1980 and in the winter of 1966/67 one associated with a flock of Collared Doves at Cleethorpes Zoo from November to February.

A passage migrant ringed at Gibraltar Point in September 1971 was shot in south-west France one month later and a nestling ringed at Donna Nook in June 1973 was shot in Portugal in the following September. One ringed on passage in Portugal in September 1960 was recovered at Metheringham Fen, near Lincoln in August 1962. One ringed at Deeping St. Nicholas in September 1985 was shot in Mali in the following March.

Rufous Turtle Dove *Streptopelia orientalis*
A very rare vagrant from Asia. One was seen by S. Lorand at Donna Nook on 25th October 1975. It was the sixth British record.

Ring-necked Parakeet *Psittacula krameri*
There are several records of this species, mainly on the coast in spring and autumn since about 1966. Feral populations have become established in several parts of England since about 1970. It seems likely that some of the records may refer to birds wandering from these feral populations and there was a small influx of about five or six birds in March and April 1988.

Great Spotted Cuckoo *Clamator glandarius*
A very rare vagrant. One seen by K. Atkin at Anderby Creek on 9th May 1971 was the fifteenth British record. S. Lorand recorded an adult at Donna Nook on 1st July 1974.

Cuckoo *Cuculus canorus*
A common and well-distributed summer visitor. There was a decrease in breeding numbers in Lincolnshire and in other eastern counties from about 1953 but the population seems to have recovered to its former level in most parts of the county during recent years. It is common in a wide variety of habitats ranging from open woodlands to the coastal marshes and dunes.

The first birds usually arrive in the third week of April, passage continuing until early June. Adult birds leave during July and early August but passage of juveniles lasts until the beginning of September with occasional stragglers later in the month. In 1976 an adult remained off-passage at Saltfleetby for several weeks until the exceptionally late date of 25th October.

An adult ringed on passage at Gibraltar Point in August 1954 was recovered in Belgium in August 1956 and a juvenile ringed at the same locality in July 1964 was found in Malta in May 1965. A nestling ringed at Gunby, near Alford in June 1967 was recovered in Italy in the following September. One ringed in the Netherlands in August 1967 was found dead at Sleaford in July 1969 and one ringed on Heligoland, Germany in July 1971 was controlled at Wragby in June 1972. One ringed at Gibraltar Point in August 1980 was controlled in County Wexford in May 1983.

Yellow-billed Cuckoo *Coccyzus americanus*
A very rare vagrant from North America. One was found dead by R. Pritchard at Welton-le-Marsh, near Spilsby on 30th October 1978. The skin is preserved in Lincoln Museum. Another was present at Rauceby Warren on 18th and 19th October 1987 and seen by D. and S. Brooks, B.J. Hancock and other observers.

Barn Owl *Tyto alba*
A well-distributed and fairly common breeding bird, chiefly in agricultural areas where suitable old buildings, barns and hollow trees provide nesting sites.

In 1932 a census located 41 pairs in an area of about 250 square miles. From these figures and assuming the areas to be representative of the county it was estimated that there were just over 400 pairs nesting in Lincolnshire. There was a marked decline of the species during the 1950s. More intensive farming with larger fields and fewer hedgerows and derelict buildings adversely affected the Barn Owl but far more serious was the extensive use of toxic chemicals which caused a sudden decrease. Fortunately numbers have recovered quite well in most areas during recent years although it is probably not so common as in 1932. Temporary setbacks in the population are caused by hard winters. In addition the species fares badly by being a regular road casualty.

Although it appears to be mainly resident, occasional birds occur on the coast in March and April and in autumn between September and November. Birds showing characteristics of the dark-breasted race *T.a. guttata* which breeds on the continent to the north and east of nominate *alba* have been recorded as follows: at Tetney on 6th October 1962; at Donna Nook on 20th March 1969; at Anderby Creek on 19th January 1974; at North Cotes from 1st to 23rd March 1975; at Donna Nook on 15th September 1976 and 19th March 1979, and at Tetney on 12th April 1979.

A nestling ringed in Dumfriesshire in June 1957 was recovered at Grantham in January 1959. Two nestlings from Nottinghamshire in July 1971 were found at Epworth and Metheringham in the following February and March respectively and another nestling ringed in Northumberland in August 1974 was found dead at Heckington, near Sleaford, in November of the same year.

Scops Owl *Otus scops*
A very rare vagrant. One was found dead and in an emaciated condition by C. Marsh at Saltfleetby on 7th April 1977. A specimen in Lincoln Museum was said to have been obtained at Dunston, near Lincoln in 1895.

Eagle Owl *Bubo bubo*
A very rare vagrant. A female shot near Stamford on 12th April 1879 was examined by T. Cullingford at Durham University Museum. He recorded that the bird appeared to have been wild and in good condition after feeding on rabbits.

Little Owl *Athene noctua*
A fairly common breeding species that has decreased in recent years. It is well-distributed in the county and characteristic of agricultural areas, but is also found in old parks, orchards, on sand dunes and within villages.

Following introductions in Northamptonshire during 1888 to 1890 single birds were shot at Coleby, near Lincoln on 13th November 1899 and 10th January 1902. One was seen at Humberston in 1904 and by 1906 it was breeding around Grantham, Bourne and Sleaford. It had spread north of Lincoln by 1914 and reached the north-west in 1917 and 1918. Some appeared on the north-east coast in 1915, and by 1920 it was reported as breeding fairly commonly throughout the county. There were decreases in several areas during the 1940s, considered to be the result of a succession of hard winters, but a more serious decline in the late 1950s has been attributed to the use of toxic chemicals. A partial recovery in numbers was made until about 1970 although it remains locally scarce, particularly in some northern parts of the county.

The Little Owl appears to be sedentary, although it sometimes occurs on the coast mainly in autumn in areas where it does not breed.

A nestling ringed at Goxhill in June 1954 was recovered in Yorkshire a year later and one ringed at Wragby in December 1970 was found dead in Nottinghamshire in the following April.

Tawny Owl *Strix aluco*
A common and well-distributed resident frequenting mature wooded districts, farmland with old trees, orchards, parks and gardens in urban and suburban areas. It is absent from much of the coast and large, open farms where old hollow trees have been cleared. Birds which appear to be on passage are occasionally seen on the coast during March and April and from September to November but ringing recoveries indicate only short-distance movements within the county and one from Nottinghamshire.

The Tawny Owl is the commonest owl in Lincolnshire.

Long-eared Owl *Asio otus*
A fairly common breeding species, passage migrant and winter visitor that has decreased during the present century. The main population is concentrated in the north and west of the county where it is often found in coniferous woods and plantations with rather fewer pairs elsewhere in small isolated woods and patches of scrub. Wintering birds frequently form communal roosts of up to a dozen or so birds at several fairly regular sites. Immigrants on the coast occur from late August to mid-November with smaller numbers in spring between late March and the end of May.

One ringed in the Netherlands in June 1932 was recovered in the county in February 1935. A passage bird ringed at Donna Nook in April 1966 was found dead in southern central Norway in June 1968 and another ringed at Gibraltar Point in October 1966 was found dead in south-west Finland one year later. A nestling ringed in Cheshire in June 1980 was found dead at Scredington, near Sleaford in March 1983.

Short-eared Owl *Asio flammeus*

A scarce breeding species and a fairly common passage migrant and winter visitor. The numbers of breeding and wintering birds fluctuate widely depending to a large extent on the vole population. It used to nest apparently with some regularity on several of the heaths and commons of the north-west during the late nineteenth century but has bred only spasmodically in those areas in the present century. In the last 30 years a few pairs have nested regularly in marshes and rough pasture on the coast, along the Humber and in the Wash and also inland in one or two old fenland areas. Some years may produce exceptional concentrations in certain areas; for example, seven nests were found on Read's Island in 1972 and 12 in the following year.

Wintering birds are fairly widespread inland and on the coast. It usually occurs singly or in very small parties although there have been gatherings of up to 40 birds. Immigrants arrive on the coast from September to the end of November with peak numbers in October. Spring passage is generally less well-marked between late March and early May.

A nestling ringed in Ayrshire in May 1956 was recovered near Louth in July 1960 and another from Norfolk in June 1957 was recovered near Sleaford in the following November. One trapped at Gibraltar Point in November 1966 was found dead in Stirlingshire two years later and another ringed in April 1983 was found dead in Sweden two months later. A nestling ringed on Read's Island in May 1973 was shot in north-west Russia in September 1975.

Tengmalm's Owl *Aegolius funereus*

A very rare vagrant. An adult was shot by E. Pretyman on the dunes north of Saltfleet Haven on 22nd October 1880.

Nightjar *Caprimulgus europaeus*

A scarce summer visitor nesting on the heaths and commons of the west and north-west and in smaller numbers in the centre and south-west of the county. Until recently, its breeding status appeared to be similar to that of the last century, but in the last few years there has been a decline in the Market Rasen, Lincoln and Woodhall Spa areas. First arrivals usually appear in the first half of May and most have deserted their nesting areas by late August.

Passage migrants are rare and irregular on the coast and occur occasionally in May and early June and from August to the beginning of October. A very late bird was shot at Humberston on 28th November 1864.

Swift *Apus apus*

A numerous summer visitor and passage migrant. It breeds most commonly in the older sections of towns and villages as most modern buildings do not offer suitable nest sites.

A few birds usually appear in late April with the main arrivals in May and early June. Between late June and early August weather movements frequently occur usually during periods of low overcast cloud and freshening winds. Most of these movements involve a few hundred birds but occasionally several thousands may head into the wind. This passage is most concentrated on the coast at Gibraltar Point with usually much smaller numbers elsewhere. Autumn passage is mainly between late July and the end of August with frequent stragglers into September. Regular records of a few birds in October and occasionally early November appear to be a recent trend.

Two birds ringed in Lincolnshire have been shot on autumn passage in Spain. One ringed in July 1965 was killed in Malawi in February 1966 and another ringed in June 1967 was found dead in Morocco in April 1974. There are quite a number of recoveries involving many other English counties, most of which are the result of the large scale trapping of Swifts in the Sleaford and Grantham areas.

Alpine Swift *Apus melba*
A rare vagrant recorded on eight occasions. One was seen at Sturton Park, near Horncastle by R. Fox and P. Prince on 23rd April 1964. A very late bird was seen at Tetney on 24th October 1969. One found in a weak condition at Healing, near Grimsby on 6th August 1971 died later. One was seen at Gibraltar Point on 11th June 1974 and another was recorded at Donna Nook on 20th July 1975. One was present at Messingham on 16th June 1979. One flew south at Gibraltar Point on 31st August 1985 and one seen there on 24th April 1987 was presumed to be the same individual as that found dead at Seacroft on 2nd May.

Kingfisher *Alcedo atthis*
A fairly common resident on a number of streams, rivers and gravel pits. Outside the breeding season it is regularly present in small numbers on coastal drains and creeks on the salt marshes.

Heavy mortality occurs during hard winters when frosts are prolonged. It fared particularly badly in the winter of 1962/63 when the county population was almost wiped out. Pollution of many rivers and streams by agricultural chemicals had already caused a decline in numbers in the late 1950s but by 1970 it was becoming more widespread and was breeding once more in several of its former haunts. A succession of mild winters further aided the recovery of the species and the population reached its highest level for many years by the late 1970s.

A bird ringed in Essex in August 1972 was found dead at Torksey on the Trent in June 1973. One ringed in Nottinghamshire in September 1982 was controlled at Theddle-thorpe nine days later.

Bee-eater *Merops apiaster*
A rare vagrant with 12 records involving 21 birds. There are two old records. One shot at Ingoldsby, near Grantham in July 1879 was recorded by J. Whitaker. One seen at Tetney Haven on 15th August 1880 was shot on the following day. More recently there was one at Gibraltar Point on 2nd September 1957, three at the same locality on 2nd

September 1958, one at Barrow-on-Humber on 29th April 1968 and two at Gibraltar Point on 10th June 1973. In 1985 one was present at Gibraltar Point during 26th to 29th August with two additional birds on 28th. Three were again at Gibraltar Point on 3rd May 1987 and there were also three at Holbeach St. Marks on 13th June. In 1988, single birds were seen at Tetney on 26th May, Friskney on 31st July and Kexby, near Gainsborough, on 7th August.

Roller *Coracias garrulus*
A rare vagrant noted at least six times. An immature was shot at Keddington, near Louth in October 1863 and recorded by T.H. Allis. Since then it has been recorded as follows: one shot at Elsthorpe Grange, near Bourne on 10th May 1871; one shot at Marshchapel in 1900; one seen near Louth on 29th August 1901— probably the same bird was recorded there again on 26th September; one shot at Grainthorpe on 13th June 1962; one present at Highall Wood, near Woodhall Spa from 2nd to 19th October 1983.

In addition, a bird shot at Muckton Wood, near Louth on 27th October 1883, and recorded as an Indian Roller *C. benghalensis,* seems more likely to have been an immature of *garrulus.* Another Roller is also said to have been seen at Gautby, near Horncastle a few years prior to 1900.

Hoopoe *Upupa epops*
A rare but almost annual passage migrant, chiefly in spring and rather irregular in autumn. There have been about 80 records during the last 35 years making a grand total of about 125 occurrences. Almost half of these reports have been from inland localities.

Early birds appear from the second week of April but most occur during the first three weeks of May with a few to June or early July. Autumn records extend from the last few days of August to the end of October with two in early November. Two are said to have been seen at Cadney, near Brigg on 17th December 1906. Most migrants occur singly although there are several records of two birds together, causing speculation about supposed breeding in the nineteenth century. None of these alleged breeding attempts are supported by any firm details.

Wryneck *Jynx torquilla*
A scarce passage migrant, chiefly on the coast but also occasionally inland. During the last 20 years it has increased quite significantly in autumn and also in spring when numbers are usually much smaller. During the nineteenth century it was a well-distributed summer visitor in the north-west and south-west of the county with a few nesting in central areas. The decline of the Wryneck extended through the latter half of the century and the early years of the present century. The last reference to breeding was by Blathwayt when he recorded it as a scarce nester in the Lincoln area in 1918. After this there were only a few records of autumn migrants on the coast until the early 1950s.

In recent years the main arrivals of passage birds have occurred during easterly winds. Reports of several birds in a day are not infrequent and exceptionally there were 12 at Donna Nook on 20th August 1977. Some migrants are in a weak condition on arrival and a number remain off-passage for long periods. Autumn passage lasts from the

Roller

Skylark

Shore Lark

second week of August to the third week of September with peak numbers in the last week of August and the first week of September. Occasional late birds occur until mid-October. Spring migrants are now recorded almost annually and generally arrive singly between the last week of April and the end of May.

Green Woodpecker *Picus viridis*
A fairly common resident, well-distributed in suitable wooded areas mainly in central and western parts of the county. It decreased in the last century when a number of mature woodlands were felled although it spread into the Marsh district in the early years of the present century as tall hedgerows with old trees increased. Much of this habitat and consequently the species has now disappeared from this area. Substantial decreases have frequently followed severe winters and were particularly noticeable after the winters of 1946/47 and 1962/63. On the coast it occurs only very rarely and at irregular intervals, usually in September and October.

Great Spotted Woodpecker *Dendrocopos major*
A fairly common resident breeding in many woodlands in the county. It is the commonest woodpecker in Lincolnshire. Extensive felling of mature woods in the nineteenth century caused a considerable decline but as elsewhere in Britain numbers recovered in the early years of the present century. Marked losses during hard winters are usually less drastic than those of the Green Woodpecker.

A few occur on the coast between mid-September and early November and less frequently on return passage in March and early April. Some migrants show character-istics of the British race *D.m. anglicus* but in some years immigrants of the irruptive northern race *D.m. major* occur in variable numbers. Few immigrants remain for any length of time on the coast as much of the habitat is unsuitable. The northern race has been identified inland on only one occasion.

Lesser Spotted Woodpecker *Dendrocopos minor*
A scarce and usually under-recorded resident found in several wooded areas in the north-west, south-west and central parts of the county. In recent years isolated pairs have bred away from traditional areas, particularly in the Fens and Humber area. One trapped at Gibraltar Point on 10th August 1988, and possibly a different bird seen there in early October appear to be the only coastal records.
In common with the other woodpeckers, this species is also adversely affected by hard winters but, apart from short-term declines, its status is not known to have changed since the last century.

Short-toed Lark *Calandrella brachydactyla*
A very rare vagrant. One at Gibraltar Point from 18th to 26th September 1971 showed characteristics of one of the greyish eastern races. It was observed by a number of observers including R.L. Swann, R.B. Wilkinson and E.J. Mackrill. One occurred at the Inner Dowsing tower on 16th June 1986 and was identified by P. Lee.

Woodlark *Lullula arborea*
A rare breeding species, coastal passage migrant and occasional winter visitor. It was formerly a scarce nesting species on several of the warrens and commons in the north-west until at least 1925. Elsewhere it may have bred at Woodhall Spa in 1898, and a pair nested at Haverholme, near Sleaford in 1902. The status of the Woodlark after 1925 is uncertain for about 20 years but, correlated with an increase in other counties during the 1940s, birds were again present in the north-west from 1946, with breeding proved from 1948. It nested at Skellingthorpe, near Lincoln until 1956 and up to four pairs bred in the Scawby area until 1959. After then no breeding attempts were reported for 25 years. Low numbers of rabbits following the outbreak of myxomatosis in the 1950s caused the Woodlark's breeding habitats to become overgrown, although climatic changes are also considered to be connected with the decline of the species. Since 1984 up to three pairs have nested successfully in cleared forest areas at one site in the north of the county and another pair bred at a second site some distance away in 1988. The male of the latter pair had been colour-ringed as a nestling in Thetford Forest, Suffolk in April 1987. At least 19 young were reared in 1988.

Spring migrants on the coast occur irregularly in late March and April. It is not quite so rare in autumn when it appears between the third week of September and mid-November. There were more records than usual in 1976 and 1977. Migrants usually occur singly but very small parties of up to five birds have been noted. Occasionally wintering birds have appeared away from the breeding areas. One was shot from a party of four birds seen at Grainsby from 27th to 31st December 1893. Another was shot near Crowland at the end of December 1920 and one was obtained from a flock of eight present at Grainsby from 6th to 9th December 1923. One was seen at Cleethorpes on 24th December 1946 and a bird remained at Donna Nook from 11th October 1976 to 8th January 1977. Another was seen at Donna Nook on 17th February 1979.

Skylark *Alauda arvensis*
An abundant breeding species, winter visitor and passage migrant, well-distributed in the open habitat that is typical of much of the county. Outside the breeding season large flocks are frequently found wherever suitable feeding conditions exist. Until the late nineteenth century Skylarks were much in demand as a table bird but there is no evidence that persecution had any noticeable effects on the population.

Large scale immigration from the continent occurs from the second week of September to mid-November when on many days Skylarks will be one of the most numerous species on visible migration, inland as well as on the coast. Return passage, usually on a much smaller scale, extends from late February to the end of April.

One ringed on Fair Isle in October 1956 was recovered at Boston in the spring of 1963.

Shore Lark *Eremophila alpestris*
A scarce winter visitor and passage migrant on the coast in variable numbers. It increased considerably from the mid-1960s until the mid-1970s when it was fairly common. The main wintering areas are at Donna Nook and Gibraltar Point where single flocks have numbered up to 120 birds in good years. Apparently some interchange of

birds occurs between the two areas as an increase at one site frequently follows a decrease at the other locality. It is invariably encountered feeding on the shore or on the adjacent coastal fields.

Until the late nineteenth century the Shore Lark was a rare and irregular winter visitor to Britain; one said to have been obtained in Lincolnshire in 1837 was only the second British record. There were no further records until 1890 when one was shot in February at North Somercotes. Three were seen at Saltfleet in January 1902 and four were shot at North Cotes in October of the same year. Fourteen were recorded at North Cotes in November 1912 and a flock of 20 to 30 birds wintered there in 1913/14, followed by 30 in November 1914 and a party of 16 in January 1919. There were no more records until 1947/48 when 20 wintered at Gibraltar Point. Since then, regular sightings have been made there with comparable records on the north-east coast from 1951. Numbers fluctuate considerably each winter but flocks, often in excess of 30 birds feeding with Skylarks and Snow Buntings were recorded in most years from 1966 to 1976.

Immigration lasts from about mid-October to early December. Numbers decline in late January and February but increase again in late March and April when passage birds reappear. Late birds are occasionally seen up to mid-May. There are four inland records of single birds, all at Covenham Reservoir.

Sand Martin *Riparia riparia*

A common summer visitor which has decreased drastically during the last 20 years, attributable to droughts in the main wintering areas in Africa. It is also a common passage migrant both inland and on the coast. Colonies are found in sand and gravel pits throughout the county although there are few in the north-east where little suitable habitat exists. Some of the former colonies are now no longer occupied.

Early immigrants arrive at the colonies in late March and early April but coastal passage is usually from the third week of April until the beginning of June. A few birds reappear on the coast at the end of June with the main movement from late July to the end of September. Late birds trickle through in October and exceptionally to the first week of November. Large roosts in reed beds are a common feature in autumn when concentrations also gather to feed at reservoirs, sewage farms and other inland waters.

A good series of recoveries has emerged following concerted trapping efforts at most of the major roosts and colonies in the county. These results formed part of the national Sand Martin Enquiry organised by the British Trust for Ornithology. Many recoveries show that migratory birds from other parts of Britain use the breeding colonies as well as reed beds to roost at while on passage. Movements to and from the county are predominantly within eastern England and Scotland with a few to southern central England. Foreign recoveries involve birds in the Netherlands, Belgium, France, the Channel Islands, the Balearic Islands, Algeria and Morocco. One worthy of fuller mention was ringed at Calceby, near Alford in June 1966 and found dead on the Cape Verde Islands in late August 1969. One ringed as a nestling at Lincoln in July 1966 was controlled, apparently breeding, at a colony in Belgium in early June 1967. There is evidence of some interchange of breeding birds from one site to another but the vast majority evidently return to the original colony as long as suitable conditions remain.

Swallow *Hirundo rustica*

A numerous and widespread summer visitor and an abundant passage migrant. The clearance of old buildings from many of the more intensive farms has caused a decrease in some areas during recent years while a significant transfer from livestock to arable farming with its associated crop-spraying operations has had an adverse effect on the species.

Early migrants may occur in March but the main passage is from the second week of April to mid-June. A few juvenile birds pass along the coast in late July but the main movement is from early August to the end of September with smaller numbers to late October. Stragglers regularly occur until mid-November and one or two have been recorded in early December. One was present at North Hykeham on 4th February 1983. Migration is most marked on the coast although large numbers pass inland, particularly along the river valleys. Very large roosts form in a number of reed beds during the autumn.

Large scale ringing of Swallows has resulted in many recoveries. Several birds trapped on passage through the county had been ringed as nestlings in northern England. Recoveries have also involved the majority of east coast counties as well as a few in southern central England, Wales and Ireland. There are a number of recoveries in western European countries between Germany, the Netherlands and Spain and east to Italy. Farther south there are several spring and autumn recoveries in Morocco, Algeria and Ghana. At least 15 birds have been recovered in their wintering areas in South Africa, in addition to two birds in South West Africa and one in Mozambique. Many breeding birds have been retrapped at the place of ringing in subsequent seasons.

Red-rumped Swallow *Hirundo daurica*

A very rare vagrant. One was seen by R. Thompson at Gibraltar Point on 29th October 1977. In 1987 there was one at Gibraltar Point from 2nd to 5th May and up to four at the same locality between 24th and 28th October.

House Martin *Delichon urbica*

A numerous and well-distributed summer visitor and passage migrant in variable numbers, chiefly along the coast. There are small colonies in most villages and suburban areas where suitable buildings exist for nesting. Several housing estates erected in recent years have attracted substantial numbers of House Martins.

First arrivals in spring vary between the second week of April and early May with passage until early June and stragglers to the end of the month. In some springs migrants are very scarce on the coast. Returning birds begin to move along the coast in late July, reaching peak numbers in late August and September. Passage continues to late October and late birds are not infrequently seen until the third week of November, with exceptional records in December.

One ringed in Buckinghamshire in May 1962 was recovered in Lincolnshire in July 1963 and another found dead at Donington-on-Bain in September 1974 had been ringed in the Netherlands in May 1972.

Richard's Pipit *Anthus novaeseelandiae*
A rare but annual autumn visitor from Asia. One was seen at Tetney on 12th October 1887 and another was shot at Marshchapel on 16th November 1912. One was reported at Saltfleetby on 6th October 1951. Since 1967, Richard's Pipits have been recorded in variable numbers each autumn. At least 80 birds were seen during this period and most have occurred on the north-east coast. Arrivals are normally between late September and early November, with occasional birds until the end of November and early December. One occurred at Donna Nook on 9th May 1985 and there is one inland record at Cadney Reservoir on 14th October 1988. Several birds have made protracted stays and have sometimes been supplemented by later arrivals to form small parties of up to five birds.

Tawny Pipit *Anthus campestris*
A rare vagrant recorded on five occasions. One at Donna Nook on 24th May 1970 was seen by S. Lorand. Another bird in the same year was present at Wisbech sewage farm on 25th September. One recorded at Donna Nook on 8th May 1975 was considered to be the same bird seen there on 17th May. Also in 1975 there was one at Tetney Haven on 15th October. One was present at Donna Nook on 10th May 1980.

Olive-backed Pipit *Anthus hodgsoni*
A very rare vagrant from Asia. One at Saltfleetby on 19th October 1980 was seen by G.P. Catley. It was the fourteenth British record.

Tree Pipit *Anthus trivialis*
A fairly common summer visitor and passage migrant. It is widespread in the north-west, central and south-west of the county where it breeds in open woodland, young conifer plantations and on heathland. The lack of suitable habitat in most eastern districts has prevented any spread into these areas.

The first arrivals usually appear in mid-April and passage birds on the coast move through from then until the end of May. Return movements extend from late August to early October with occasional late birds to the third week of October. Many migrants are observed singly or in very small parties but occasionally larger numbers arrive during falls of other migrants from the Continent.

One ringed at Bardney Forest in May 1970 was found dead in southern Norway one year later.

Meadow Pipit *Anthus pratensis*
A numerous breeding bird and winter visitor and an abundant passage migrant on the coast and inland. It is found commonly in many types of open country including rough grassland, heaths, sand-dunes and marshes but is absent from the extreme south-west of the county. Many of the breeding areas are deserted by the early autumn and are later occupied by wintering birds although in some exposed coastal areas Meadow Pipits are absent in winter.

Autumn migration lasts from early September until the beginning of November. Movements are frequently very heavy and it is often one of the most numerous diurnal migrants. Parties frequently follow the coastline but many also head over the coast and inland on a broad front.

A return to the breeding areas begins in late February coinciding with the start of small but regular movements along the coast that extend to the end of April or early May. British birds and those from the Continent belong to the race *A.p. pratensis*. Some birds showing characteristics of the race *A.p. theresae* which breeds in Iceland have been identified in late September and early October in recent years.

Nine autumn migrants ringed on the coast have been recovered in Portugal and Spain between October and February and another was in southern Spain in the following August. One ringed at Gibraltar Point in September 1964 was recovered on the west coast of Italy six weeks later. Another Gibraltar Point bird ringed in September 1982 was found dead in Morocco in November 1985.

Red-throated Pipit *Anthus cervinus*
A very rare vagrant. One was seen by S. Lorand at Grainthorpe Haven on 21st and 22nd September 1977.

Rock Pipit *Anthus petrosus*
A fairly common winter visitor and passage migrant. It is found chiefly on the coast where creeks in salt marshes are particularly favoured. A few birds occur inland on passage but sometimes remain all winter at reservoirs, sewage farms and one or two other suitable waters.

Autumn immigrants occasionally appear in late September but the main arrivals are between early October and the end of November. Return passage lasts from early March to the third week of April.

Winter visitors and passage migrants belonging to the British race *A.p. petrosus* are frequently recorded but birds of the race *A.p. littoralis* which breeds in Scandinavia and on islands in the Baltic are regularly identified in spring and probably form a significant proportion of the wintering population. The two races are usually inseparable in winter plumage.

Water Pipit *Anthus spinoletta*
A rare passage migrant and winter visitor. One was shot at Tetney on 5th April 1895 but since 1957 it has been recorded almost annually. It has occurred from mid-October to late April mainly in the Humber and on the north-east coast, with rather fewer in the Wash. Wintering birds have been more frequent in the last ten years with up to three birds present at Saltfleetby during 1980 to 1985. A few birds have been recorded inland.

Yellow Wagtail *Motacilla flava*
A common summer visitor and passage migrant. Its distribution, however, is somewhat irregular. It breeds quite commonly in the north-west, South Humberside, the Wash, and much of the Fens and along the Trent Valley and on the north-east coast. Few are present in the well-wooded districts of the south-west while the dry chalk and peripheral areas

of the Wolds are completely avoided. Most birds nest in fairly damp situations, favouring marshes, rough pasture and arable fields and are often most plentiful when these habitats coincide with sewage farms, reservoirs and other waters.

It is common as a passage migrant inland as well as on the coast. Early birds have been recorded in late March but the main passage is from mid-April to early June with peak numbers between the end of April and mid-May. Return passage involves a few juveniles in July but most movement is in August and September with occasional birds in early October. A late bird was present at Bardney from 29th November to 27th December 1974 and another was at Donna Nook from 17th November to 1st December 1983. British birds belong to the race *M.f. flavissima*.

One ringed in Yorkshire in August 1983 was controlled at Ancaster one month later.

The central European race *M.f. flava* known as the Blue-headed Wagtail is a very scarce but annual passage migrant, chiefly in spring although occasionally in autumn. There are only two old records of single birds in 1894 and 1932 but since 1954 this race has been identified regularly with peaks of about 15 birds in both 1978 and 1979. This race has bred on a few occasions since 1970 at Donna Nook, Covenham Reservoir, Cadney and Goxhill.

The Grey-headed Wagtail *M.f. thunbergi* which breeds in Scandinavia and Russia, north of the range of flava, is a rare spring vagrant. Since 1955 there have been 18 records all in May apart from two in June.

The Ashy-headed Wagtail *M.f. cinereocapilla* which breeds in southern central Europe has been recorded twice. Single birds were present at Covenham Reservoir on 4th May 1983 and 31st May 1984.

Citrine Wagtail *Motacilla citreola*
A very rare vagrant from Asia. An immature bird at Gibraltar Point from 4th to 10th September 1983 was recorded by K.W. Winfield, R.K. Watson, P.J. Keller and other observers.

Grey Wagtail *Motacilla cinerea*
A scarce winter visitor and passage migrant and a rare, irregular breeding species. The county possesses very few of the fast-flowing streams much favoured by the Grey Wagtail, hence the paucity of breeding records. It bred near Scunthorpe, apparently annually, between 1868 and 1875, at Great Coates in 1897, near Sleaford about 1908 and in 1958, and near Grantham in 1914 and 1959. More recently breeding occurred at Scunthorpe in 1974 and 1975, at Stamford in 1980, Louth in 1980 and 1982, at Scredington, near Sleaford in 1985 and Tealby, near Market Rasen, in 1988. There are also several summer records of single and paired birds which may also refer to breeding attempts.

Passage migrants on the coast appear in variable but always small numbers. Occasional birds may be seen in late June or July but movements are usually between the last week of August and late October with odd birds during November. It is rare in spring from early March to mid-April. Most migrants occur singly or in very small numbers. Wintering birds are widely but thinly distributed at inland waters between late September and March.

Pied Wagtail *Motacilla alba*

The Pied Wagtail *M.a. yarrellii* is a numerous breeding species and a common passage migrant. It is well-distributed throughout the county, occurring mainly in open country particularly in the vicinity of farms and human habitation, sewage farms and reservoirs. It has decreased in several areas during recent years, probably as a result of increased farm mechanisation and more intensive agricultural methods. Declines are also apparent following severe winters despite the emigration of many breeding birds. Autumn and winter roosts sometimes of up to several hundred birds are present in a number of diverse situations such as sewage farms, pumping stations, greenhouses, urban roadside trees, reed-beds and sugar beet fields.

Passage birds either moving singly or in very small parties occur between late August and early November. The return movement is usually quite small from the end of February to late April.

The White Wagtail *M.a. alba* which breeds on the continent and in Iceland is a scarce but regular passage migrant chiefly in spring. Occasional birds arrive during late March but the main passage is in April and the first week of May with stragglers to the third week of May. There are three midsummer records and one in winter. Autumn migrants are probably often overlooked although many *alba* wagtails pass too high for subspecific recognition. A few birds have been noted in late August but most occur during September and the first half of October. White Wagtails are recorded chiefly on the coast but there is evidently a small regular passage inland.

Ringing recoveries all involve Pied Wagtails. Two birds ringed in August and September and a nestling ringed at Ancaster have been recovered in Portugal between November and February during their first winters. Another ringed in August 1970 was in south-west France in February 1972. One recovered in Sussex in November was ringed in the county in the previous August and one ringed in Surrey in January 1962 was at Blankney, near Lincoln in September 1963.

Waxwing *Bombycilla garrulus*

A winter visitor and passage migrant somewhat erratic in numbers. A few occur most winters between late October and March with periodic invasions of large numbers in some years. During invasions parties of birds roam the countryside and many birds inhabit towns and villages where they are tame and confiding during their search for berries in gardens and parks. Their length of stay is governed by the supply of food and birds have sometimes deserted the county by mid-winter but have remained until spring in other years. Spring migrants occur during March with a few records in April. One remarkable record was of a bird which appeared during a freak snowstorm at Kirton in Lindsey on 3rd June 1975.

The dates of Waxwing invasions into Lincolnshire can be traced back for about 130 years. The main years are as follows: 1849-50, autumn 1863, 1866-67, 1892-93, 1913-14, 1932-33, 1936-37, 1946-47, 1956-57, 1957-58, 1958-59, 1959-60, 1961-62, 1963-64, 1965-66, 1970-71 and autumn 1988.

Wren

Waxwing

Comparative numbers during these years are difficult to assess especially when large numbers are scattered in urban and suburban areas but one of the largest invasions was the recent one in 1965-66. Small numbers appeared on the coast in late October followed by more birds in early November so that by the second week of November birds were spread over all areas of Lincolnshire. Many flocks were quite large and between 500 and 1,000 birds were estimated in the Louth area. Numbers gradually declined as birds moved on and only small parties remained by the following January and February.

Dipper *Cinclus cinclus*
A rare and irregular winter visitor and passage migrant recorded mainly on inland waters but also occasionally on the coast.

The British race *C.c. gularis* has been recorded about 20 times since 1870, mainly in October and November. An early bird was noted at North Cotes on 27th August 1935 and others have occurred in winter or early spring. One bird, probably the same individual, wintered on the River Lud at Louth in five successive winters from 1951-52 and one also wintered there in 1963-64. Two summer records seem somewhat doubtful. One is said to have been seen near Brigg on 9th June 1905 and two were reported at Boston in early June 1966.

Several records are of birds showing characteristics of the north European Black-bellied race *C.c. cinclus*. One was seen at Great Coates for several days from 15th April 1879 and single birds were shot at Louth in the autumn of 1884 and at Stallingborough on 24th October 1885. One was present at Tealby, near Market Rasen from 3rd February to 17th March 1963 and another was trapped at Humberston during its stay from 11th to 15th April 1967. One was seen at Louth on 15th February 1969. In 1980 there were single birds at Donna Nook on 21st to 25th November, at Louth on 8th December and at Riseholme from 27th November to 4th January 1981. One was present at Little Cawthorpe, near Louth, from 5th to 7th March 1988.

Wren *Troglodytes troglodytes*
An abundant breeding species, winter visitor and passage migrant, occurring practically everywhere except in the most built-up areas in town centres. Even in intensively farmed districts with few bushes or trees, Wrens can usually utilize a niche in such bare situations at the side of a dyke or a farm building. Numbers fluctuate markedly according to the severity of the winters and particularly high numbers succumbed in the winters of 1962-63 and 1978-79.

Passage on the coast is frequently quite pronounced from mid-September to mid-November but the return movement between mid-March and the end of April is generally quite small. Some migrants evidently winter farther south in Britain. Birds ringed on the coast in autumn have been recovered between January and April in Norfolk, Essex, Huntingdonshire, Middlesex, Hampshire and Sussex. One ringed at Gibraltar Point in August 1974 was controlled at Dungeness Bird Observatory, Kent two months later. Another ringed at Gibraltar Point in October 1967 was found long dead, perhaps in its breeding area, in North Yorkshire in June 1968. One ringed at Grimsby in August 1981 was found dead in Cheshire two years later and one ringed in

166

Bedfordshire in November 1982 was controlled at Gibraltar Point in September 1983.

Dunnock *Prunella modularis*

An abundant breeding species, winter visitor and passage migrant. It is widespread throughout the county, nesting in woodlands, hedgerows, scrub, parks and suburban gardens. Very high densities breed in the sea buckthorn along the coast.

Ringing has shown that a proportion of birds are sedentary although eruptive movements are sometimes evident in autumn. Large numbers may move along the coast between late August and early November and immigration of continental birds occurs probably annually during September and October. Birds of the continental race *P.m. modularis* have been trapped many times in autumn and some have been identified apparently wintering in the county and on spring passage in late March and April. Spring movements of this race and the endemic race *P.m. occidentalis* are usually very small.

A bird of the Continental race ringed at Tetney in April 1962 was controlled in the Netherlands 11 days later. One ringed at Donna Nook in October 1983 was controlled in Belgium also 11 days later. Birds ringed at Gibraltar Point have been recovered in Norfolk and Essex in the same autumn. Two birds from Spurn, Yorkshire have been controlled on the coast in October and one ringed in Northumberland in April 1980 was controlled at Gibraltar Point one month later.

Rufous Bush Robin *Cercotrichas galactotes*

A very rare vagrant. An adult male showing characteristics of the western race *C.g. galactotes* trapped at Ingoldmells, near Skegness was present from 2nd to 9th September 1963. It was seen by F.J. Lambert and later by several other observers. This was the eighth British record.

Robin *Erithacus rubecula*

An abundant breeding species, winter visitor and passage migrant. It is well-distributed in all parts of the county, nesting wherever there are trees and shrubs and is absent only from areas of high cultivation, town centres and sections of the coastline where the vegetation is sparse.

Many birds appear to be sedentary although good numbers of the British race *E.r. melophilus* appear as migrants and winter visitors. Birds of the continental race *E.r. rubecula* occur in variable but sometimes very large numbers on the coast. Passage on the coast extends from mid-August to late November although continental immigrants do not usually appear before mid-September. Spring passage of British birds is generally very light but during periods of easterly winds large numbers of continental Robins may arrive between late March and the middle of May.

There are six recoveries of birds ringed in the county in autumn and found in France between October and February. Two birds ringed on the coast in September and October were wintering in central Spain and another ringed in April was in Portugal by the following December. Others ringed in autumn have been recovered in Denmark, the Netherlands, West Germany and southern Norway. Birds from Norway and West Germany have been controlled in the county.

One ringed in May 1978 was found dead on a North Sea oil-rig north-east of Aberdeen three months later and a passage bird ringed on the Isle of May in October 1951 was wintering in the county in February 1955. Two coastal migrants in autumn were recovered wintering in Hertfordshire and Kent. Other recoveries involve neighbouring counties, Lancashire and Staffordshire.

Thrush Nightingale *Luscinia luscinia*
A very rare vagrant. One was trapped by P.J. Wycherley at North Somercotes Warren on 22nd May 1977. Another trapped by R.M. Jones at Theddlethorpe on 3rd September 1977 was retrapped on 6th and 9th September. Both birds were examined in the hand by several other observers. One was trapped at Theddlethorpe by M. and F.E. Boddy on 2nd September 1984.

Nightingale *Luscinia megarhynchos*
A fairly common and well-distributed summer visitor in suitable woodlands. The main strongholds are in the well-wooded districts of the south-west and central areas with birds becoming more local in northern parts. It is absent from much of the north-east, the coastal strip and south-eastern areas where there is no available habitat. In the mid-nineteenth century it was quite rare outside the south-west, but an increase and subsequent spread to the north was recorded from 1870 and it became quite common in many woods by the end of the century. During the last 20 years, however, there has been a noticeable decline in a number of areas.

Nightingales usually return to their breeding sites in the second half of April or early May and most have departed again by August. On the coast it is rare and not quite annual. Most of these occurrences have been in spring between mid-April and the third week of May. Autumn birds are mainly in August with occasional records in September.

One ringed at Gibraltar Point in May 1979 was controlled in Warwickshire in May 1981.

Siberian Rubythroat *Luscinia calliope*
A very rare vagrant. Good views of one were obtained by R. Lorand over a period of several hours at Donna Nook on 14th October 1977. It was the second British record of this Asiatic species.

Bluethroat *Luscinia svecica*
A rare and irregular passage migrant on the coast but also recorded twice inland. Seven birds, all in autumn, were recorded on the north-east coast between 1892 and 1924 but during the last 40 years there have been about 65 records with the majority since 1969.

Until recently it was very rare in spring. The first was recorded at Donna Nook on 31st May 1969 and since then there were eight records in 1970, four in 1977, one in 1981, 11 in 1985 and seven in 1987. Apart from one in early April all the spring records are in the second half of May. There are three instances of birds in late August and seven in October, with the remainder of records concentrated in September. Three of the October birds were very late; one was at Tetney on 24th October 1962 and others at Gibraltar

Point on the same date in 1977 and on 29th October 1979.

Males of the Red-spotted race *L.s. svecica* which breeds in Scandinavia and eastwards have been identified on many occasions. A male showing characteristics of the White-spotted central European race *L.s. cyanecula* was seen at Chapel Point on 4th September 1963 and a singing male was holding territory at Whisby gravel pits from 21st June to 4th July 1987.

Red-flanked Bluetail *Tarsiger cyanurus*
A very rare vagrant. An adult male seen by G.H.C. Haigh and F. Bacon at North Cotes on 23rd September 1903 was the first British record. One seen by S. Lorand at Donna Nook on 10th October 1978 and another trapped by M. and F.E. Boddy at Theddlethorpe on 12th October 1988 were the eighth and eleventh British records.

Black Redstart *Phoenicurus ochruros*
A scarce but regular passage migrant, chiefly on the coast but also occasionally inland. It has increased in recent years and has become a regular breeding species. There are a few winter occurrences.

Spring passage usually extends from the third week in March to mid-May with similar numbers in autumn between the first week of October and mid-November. Formerly the Black Redstart was only a vagrant to the county. The first record was of one obtained at Gedney Drove End in the Wash on 25th October 1867. Between 1902 and 1915 seven birds were recorded on the north-east coast during October and one appeared on the Inner Dowsing Lightship on 14th April 1905. There were no further records until 1933 when one was seen at Limber in late March. One or two birds were recorded annually during the next 15 years or so with sightings rising to their present level by the 1960s.

Breeding was recorded at Scunthorpe in 1970, 1974, 1984, 1986 and 1987. In 1980 single pairs bred at Grimsby Docks, Immingham Docks and at South Killingholme. Five pairs bred along the Humber bank in 1981, with two pairs in 1982, one pair in 1986 and three pairs in 1987 and 1988. One pair also bred at Spalding in 1986, with two pairs in 1987 and 1988. In addition there have been several records of unattached birds in various localities between late May and late August, although some of these birds, particularly in coastal areas, may have been migrants. There are several recent records of birds in winter, all since 1978 and mainly on the coast.

An adult male showing characteristics of one or other of the eastern races *P.o. ochruros* or *phoenicuroides* was seen at Saltfleetby from 15th to 17th October 1978 and another male was at Donna Nook on 21st October 1988. British birds belong to the race *P.o. gibraltariensis*.

Redstart *Phoenicurus phoenicurus*
A very scarce summer visitor although a fairly common or sometimes common passage migrant on the coast. Breeding birds favour the mature woods and parkland of the south-west. It occurs more locally in the north-west and central areas where breeding is irregular at several localities. There appears to have been little change in its breeding status since the nineteenth century.

Spring migrants usually in small numbers are recorded between the third week of April and early June. The return movement from late August to the end of October is generally much more pronounced. Peak numbers occur during September and in some years arrivals of many hundreds have been recorded. During the last ten years however, only small numbers have occurred. Late birds have been seen several times in early November.

Three recoveries indicate the origin of migrants. A nestling ringed in southern Sweden in June 1964 was controlled at Tetney in August 1966. Two birds ringed on the coast in late August have been found dead in southern Norway in the following May. Two birds have been recovered in France later in the same autumn and three birds have been found in Spain in autumn. One ringed at Gibraltar Point in September 1977 was recovered in Algeria in May 1978. Another ringed at Gibraltar Point in September 1963 was controlled at Dungeness Bird Observatory, Kent one week later and another caught in September 1976 was trapped at Walney Island, Lancashire ten days later.

Whinchat *Saxicola rubetra*

A scarce summer visitor and a common passage migrant mainly on the coast but also in small numbers inland. In the nineteenth century it was described by Cordeaux and others as one of the most abundant summer visitors in the county, breeding along many country lanes, railway embankments and in uncultivated areas. More intensive farming brought about the loss of much suitable habitat and the species was decreasing in the early years of the present century. By 1950 it was reduced to a few pairs in the north-west, the north-east coast and the Fens. The coastal birds ceased breeding a few years afterwards but a few still nest in the north-west and occasional pairs breed sporadically elsewhere.

Spring passage between late April and early June is usually light although larger numbers sometimes occur during easterly winds. The autumn movement is generally much more pronounced. A few juveniles often appear on the coast in late July merging with migrants from mid-August onwards. Migration continues until early October and large arrivals in late August and early September are quite frequent. Late birds are sometimes present until the end of October and first half of November.

One ringed in central Sweden in August 1966 was controlled at Skegness 19 days later.

Stonechat *Saxicola torquata*

A fairly common winter visitor and passage migrant on the coast, with smaller numbers inland. Numbers may vary according to the severity of winters.

Stonechats were formerly local breeding birds of the heath district of the north-west, the north-east coast, the Fens and possibly elsewhere. It declined in the 1930s and 1940s in several areas as a result of the combined effects of several cold winters and loss of habitat to agriculture. It ceased breeding regularly in the county after 1947 although a pair were thought to have bred at Cowbit Washes from 1953 to 1955 and single pairs nested at Lincoln sewage farm in 1961 and at Saltfleet in 1980.

Passage birds usually occur from late September to early November. Wintering birds have usually left again by the end of March but a few migrants move through in April and occasionally May.

There are four records of birds showing the characterisitcs of one or other of the eastern races *S.t. maura* or *stejnegeri*, colloquially known as Siberian Stonechats. All the records are from Donna Nook. In 1978 an adult male considered to be *stejnegeri* was seen on 23rd May and an immature male was identified on 7th and 8th October. A female or immature bird was seen on 9th November 1980 and another was present on 2nd October 1987. British birds belong to the race *S.t. hibernans.*

Wheatear *Oenanthe oenanthe*
A common or sometimes numerous passage migrant on the coast, with smaller numbers inland. Isolated pairs may still occasionally breed in the north-west of the county, although there has been no proof for many years. Nesting birds were uncommon in the latter half of the nineteenth century and were apparently restricted to several heaths and commons in the north-west and to the north-east coast. The date of its disappearance from the coast is unknown but we have been unable to find any breeding records after one at North Somercotes Warren in 1899. Increased cultivation and afforestation leading to loss of suitable habitat has been blamed for the decline of the Wheatear in many parts of England, although there are still quite a number of apparently suitable breeding areas in Lincolnshire. In recent years migrant birds have been observed prospecting and displaying until mid-June at one or two coastal sites, but none of these records has culminated in successful breeding.

Early birds occasionally appear from about the second week of March but the main arrivals begin in the last week of March or the first week of April and continue to the end of May with stragglers to mid-June. Odd juveniles reappear on the coast from mid-July onwards with the main migration from mid-August to late October and occasional birds to late November. Numbers are variable but during easterly drift conditions large arrivals may occur between late August and the third week of September. The population known colloquially as the Greenland race *O.o. leucorrhoa,* which also breeds in north-eastern Canada, Iceland and the Faeroes, is a very scarce annual migrant. It is usually identified between late April and the end of May and more rarely in autumn, in September and early October. British birds and migrants from the continent belong to the nominate race *O.o. oenanthe.* One ringed at Gibraltar Point in August 1960 was recovered in southern France in September 1961 and another Gibraltar Point bird trapped in August 1970 was found dead in Berkshire in March 1972.

Desert Wheatear *Oenanthe deserti*
A very rare vagrant. An immature male was seen by B. Childs and S. Lorand at Donna Nook on 23rd September 1970. It was the eighteenth British record of this species which breeds in North Africa and central Asia.

Ring Ouzel *Turdus torquatus*
A passage migrant mainly on the coast but also occasionally inland. It is usually scarce but may be fairly common in some years.

Spring migrants which have occurred more regularly in recent years move through between early April and mid-May although there are several records of birds from the second week of March. In autumn when the species is sometimes more plentiful the main passage is from mid-September to early November with occasional later stragglers. Most migrants occur singly or in small parties but flocks of up to 30 birds have been recorded occasionally in autumn. A late bird was shot at Crowland at the end of December 1920 and others were seen at Gibraltar Point on 22nd December 1963, 11th December 1976 and 18th December 1986. One at Rippingale Fen, near Bourne on 28th December 1980 stayed until 17th February 1981.

Ring Ouzels are said to have nested near Gainsborough and at Grayingham, near Kirton in Lindsey in the nineteenth century but confirmatory eivdence is lacking in both cases. The only recent summer record is of one in song at Donna Nook on 13th July 1986.

A bird ringed at Donna Nook in late October 1969 was shot in south-west France one week later and another bird found dead in the same area of France in November 1966 had been ringed at Gibraltar Point five weeks previously. There are two other recoveries of birds trapped at Gibraltar Point. One ringed in September 1968 was recovered on the east coast of Spain in the following December and one ringed in September 1959 was shot in north-east Morocco in February 1962.

Blackbird *Turdus merula*

An abundant breeding bird, passage migrant and winter visitor. Nesting birds are found commonly in practically all areas throughout the county. Many woods and copses attract very large numbers of roosting Blackbirds in winter.

Dispersing juvenile birds appear on the coast in late summer and early autumn but these are overshadowed by immigrants, sometimes on a huge scale between mid-September and late November. Numbers of immigrants vary considerably from year to year. In some years migrants arrive in a steady flow but in others large flocks follow each other, often with other thrushes over periods of several days. A remarkable influx occurred on 5th November 1961 when tens of thousands of birds poured in all along the coast. Severe weather has considerably less effect on this species compared with other thrushes and consequently it is seldom noted in any significant numbers during hard weather movements. Spring passage is usually much lighter than in the autumn although in common with other thrushes many leave overnight and are only heard as they pass overhead. These movements generally last from early March to the end of April although some migrants may still be on the coast in the first half of May.

Very large numbers of Blackbirds have been ringed in the county and the recoveries provide a fairly comprehensive picture of movements. The vast bulk of immigrants arrive from Norway, Sweden, Finland, Denmark and Germany. Rather few from Holland and Belgium are probably transient birds through these countries. The Finnish recoveries are a recent development and coincide with the Blackbird's extension of range there. Beyond Germany the only recoveries are one in Poland in March and another in Latvian Russia in July. There are several recoveries of birds found farther south in France and Spain in subsequent winters. Most coastal migrants, however, evidently continue to winter in more western areas. Many have been recovered in Ireland in winter and also in Wales and central and south-west England. Birds apparently still

Wheatear

Blackbird

on passage have been recovered in most other east coast counties and some of these in later years probably indicate foreign birds returning to winter in Britain. Coastal birds are not infrequently trapped in successive autumns within a few days of the date of the first capture, apparently showing a remarkable fidelity to migration routes and times. One bird ringed at Spurn Bird Observatory, Yorkshire in April 1955 was wintering in County Wexford in the following February and had returned to the Humber estuary at Cleethorpes by June 1956. Nestlings ringed in the county have produced mainly short distance recoveries although single birds have reached County Mayo and Pembrokeshire in winter.

Fieldfare *Turdus pilaris*

An abundant winter visitor and passage migrant recorded several times during summer in recent years. Arrival times and numbers often vary considerably. In some years there have been records of a few birds from the second week of August but the main immigration is not usually until early October or even later. Migrant flocks sometimes of huge numbers continue to arrive until late November although hard weather on the continent may cause further immigration later in the winter. Return passage extends from late March to the end of April with smaller numbers in early May.

Many immigrants cross the Lincolnshire coast and continue inland without hesitation but flocks totalling thousands remain on the coast where they exploit the plentiful supply of sea-buckthorn berries. By early December berry stocks are usually exhausted and the birds leave for inland winter quarters. Wintering birds are well-distributed mainly in open country, resorting to gardens and parks during severe weather. Hard weather movements, often with Redwings, are sometimes quite heavy and may last for several days. During the last few years there has been a growing number of records in summer, chiefly of single birds.

There is a good selection of recoveries of birds ringed in Lincolnshire. The majority of birds returning to Scandinavia have been recovered in Norway and Finland with fewer in Sweden and one in Denmark. Birds in later winters or on subsequent passage have been recovered in a number of countries but to date none have been found again in Britain. Six were found in France, two in Portugal and two in Italy, with single recoveries from Poland, Belgium, Austria and Yugoslavia. One ringed at Lincoln in December 1967 had reached north-west Spain within six weeks. Another shot in western Turkey in November 1969 had been ringed at Tetney in the previous February.

Song Thrush *Turdus philomelos*

An abundant and widespread breeding species, passage migrant and winter visitor. It breeds in all areas provided there are some trees or bushes and is absent only from the most built-up urban districts. Serious declines may follow severe winters.

Movements of juvenile birds to the coast occur in August with passage becoming more pronounced in September. Immigrant birds often in the company of Redwings arrive between late September and the end of November. Many of these birds are referable to the continental race *T.p. philomelos* whereas British birds belong to the race *T.p. clarkei.*. Return passage between March and early May often involves some *philomelos* birds, particularly during easterly winds when birds may occasionally arrive in numbers comparable with those in autumn.

Ringing recoveries show that many immigrants continue to winter inland and farther west in Britain while others move to areas in south-west Europe. The origin of migrants is indicated by breeding season recoveries in Norway, Finland, Denmark and Belgium. About 50 recoveries, mostly of autumn-ringed birds, are in wintering areas in France and the Iberian Peninsula. Three ringed as nestlings were also wintering in France with others in Spain and Portugal. Single birds recovered in Belgium in October and in the Netherlands in March and August were probably on passage through these countries. One ringed in the Netherlands in August was controlled in the county in autumn. One ringed on the coast in September was found dead in Cornwall two months later and one ringed in winter in County Wexford was controlled in the county in the following August.

Redwing *Turdus iliacus*
An abundant winter visitor and passage migrant. Small numbers usually occur in the second half of September with the main immigration in October and rather fewer to the end of November. On peak days flocks totalling many thousands arrive all along the coast and are often heard continuing inland at night. The largest arrivals often occur with other species of easterly origin and ringing recoveries indicate that many Redwings come from farther east than other thrushes. Good numbers remain on the coast in autumn in the sea-buckthorn but most birds have moved to inland areas by late December. Return passage, usually on a much smaller scale, lasts from mid-March to the end of April with stragglers in early May. Many leave at night and significant numbers on the coast occur only during adverse weather. Occasional late migrants have been recorded until the second week of June and early birds have arrived in mid-August. The only summer records were single birds at Gibraltar Point and Marshchapel in July 1978. One was observed several times carrying food in a conifer planatation at North Somercotes on 22nd May 1977 but was not seen subsequently. The nominate race *T.i. iliacus* is the typical form occurring in Lincolnshire. The Icelandic race *T.i. coburni* which also breeds in the Faeroes has been identified with certainty on only four occasions. These birds, all shot at North Cotes, were on 16th October 1935, 9th December 1936, 15th December 1937 and 17th January 1945.

Severe winters often wreak havoc on the Redwing as it is one of the earliest species to succumb during long periods of snow. At these times it is often the commonest species recorded on weather movements. Wintering birds usually feed in the open countryside and form large roosts in a number of woodlands but during cold spells many resort to towns, villages, farmyards and other areas where they may obtain food.

Recoveries of birds ringed in the county indicate that they may winter over wide ranges in succeeding years. There are several instances of birds wintering in France and Italy in later years with single examples in Portugal, Spain, Belgium, Cyprus, Turkey and the Lebanon. Easterly recoveries in Russia are of one between Leningrad and the Ural Mountains in September, one east of the Urals on the Siberian Plain in August and two birds near the Black Sea, in Georgia in January and March. The only Scandinavian recovery is of one in south-west Finland in June. The fact that some birds return to winter in Britain in later years is shown by recoveries of one ringed at Tetney in January 1967 and found dead in Shropshire in April 1968 and of another ringed in Staffordshire in March 1967 and controlled at Cleethorpes in October 1968. One found dead in Boston in February 1978 had been ringed on passage through the Frisian Islands in the previous October. One ringed in Orkney in October 1977 was controlled at Gibraltar Point three years later.

Mistle Thrush *Turdus viscivorus*
A common and well-distributed breeding species and a passage migrant in small numbers. It is found in most woodlands and open country with some trees as well as suburban parks and gardens. It increased in the county, as in other parts of Britain, during the nineteenth century.

Some parties of juveniles disperse to coastal districts from early June onwards but true passage migrants occur between mid-September and the end of November. Numbers are usually very small and most birds are probably of British origin as only very few birds accompany the immigrant flocks of other thrushes from the continent. Spring passage is very light, usually of odd birds from mid-February to early April.

One ringed at Gibraltar Point in September 1955 was recovered in Essex in the following March and one ringed in Hertfordshire in June 1971 was trapped at Gibraltar Point in August 1972.

Cetti's Warbler *Cettia cetti*
A very rare vagrant. Despite the recent dramatic colonisation by this species of south-east England as far north as Norfolk, there are only two county records. One was seen by G.R.M. Pepler at Barrow Haven on 6th March 1977 and one was trapped at Theddlethorpe by M. Boddy and other observers on 1st October 1983.

Lanceolated Warbler *Locustella lanceolata*
A very rare vagrant. One was shot by Haigh at North Cotes on 18th November 1909. It was the second British record of this Asiatic species.

Grasshopper Warbler *Locustella naevia*
A fairly common summer visitor in fluctuating numbers. During the late nineteenth century and early years of the present century it was generally scarce although a few pairs were found in several widely scattered areas and in some years it was described as being unusually common. The increase of young conifer plantations in the 1950s and 1960s assisted the spread of the species and it bred in quite high densities in some localities. As these plantations mature the habitat becomes unsuitable for the Grasshopper Warbler but populations are maintained provided that felling and replanting continues. Breeding birds are absent from most parts of the Wolds and the Fens.

It is a regular migrant in very small numbers on the coast between mid-April and late May and a few remain to breed there in some years. Most breeding birds have departed by the end of August. Autumn migrants usually during the first three weeks of September are quite rare though doubtless overlooked. There are one or two coastal records in early October.

Savi's Warbler *Locustella luscinioides*
A rare vagrant. There are five recent records of this species which has recolonised parts of south-east England during the last 30 years. The first bird was trapped at Pyewipe Marsh near Lincoln by P. Prince. It was present from 9th to 11th May 1967 and was also seen by K. Atkin and A.D. Townsend. Since then there have been sight records at Theddlethorpe on 3rd August and Bardney on 22nd August 1969 and at Saltfleetby from 5th to 7th September 1976. One was present at Lincoln Ballast Pit from 18th to 25th June 1986. All records apart from the Saltfleetby individual involved singing birds.

The Savi's Warbler formerly bred in the fens of Norfolk, Cambridgeshire and Huntingdonshire until the mid-nineteenth century. It seems probable that it may also have nested in the Lincolnshire Fens but we are unable to find any reference to it ever having been identified there.

Aquatic Warbler *Acrocephalus paludicola*
A very rare vagrant. An immature bird was trapped by R.M. Jones, C.F. Mapletoft and J.B. Harrison at Theddlethorpe on 8th September 1971. One was seen by E.J. Mackrill at Saltfleetby on 29th October 1979.

Sedge Warbler *Acrocephalus schoenobaenus*
A numerous and widespread summer visitor which has decreased in several areas during the last few years. It is less confined to wet habitats than the Reed Warbler and occurs in several quite dry areas such as young conifer plantations, oil-seed rape fields and stretches of sea buckthorn on the coastal dunes.

Passage on the coast is recorded from late April until the first week of June. Autumn movements are less apparent with dispersing juveniles in late July and early August and a few migrants until the third week of September. Occasional stragglers have occurred until the second week of October.

Birds ringed in July and August have been recovered in autumn in several southern and eastern counties. Birds from several southern counties have also been recovered in Lincolnshire. Two ringed in the county in autumn were found dead in north-west France in spring and autumn and another ringed in August 1965 was found dead on an island in the Bay of Biscay three weeks later. One recovered in northern Spain in October 1967 had been ringed in the county two months earlier. One ringed in the Channel Islands in May 1978 was controlled in Lincolnshire one year later. One ringed at Gibraltar Point in September 1983 was controlled at the same site on Merseyside in May 1984 and May 1985.

Marsh Warbler *Acrocephalus palustris*
A rare vagrant recorded on 12 occasions. One trapped at Tetney on 8th October 1961 was examined by several observers including R.K. Norman, L. Watkinson and S. Lorand. A singing male was present at Bardney from 14th to 22nd June 1964. Another was trapped

at Ancaster gravel pit on 16th August 1966. Singing males were recorded at Donna Nook on 28th May 1978 and 5th to 7th June 1979, the latter bird being trapped on the first date when another was also trapped at Saltfleetby. One was seen at Theddlethorpe on 17th May 1980. Singing males were present at Messingham from 4th to 10th June 1983 and on 3rd June 1985, then at Chapel Pit on 4th June 1986. Also in 1986 one was seen at Saltfleetby on 24th August and in 1988 one was present at Chapel Point on 22nd and 23rd October.

Reed Warbler *Acrocephalus scirpaceus*

A common summer visitor which is well-distributed wherever there are beds of *Phragmites*. It frequently breeds in dykes and ditches containing this reed and large concentrations occur in some reed beds, particularly along Humberside. Nesting is not always confined to reed beds as at some colonies nests may also be found in adjacent willow herbs, lesser reed mace, nettles and other plants.

The first arrivals are in late April and early May but some birds do not appear until the first week of June. Passage birds are scarce on the coast in spring, their presence usually being obscured by breeding birds. Migrants are fairly common between early August and late September and some inland movement is indicated by birds occurring away from their usual habitats in such places as woods and hedgerows. Stragglers occasionally occur in early October and very late birds have been recorded at Donna Nook on 27th October 1976 and at Gibraltar Point on 28th October and 12th to 13th November 1982.

A singing male showing characterisitcs of the eastern race *A.s. fuscus* was recorded at Humberston Fitties on 23rd May 1984. British birds belong to the nominate race *A.s. scirpaceus*.

There are several instances of birds ringed in the county between July and September and subsequently recovered on passage in the Channel Islands, France, Spain and Portugal. One from Skellingthorpe, near Lincoln in August 1968 was found dead on the north Spanish coast only four days later. More distant recoveries are four birds in Morocco in August, November, April and May. One ringed at Huttoft in July 1967 was found dead in the Spanish Sahara in the following October and another ringed at Tetney in September 1965 was recovered in Senegal in April 1969. One ringed at Gibraltar Point in September 1978 was controlled in the Ivory Coast in March 1979. Two passage birds ringed in Morocco in May were controlled in the county in spring and one ringed in Belgium in September was controlled on the coast in the following June. There are several recoveries relating to birds in Yorkshire and Nottinghamshire while others concern birds on migration in southern and eastern counties of England.

Great Reed Warbler *Acrocephalus arundinaceus*

A rare vagrant recorded on five occasions. One was present in a reed bed near Tetney Lock for several weeks in July 1897 and was heard singing by several people including Cordeaux. One was trapped at Huttoft on 3rd May 1969. A singing bird held a territory at Chapel Pit from 23rd May to the end of June 1976 and what was presumably the same bird was recorded nearby in July at Wolla Bank on 11th and at Huttoft Pit from 26th to

Wood Warbler

Reed Warbler

28th. Other records both involved singing birds: one at Burton gravel pits from 6th to 22nd July 1979 and one at North Cotes on 20th May 1980.

Booted Warbler *Hippolais caligata*
A very rare vagrant from Asia. One trapped by M. Boddy and B. Watkins at Theddle-thorpe on 12th October 1980 was the eleventh British record.

Icterine Warbler *Hippolais icterina*
Formerly the Icterine Warbler was a rare and irregular vagrant but records have increased in recent autumns so that it is now a regular migrant, very scarce in some years and rare in others. The first record was of one shot at North Cotes on 4th September 1922. Between 1951 and 1963 it was recorded seven times at Gibraltar Point with one record of five or six birds in 1958. Since 1965 it has been recorded regularly at Donna Nook and at Gibraltar Point, together with a good number of records from other coastal localities. In all over 120 have been recorded. Most reports refer to single birds but there are several records of two or three together with exceptional occurrences of up to six.

Early birds may appear from the first week of August but main arrivals are usually during the last ten days of August and the first three weeks of September. A few have occurred in late September and early October. There are only four spring reocrds. One trapped at Norton Place, near Gainsborough on 20th June 1970 is also the only inland record. Another was trapped at Seacroft golf course on 28th May 1977. A singing male was present at Donna Nook on 20th May 1979 and another was recorded at Gibraltar Point on 28th May 1982. A singing male was also present at Gibraltar Point from 5th to 8th July 1982.

Dartford Warbler *Sylvia undata*
A very rare vagrant. A male at Tetney on 2nd and 3rd June 1984 was trapped by H. Bunn, G.P. Catley and M. Mellor. The bird showed characteristics of the Mediterranean race *S.u. undata*.

Subalpine Warbler *Sylvia cantillans*
A very rare vagrant. A male in song was recorded by P. Shooter at Ingoldmells Point on 11th May 1970. Another singing male was trapped at North Cotes on 14th May 1976 and a male was seen at Tetney on 12th and 13th May 1981. A female trapped at Gibraltar Point was present from 7th to 14th May 1983 and a singing male was recorded at Pye's Hall on 23rd May 1985. The Tetney bird showed characteristics of the eastern race *S.c. albistriata* and that at Pye's Hall was considered to be the nominate race *S.c. cantillans*.

Sardinian Warbler *Sylvia melanocephala*
A very rare vagrant. An adult male was trapped at Gibraltar Point on 30th June 1979 and recorded by R. Lambert, S. Davies, P.R. Boyer and other observers. It was retrapped on 28th July and 6th September and was present until at least 15th September. Another adult male was trapped at the same locality on 6th July 1986, retrapped on 24th August and seen again on 31st August. It was seen by I. Hartley, J. Halls, K.W. Winfield and other

observers. These were the seventh and fourteenth British records.

Barred Warbler *Sylvia nisoria*
A scarce annual passage migrant on the coast in autumn. The first county record was of one shot at North Cotes on 5th September 1898. There were eight more records until 1927 then none until the commencement of regular reports in 1951. It remained rare or perhaps largely unobserved for a number of years but since 1968 increased mist-netting and more intensive coastal watching have produced a marked rise in the number of records with a maximum of 18 and an average of about seven birds a year. Most records have been between the third week of August and the end of September with a scattering of October occurrences. A particularly early bird was seen at Tetney on 4th August 1967. Late migrants have been noted at Saltfleetby on 11th November 1956 and at Donna Nook from 2nd November to 6th December 1971, between 3rd and 5th November 1974 and on 5th November 1978.

Lesser Whitethroat *Sylvia curruca*
A fairly widespread and common summer visitor and a passage migrant in small numbers. It occurs in many habitats alongside Whitethroats although it shows a distinct preference for areas containing denser and taller bushes. Breeding birds are absent from much of the Fens and most of the coastal districts.. After the crash of the Whitethroat population in 1969, there was an increase and spread of Lesser Whitethroats in a number of localities.

Spring birds begin to arrive in the third week of April and small numbers are present on the coast until late May or early June. Return migration lasts from the second week of August until mid-October or exceptionally mid-November. Migrants showing characteristics of the Siberian race *S.c. blythi* have occurred on the coast on several occasions during recent years between September and November. European birds belong to the nominate race.

Three birds ringed in the county have been recovered in Italy in autumn and another ringed at Boston in July 1972 was recovered in the Lebanon in April 1973. One ringed at West Deeping in June 1983 was controlled in Hungary in the following October and one ringed at Theddlethorpe in August 1984 was found dead in Syria in March 1986. One ringed at Anderby Creek in May 1967 was found dead in Yorkshire three days later and another ringed at Theddlethorpe in September 1976 was found dead in Northampton-shire in July 1978. One controlled in Nottinghamshire in May 1981 had been ringed at Gibraltar Point two years earlier and one ringed at Saltfleetby in September 1981 was recovered in Tayside in the following spring.

Whitethroat *Sylvia communis*
An abundant summer visitor and a common coastal passage migrant. It breeds through-out the county particularly in scrub, hedgerows, edges of woods and generally neglected areas where there is plenty of thick undergrowth. Exceptionally high densities are found in young forestry plantations and in the sea-buckthorn of the coastal dunes. In 1969 the Whitethroat population suffered a near catastrophic collapse. Few birds returned to

Britain in the spring and it seems most likely that a drought in the African wintering grounds caused excessive mortality of the species. Breeding success amongst the depleted numbers was good during the next few years and it had apparently returned to its former abundance by the late 70s.

The first arrivals usually appear during the third week of April and are supplemented by fresh birds until the third week of May. Spring passage migrants are often difficult to detect on the coast owing to the presence of many breeding birds. Juveniles disperse in late July and migration is quite marked from late August to the beginning of October with occasional birds to the end of the month. A late bird was recorded at Tetney on 12th November 1966 and one in winter was present at Stoke Rochford, near Grantham on 26th February 1968.

Thirteen birds ringed in Lincolnshire have been recovered on passage in France, Spain and Portugal. One ringed at Donna Nook in August 1980 was controlled at Gibraltar Point in September 1982 then found dead in Morocco in April 1984. One ringed at Gibraltar Point in September 1967 was recovered in Senegal in April 1968. Two ringed on the coast in September had returned to Yorkshire and Stirlingshire in May of the following year and three birds ringed as migrants in Sussex, one from Norfolk and one from Worcestershire, were found in the county in the next breeding season. Two birds recovered in Kent in August and September had been ringed earlier in the autumn at Gibraltar Point and one ringed near Bourne in August was controlled in Hampshire in the following May.

Garden Warbler *Sylvia borin*

A common summer visitor and coastal passage migrant. It is not quite so well-distributed as the Blackcap and is less common in most woodlands. It seems to have decreased in several areas during the last few years.

On the coast it is usually fairly scarce in spring when passage is noted between late April and the end of May. In autumn it is more common with migrants of continental origin mainly from late August to early October. There has been a slight increase in the number of late birds in recent years, hence several records in late October and early November and even late November in 1974 and 1982. One was present at Sleaford sewage farm on 1st January 1961.

A juvenile ringed in Cornwall at the end of July 1973 had moved north-east to Anderby Creek by September of the same year. Two birds ringed on the coast in September 1981 had reached Devon later in the same month and Anglesey by November. A passage migrant ringed at Gibraltar Point in September 1967 was shot in southern Spain three weeks later. Another bird controlled at Gibraltar Point in August 1984 had been ringed in Sweden one week earlier.

Blackcap *Sylvia atricapilla*

A common summer visitor and coastal migrant. Very small numbers are also present in winter. It is well-distributed in many woods, plantations and large mature gardens. In the late nineteenth century it was a quite local breeding bird easily outnumbered by the Garden Warbler but at present it is the commoner species in most areas. The lack of suitable habitat has prevented it from spreading into the Fens and along much of the coast.

Spring movements are generally small between early April and the end of May. Migrants in autumn have increased significantly in recent years. A few appear on the coast in late August but the main migration is from mid-September to early November with late birds until the end of the month. Wintering individuals have been reported increasingly since the first record in 1947. There were about ten records in the 15 years from 1953, then two or three annually from 1969 to 1974, and about ten each year from 1975. Some of the occasional migrant records in March may refer to birds that have wintered in Britain.

Three birds ringed as coastal migrants in October have been recovered wintering in the Netherlands, France and Portugal and two were controlled later in the autumn, probably still on passage through Belgium. Another October-ringed bird was found dead in southern Spain in early June. Three birds ringed during June to August have been recovered in Morocco in winter or early spring. A migrant ringed on Heligoland in October 1960 was trapped at North Cotes five days later and one from West Germany in August 1979 was controlled at Saltfleetby two months later. Another caught at Gibraltar Point in October 1975 had been ringed in Belgium five weeks earlier. One ringed at Theddlethorpe in September 1982 was found dead in the Lebanon in April 1983. There are a number of recoveries involving movements within Britain.

Greenish Warbler *Phylloscopus trochiloides*
There are ten records of this autumn vagrant. One shot by Haigh at North Cotes on 5th September 1896 was the first British record. One was trapped at Gibraltar Point on 3rd September 1958. In 1976 one was caught at Anderby Creek on 14th August and others were seen at Saltfleetby on 22nd and Donna Nook on 23rd August. One at Saltfleetby on 21st and 22nd August 1977 was followed by another at Seacroft golf course, trapped on 23rd and still present on 24th August. In 1981 one was seen at Saltfleetby on 31st August and another was trapped at Gibraltar Point during 2nd to 4th September. One was also trapped at Gibraltar Point on 22nd September 1984.

Arctic Warbler *Phylloscopus borealis*
A very rare vagrant noted on six or seven occasions. One shot by Haigh at North Cotes on 24th October 1932 was the eleventh British record. One was at Gibraltar Point from 19th to 27th September 1976 and another was recorded at Humberston on 10th October 1978. One was trapped at Theddlethorpe on 10th September 1985 while in 1986 one at Gibraltar Point on 20th and 21st September was trapped and another was seen at North Cotes from 26th to 29th September. A spring bird trapped at Gibraltar Point on 14th May 1983 is still under consideration by *British Birds*.

Pallas's Warbler *Phylloscopus proregulus*
There are 23 records of this Asiatic vagrant. The first occurrences were of single birds caught simultaneously on 19th October 1968 at Anderby Creek and at Gibraltar Point. Most of the records are from the north-east coast in the second half of October. The

earliest date was of one at Saltfleetby on 10th October 1982 and there are three November records up to 9th.

Yellow-browed Warbler *Phylloscopus inornatus*
A scarce autumn visitor from Asia recorded on over 125 occasions mainly on the coast.

Haigh obtained 13 birds at North Cotes between 1892 and 1932, then there were three records at Gibraltar Point from 1949 to 1952 with the remaining birds all since 1960. There were more records than usual in 1985 and 1986 when there were about 20 sightings in each year and a record 25 in 1988.

Most arrivals have fallen into the period from mid-September to late October and show a marked peak in the first three weeks of October. A few have been seen in early November and a late bird at Saltfleetby was last recorded on 15th November 1981. One at Normanby, near Scunthorpe on 20th and 21st October 1972 and one at Scopwick, near Lincoln on 29th October 1983 are the only inland occurrences.

Radde's Warbler *Phylloscopus schwarzi*
An immature female shot by Haigh at North Cotes on 1st October 1898 was the first British record of this very rare vagrant from Asia. One was trapped by M. and F.E. Boddy at Theddlethorpe on 16th October 1988.

Dusky Warbler *Phylloscopus fuscatus*
A very rare vagrant from Asia. One trapped by J.F. Cooper at Huttoft on 1st November 1964 was the fourth British record. One seen by S. Lorand at Donna Nook on 3rd November 1980 was later trapped by C.R. Morrison and seen by other observers during its stay to 9th November. One seen by W.P. Brooking, S.J. and W.J. Meek at Pye's Hall, near Donna Nook on 13th October 1988 is under consideration by *British Birds*.

Wood Warbler *Phylloscopus sibilatrix*
A rare or sometimes scarce passage migrant mainly on the coast. One or two pairs of Wood Warblers could still occasionally breed in suitable habitat in the county but it has not been a regular summer visitor for a number of years. Singing males have been recorded at several inland localities in recent years but seldom remain for more than a few days. In the late nineteenth century and early years of the present century it was apparently a local but regular summer visitor nesting in several beech woods in the north-west of the county and probably in the woods of the south-west and around Woodhall Spa. It seems to have declined at some time in the 1920s. Four or five pairs were breeding in Manby Woods, near Scunthorpe in 1920 and two were singing there in the summer of 1926. Lack of observations are probably to blame for no further records until 1951 when singing males were recorded from the same area and in several years since then. However, there have been no recent confirmed breeding records in the county.

As a passage migrant it is rather rare but annual. Spring records are confined to late April and the first half of May. It is less rare in autumn when it is usually noted between mid-August and the end of September. A very late bird was seen at North Cotes on 23rd

October 1988. There has been an increase in the number of records during the last 20 years with peaks of up to 15 birds in some years.

Chiffchaff *Phylloscopus collybita*
A very common summer visitor and a passage migrant in variable numbers on the coast. A few birds winter in the county. Smith and Cornwallis (1955) described it as scarce and local except in the south-west but there has evidently been an increase since then. This is probably attributable to the increase and spread of forestry plantations as the species is now well-distributed in woodlands throughout the county. It is largely absent from the Fens where there is little suitable habitat and it is seldom found breeding on the coast.

The first migrants usually arrive in the third week of March or sometimes even earlier and coastal pasage lasts until mid-May with late birds to the end of the month. Return movements are usually from the end of August to early November but stragglers until early December are not infrequent. Most migrants are referable to the western European race *P.c. collybita* but there are regular appearances mainly in late autumn of birds showing characterisitcs of *P.c. abietinus* which breeds in Scandinavia and western Russia. Some Chiffchaffs associated with late autumn arrivals of Asiatic migrants in recent years have shown characteristics of the east Siberian race *P.c. tristis* although some of these records may include birds of the west Siberian race *P.c. fulvescens*.

There has been an increase in the number of wintering individuals in recent years and although it remains rare it is noted annually at coastal and inland localities. Some of these wintering birds have included birds of the eastern races.

One ringed on passage at Gibraltar Point In September 1956 was recovered in Spain in October 1959. One ringed in Rand Wood, near Wragby in July 1967 was shot in southern Spain one month later and another ringed in the same wood in August 1968 was shot in southern Portugal in the following November. One found dead in Morocco in November 1980 had been ringed at Ancaster two months earlier. One ringed on the Calf of Man in April 1979 was controlled twice in the following summer at Gibraltar Point. Birds ringed on autumn passage in the county have been recovered in Northamptonshire, Kent and Sussex and one from Kent in May was controlled on the coast one month later.

Willow Warbler *Phylloscopus trochilus*
An abundant summer visitor and passage migrant. There is one winter record. It is widespread in all open woodland, plantations, and uncultivated areas where undergrowth includes some bushes or trees. It is a scarce breeding bird in some Fenland areas and along the coast although there has been a recent increase of small numbers at suitable coastal localities.

First arrivals are normally during the second week of April though occasionally from late March and migrants continue moving through until early June. Peak numbers usually occur in the last week of April and the first few days of May. Autumn passage lasts from early August to the first week of October with the heaviest movements in late August and early September. Late birds are occasionally seen until the end of October and a very late bird was seen at Anderby on 10th November 1982. A wintering bird was seen near Covenham Reservoir between 9th and 28th February 1975. There is a regular passage of small numbers of the northern race *P.t. acredula* on the coast in spring and autumn. This subspecies breeds in Scandinavia and east into Siberia although some birds breeding in northern Britain resemble this race. The endemic race is *P.t. trochilus*. A bird considered to show characteristics of the Siberian race, *P.t. yakutensis* was seen at Donna Nook on 21st and 22nd October 1987.

Ten birds ringed in the county have been recovered on passage in the Channel Islands, France and the Iberian Peninsula. One ringed at Theddlethorpe in August 1977 was found dead in southern Norway in May of the following year and one ringed at Donna Nook in August 1979 was recovered in Finland in May 1982. One found dead at Woodhall Spa in May 1967 had been ringed in northern France three weeks earlier and one ringed in Belgium in April 1984 was controlled at Gibraltar Point one year later. Several birds ringed or recovered on passage in the county have been from breeding areas in Scotland and northern England. Quite a number of recoveries also involve counties in southern and eastern England and one bird to Wales.

Goldcrest *Regulus regulus*

A common breeding species concentrated in coniferous woods and plantations with smaller numbers in mixed woodland, parks and large gardens. It is a numerous passage migrant especially on the coast in autumn and a widespread winter visitor. Extensive afforestation of conifers has enabled it to increase and spread since the last century and some of these woods contain substantial populations in winter. The species often suffers a serious decline in numbers during hard winters.

The first autumn migrants usually appear on the coast about mid-September but it is during October when the main passage occurs. In some years there are very large influxes often associated with arrivals of continental thrushes and Robins. Immigrants continue to arrive in reduced numbers during November and a few birds remain on the coast in most winters. Return migration is usually on a small scale between the second week of March and the end of April with occasional late birds to the second week of May.

Recoveries of birds ringed on the coast in autumn have included three in the Netherlands and two in Belgium, all later in the same autumn or winter. One ringed in October 1976 was recovered in Poland one year later, and another ringed in Poland in September 1980 was controlled in the county one month later. Two birds from Norway and one from the Netherlands have also been recovered in the county on passage. There are also a number of recoveries involving eastern counties of England.

Firecrest *Regulus ignicapillus*

A scarce passage migrant mainly on the coast and a very rare and irregular winter visitor. There are about 370 records and all but seven have been since 1966. The first bird was shot at North Cotes on 9th November 1901 and others were obtained there in September 1925 and October 1931. No further occurrences were noted until one at Gibraltar Point in April 1952, followed by single birds at the same place in 1960, 1963 and 1964. Nine were recorded in the county in 1966 and small numbers have appeared annually since then with peaks of at least 35 in 1979, 50 in 1980 and just over 30 in 1982.

Just under half of the records refer to spring migrants between the second half of March and late May. A singing male held a territory at Bourne between 19th April and 17th May 1980 and another held a territory at Gibraltar Point from late May to July 1987. There had been an earlier summer record of one at Skegness on 16th July 1975. Autumn migrants occur from the last week of September to November. One ringed at Gibraltar Point in October 1972 was still there on 6th January 1973. Another bird wintered inland at Lincoln where it was seen from 17th December 1966 to 4th February 1967. In 1980/81 about eight birds were recorded wintering in the county and several have been recorded in December in most recent years with two in January and February 1988.

Spotted Flycatcher *Muscicapa striata*

A common summer visitor and a fairly common passage migrant on the coast. It is widespread throughout the county breeding in open woodland, copses, orchards, parkland and mature gardens.

One or two birds occasionally appear in late April but the main arrivals are in the second week of May. Small numbers continue to move along the coast until early June. Return passage extends from mid-August to early October with a few records later in the month. Very late birds were noted at Gibraltar Point on 6th November 1966, 20th November 1973 and 8th November to 5th December 1981.

One ringed at South Willingham, near Market Rasen in July 1970 was shot in central Algeria in May 1972. One ringed on the Isle of May, Fifeshire in May 1973 had apparently overshot its destination and was controlled at Gibraltar Point two weeks later.

Red-breasted Flycatcher *Ficedula parva*

A rare coastal migrant recorded almost annually in autumn in recent years and twice in spring. There have been 92 records since the first bird was shot at North Cotes on 16th September 1909. Another was recorded at North Cotes in 1922 followed by two in 1929. There were no further sightings until one at Humberston and two at Gibraltar Point in 1949. Five birds were noted during the 1950s and it has been seen in most autumns since 1960.

Most migrants arrive between mid-September and late October although it has been seen as early as 23rd August. One was recorded inland at Spalding on 1st October 1961. Single birds at Donna Nook on 24th May 1976 and 22nd May 1985 are the only spring occurrences.

Pied Flycatcher *Ficedula hypoleuca*

A fairly common passage migrant mainly on the coast in autumn. In good years it can occur in quite large numbers. It is usually rare in spring. During much of the nineteenth century it was apparently a rare and irregular migrant. In 1872 Cordeaux could cite only one record of a migrant seven years earlier although it was being recorded fairly regularly by the end of the century. Coinciding with its change in status, there were five instances of breeding in the county. It nested at Scawby in 1871, West Rasen, near Market Rasen in 1891, Normanby, near Scunthorpe in 1896 and Gainsborough and

Red-breasted Flycatcher

Red-backed Shrike

Haverholme, near Sleaford in 1901. There have been no breeding records since then.

Spring birds, usually in ones and twos, appear on the coast between the third week of April and the end of May. There was an exceptionally large fall of birds on 7th May 1936 when considerable numbers were recorded along the coast between Cleethorpes and Donna Nook. Autumn migrants arrive in variable numbers mainly from the second week of August to the end of September with stragglers during October. A late bird was seen at Donna Nook on 4th November 1982. Large arrivals in late August and early September are usually preceded by winds from an easterly quarter.

Five autumn migrants ringed at Gibraltar Point have been recovered in France, Spain and Portugal in the same or subsequent autumns and two others were recovered in Portugal in March and early June. One ringed in September 1958 had returned to Sweden by June 1959. One ringed at Gibraltar Point in September 1981 was recovered in the Central African Republic in the following February. One ringed in Northumberland in July 1951 was found dead at Lincoln in April 1953.

Bearded Tit *Panurus biarmicus*
A scarce breeding species at several sites on the Humber Bank and a scarce passage migrant and winter visitor, chiefly on the coast but also inland. Prior to the drainage of the Fens it was probably quite common and widespread. It was recorded as being not uncommon in the large reedy areas near Cowbit as late as 1830 although it may have become extinct there very shortly afterwards. Its former status in the north-west is unknown but one shot at Brumby Common about 1840 proved to be the last county record for over 100 years.

During the late 1950s and early 1960s there was a large increase in the breeding numbers of East Anglia resulting in several long distance eruptions. Two birds at Gibraltar Point on 27th September 1956 were the first of the series of recent records. Very small numbers were recorded in the county during the next few autumns with some birds remaining until spring. In the autumn of 1965 there was a huge eruption of birds from the Netherlands which resulted in reports of parties of up to 20 birds at several localities. Breeding was first recorded in 1968 when three pairs nested on the Humber Bank. It has bred at several sites in this area each year since then and a fairly stable population of up to 30 pairs has been maintained during the last 20 years. Numbers have perhaps been augmented by birds from Blacktoft Sands in Yorkshire as some movements certainly originate from there in autumn. Passage on the coast, usually of very small parties, is mainly from mid-October to late November with a smaller return movement in March and early April.

Long-tailed Tit *Aegithalos caudatus*
A common breeding species and passage migrant. It nests in many woodlands, hedgerows and overgrown areas of scrub throughout the county but is absent from much of the coast and Fens. Numbers fluctuate widely as Long-tailed Tits are especially susceptible to severe winters. Recently, following a succession of relatively mild winters during the 1970s, the population has been at a high level with a few pairs also nesting at one or two coastal sites since 1972.

Outside the breeding season wandering parties are a regular feature of towns and countryside. Along the coast small flocks often moving south, occur between late September and early December. In some autumns hundreds may be seen but in others only a few parties move through. Spring movements are much smaller and normally relate to paired birds in March and early April. Cordeaux recorded that he saw a bird of the northern race *A.c. caudatus* at Great Coates in November 1972. British birds belong to the race *A.c. rosaceus*.

Ringing recoveries indicate that migrating family parties frequently remain together. Seven birds ringed at Donna Nook in October 1967 were controlled at Gibraltar Point, 27 miles SSE, four days later. Two ringed at Wragby on 7th October 1973 were controlled 36 miles NNE at Withernsea in Yorkshire on 27th October and a party of seven ringed in Northamptonshire on 29th September 1973 was caught at Mablethorpe, 67 miles NE, on 23rd October. One ringed at Harmston near Lincoln in June 1971 had moved to Nottinghamshire by March 1972 and another ringed at Donna Nook in October 1974 was controlled at Withernsea, Yorkshire in March 1975. A remarkably rapid recovery concerned a bird ringed at Donna Nook on 16th October 1976 and controlled 32 miles NW at Beverley, Yorkshire on the following day. One ringed at Gibraltar Point in October 1978 was controlled in Leicestershire in March 1979.

Marsh Tit *Parus palustris*

A fairly common resident mainly in deciduous woodland. It is fairly well-distributed in south-western parts of the county, north to the Lincoln area. A few pairs occasionally breed elsewhere but there is no stable population away from the main strongholds. Early accounts of its status are not reliable owing to the confusion between this species and the Willow Tit but at present it appears to be much less common and more local than the Willow Tit. Between 1967 and 1976 only 67 Marsh Tits were ringed in the county compared with over 1,000 Willow Tits in the same period. On coastal passage it is rare and irregular with only 14 records of one or two birds during the last 30 years. Six of these were in April, one in late August and the remainder in September and October.

Willow Tit *Parus montanus*

A common and widespread resident that has increased in recent years. It may occur alongside the Marsh Tit in some woodlands but it is also regularly found in small copses, hedgerows and overgrown areas. This species was not recognised until 1900, hence its distribution and numbers have remained obscure until recent years.

Coastal migrants were formerly rare and irregular. Seven birds were shot by Haigh on the north-east coast between 1894 and 1899. These were originally recorded as Marsh Tits but later examination proved that all were in fact Willow Tits. There appear to be no further records on the coast until the establishment of Gibraltar Point Bird Observatory produced a few annual records from 1949 onwards.

Regular coastal appearances began about 1965 in most other areas mainly in March and April and between late July and November, suggesting some migration dispersal. These have continued to increase and Willow Tits have bred at several coastal sites since 1972, some remaining there in winter.

One ringed at Theddlethorpe in August 1973 was found dead at East Halton in October 1973 and another ringed at Gibraltar Point in August 1977 was caught at Donna Nook two months later.

Coal Tit *Parus ater*

A common and well-distributed resident except on the coast and in many parts of the Fens. It is most plentiful in conifer plantations, where it is usually the commonest tit, but smaller numbers are regularly present in many other woodlands.

Coastal records mainly between late September and early November concern occasional single birds or very small parties although it occurs more regularly during irruptions of Blue and Great Tits. A bird showing the characteristics of the continental race *P.a. ater* was trapped at Donna Nook on 28th October 1969. Sight records of this race have been claimed on several occasions in autumn and some probably occurred in the 1957 tit irruption. British birds belong to the race *P.a. brittanicus*.

Blue Tit *Parus caeruleus*

An abundant resident found in practically all woods, copses, hedgerows, orchards, parks, farms and gardens. It is also a regular coastal passage migrant in small numbers although large autumn irruptions occur at irregular intervals.

Many movements are relatively local but irruptions involving large numbers of birds occurred in the autumns of 1878, 1889, 1898, 1899, 1901, 1919, 1923, 1949 and 1957. Coastal movements begin in mid-September with the main passage in October and early November. Return passage in late March and April is almost invariably on a small scale.

A nestling ringed in Berkshire in May 1957 was found at Louth in the following February and a Yorkshire nestling ringed in May 1975 was controlled at Mablethorpe in January 1980. Lincolnshire-ringed birds have produced recoveries in the neighbouring counties of Yorkshire, Nottinghamshire, Leicestershire and Northamptonshire, and one ringed in February 1950 was recovered in Suffolk in March 1951. One ringed in July 1978 was controlled at Warwickshire in the following May. One ringed at Grantham in December 1957 was found dead in northern France in January 1959.

Great Tit *Parus major*

A numerous breeding bird in woodlands, hedgerows, orchards, parks and gardens. It is a regular passage migrant on the coast in variable but usually small numbers although in some years considerable irruptive movements take place.

Autumn movements are most marked between mid-September and early November but return migration in late March and April is often almost negligible. Large numbers were observed on the coast in October and November in 1878, 1883, 1884, 1886, 1889 and 1901 and these were considered to have belonged to the continental race *P.m. major*. Birds of this race were obtained on the coast during a huge immigration in October and November 1910. More recently influxes of continental birds occurred in 1949 and 1957. British birds belong to the race *P.m. newtoni*.

There are several ringing recoveries in Yorkshire, Derbyshire, Northamptonshire and Cambridgeshire. One ringed in October 1949 was recovered in Sussex in June 1951 and another ringed in March 1962 was found in the same county six weeks later. One ringed in April 1984 was controlled in Wiltshire in February 1986. One controlled in Hertfordshire in May 1976 had been ringed in the previous October. Two ringed in Staffordshire and one from Shropshire in winter have been controlled in the county in spring. One ringed in March 1967 was found dead in the Netherlands in October 1968.

Nuthatch *Sitta europaea*
A fairly common resident largely confined to mature deciduous woods in the south-west. At present, breeding birds extend as far north as Potterhanworth Woods. There were sight records of single birds at Bottesford, near Scunthorpe in 1879 and 1889 and it was recorded breeding in nearby Manby Woods at about that time but it is not known whether it ever occurred as a regular breeding bird in the north-west. Isolated occurrences of breeding and wandering birds away from the south-west are sporadic. A pair bred at Grimsby in 1904, and single birds were recorded near Louth in November 1916 and at Grimsby in December 1954. One pair bred at Brocklesby in 1960 and another pair near Gainsborough in 1962 and perhaps in the previous two years. In the last 15 years there have been a number of records in other parts of the county, particularly in the north-west and the Wolds. One was also trapped at Gibraltar Point on 25th April 1987.

Treecreeper *Certhia familiaris*
A common resident in all types of woodland. It is well-distributed throughout the county except in the Isle of Axholme, the Fens and on the coast where there is little suitable habitat. It wanders a good deal in winter often in association with tits and in common with those species it is particularly susceptible to hard winters. The breeding population was drastically reduced following the 1962/63 winter but managed to recover within the next four or five years.

Fairly regular appearances of birds at Gibraltar Point and Theddlethorpe mainly between late July and November probably originate from nearby breeding areas. Elsewhere on the coast it is a vagrant with only irregular records.

A bird of the northern race *C.f. familiaris* was shot by Dr. J.M. Harrison at North Cotes on 13th March 1947. British birds belong to the race *C.f. brittanica*.

Golden Oriole *Oriolus oriolus*
A rare passage migrant chiefly in spring but also occasionally in autumn. A pair is said to have started building a nest in a garden near Scunthorpe in 1871 and others were alleged to have bred at least twice in Broughton Woods, near Scunthorpe around the turn of the century. These reports and six sight records all from the north-west between 1899 and 1912 seem unreliable. The only acceptable early record is of one killed against telegraph wires near Gainsborough in August 1908. Since 1958 it has occurred on about 40 occasions. One arrived on 24th April, otherwise spring birds were concentrated in May with nine records in June and two in July. One at Friskney Decoy on 6th and 7th August 1968 and another at Wisbech sewage farm from 7th to 14th August 1971 are the only recent reports in autumn.

Isabelline Shrike *Lanius isabellinus*
A very rare vagrant. One at Donna Nook from 28th to 30th October 1978 was trapped by C.R. Morrison and subsequently seen by many observers. The bird showed charac-teristics of the race *L.i. phoenicuroides* which breeds in Russia and Iran, east of the Caspian Sea. Another was seen at Anderby Creek on 7th and 8th November 1982 by M.J. Warren and other observers and later at Gibraltar Point on 15th November. This bird which was an adult male showed characteristics closest to the race *L.i. speculigerus* which breeds east of the range of *phoenicuroides*. These were the 14th and 17th British records.

Red-backed Shrike *Lanius collurio*
A scarce passage migrant mostly on the coast and a rare and irregular summer visitor. Migrants have increased significantly during recent years. There are several instances of single or paired birds in summer but fully authenticated records of breeding are few. It is said to have nested in the south of the county in several years prior to 1883 but no actual details are recorded. Shortly afterwards, single pairs bred at Hibaldstow and Raventhorpe, both near Scunthorpe. In 1907 and 1908 a pair bred at Haverholme, near Sleaford and in 1945 breeding was proved at Barrow-on-Humber. More recently two pairs nested in close proximity to each other near Alford in 1977 and a pair bred near Grimsby in 1978.
    During the late nineteenth century and the first half of the present century, it occurred on the coast only very rarely and at irregular intervals. Haigh recorded only two birds during almost 50 years of regular observations on the north-east coast. Migrants began to appear fairly regularly in the 1950s. There was a steady increase of records and it has been seen annually in small numbers since 1963 with a sudden sharp peak in 1977 when more than 50 were seen. Most records in early May refer to inland birds whereas migrants on the coast usually occur from the third week of May to mid-June. Occasional birds sometimes appear on the coast in summer with return passage between the third week of August and early October. Autumn records almost invariably concern juvenile birds and are about three times more frequent than spring occurrences.

Lesser Grey Shrike *Lanius minor*
A very rare vagrant. One was seen by N.J.P. Wadley at Gibraltar Point on 11th October 1960. Several observers including R. May recorded one at Saltfleetby on 5th October 1969 and another present at Donna Nook on 25th and 26th May 1970 was seen by B. Childs and S. Lorand.

Great Grey Shrike *Lanius excubitor*
A scarce passage migrant on the coast and a winter visitor chiefly inland. There are two summer records. Numbers vary from year to year but it is regularly recorded at coastal localities between early October and mid-November with a few birds sometimes remaining into December. Early immigrants occasionally arrive in the second half of September. Wintering birds are usually very scarce but may be found in almost any suitable open habitat inland, particularly in the vicinity of young conifer plantations.

Spring passage is more variable than autumn but a few are seen in most years between mid-March and mid-April with one or two records in early May. An increase in the number of migrants and wintering birds in the last 20 years is probably a reflection of more intensive observations although it has been scarcer in the last five years. Single birds in summer were present at Grebby Park, near Spilsby from mid-May to mid-July 1971 and at Kirkby Moor, near Woodhall Spa from 25th May to 14th June 1975.

One ringed at Spurn, Yorkshire in October 1966 was found dead at Crowland four weeks later.

Woodchat Shrike *Lanius senator*
A rare vagrant recorded on five occasions. One was seen by D. Hill at Gibraltar Point on 7th June 1960 and another was recorded at the same locality on 26th May 1968 during a spring which produced exceptional numbers of Woodchat Shrikes in Britain. The remaining records are of immature birds in autumn. One was seen at Skidbrooke North End, near Saltfleet on 21st September 1974, one was present at Saltfleetby on 21st and 22nd August 1977 and another was recorded at Donna Nook on 6th August 1978.

Jay *Garrulus glandarius*
A common resident, breeding in many woodlands in the county. It is absent from coastal areas and the Fens where there is little suitable habitat. It has increased during the present century as persecution pressures have lessened, while increased afforestation in some areas has been readily exploited.

As a coastal migrant, its appearances are generally rare, usually in October and November and sometimes in April. Influxes have been recorded on a number of occasions, however, and these may be birds of European origin which are subject to periodic irruptions governed by the supply of acorns. At these times flocks of up to 25 birds have been recorded on the north-east coast and Jays were especially numerous in 1880, 1886, 1890, 1892, 1920, 1923, 1930 and 1935. More recently, flocks of up to 50 occurred all along the coast in the autumn of 1983, with some remaining to winter and a return movement in May and June 1984. On ringed at Donna Nook in October 1983 was found dead at Boston in March 1984 and one ringed at Gibraltar Point in April 1984 was found dead in Norfolk in the following winter.

Magpie *Pica pica*
A very common resident that has increased in recent years. It is fairly well-distributed in the county except in intensively cultivated areas devoid of trees and hedgerows. The Magpie was a regular target for persecution during the nineteenth century but still managed to hold its own in many areas. Its increase in the present century was directly linked to less gamekeeping activity but a widespread decline in the late 1950s and early 1960s is probably attributable to the combined effects of intensive hedgerow removal and the use of toxic chemicals in agriculture. Breeding numbers were also down in many places especially inland following the severe winter of 1962/63. A full recovery has been evident in several areas, particularly on the coast and recent rapid increases have probably returned its status to that of the early 1950s. There is no evidence of any regular

Magpie

Siskin

passage on the coast. Local fluctuations and wanderings in autumn and occasionally hard weather movements in winter have been recorded but due to a high coastal population any real movement is difficult to detect.

Nutcracker *Nucifraga caryocatactes*
A rare vagrant recorded on seven occasions. One killed near Sleaford in March 1833 and preserved in Lincoln Museum was recorded by A. Fieldsend. One was shot at Marshchapel on 6th November 1888. In the autumn of 1968 there was an unprecedented invasion across Europe of the Slender-billed race *N.c. macrorhynchos* of north-east Russia and Siberia. British records were largely concentrated in East Anglia but single birds were seen in September at Theddlethorpe on 12th and at Sutton-on-Sea and Gibraltar Point on 17th. One was seen at Metheringham, near Lincoln on 9th April 1969 and another was recorded at Donna Nook on 12th September 1976.

Jackdaw *Corvus monedula*
A numerous and well-distributed breeding bird and a passage migrant and winter visitor in smaller numbers. It has increased since the late nineteenth century and may be found nesting in a wide range of habitats, mainly in mature woods and copses, hollow trees in hedgerows, parks, quarries and old buildings. It is quite common in a number of towns and villages where churches and disused chimneys are much-favoured nest-sites.

Immigration and coastal movements in common with the other crows are now less spectacular than in the last century and early part of the present century. Heavy passage used to be a regular feature of autumn but in recent years migration has been recorded only on a modest scale between late September and mid-November, with a return movement from early March to the end of April. Single birds of the Scandinavian race *C.m. monedula* were shot by Haigh at Fenby Wood, near Grainsby on 20th January 1919, 4th March 1920 and 14th February 1926. One showing characteristics of this race was seen at Donna Nook on 1st April 1979 and another was seen at Barton-on-Humber on 6th November 1983. British birds belong to the race *C.m. spermologus*.

One ringed at Deeping St. James in December 1965 was recovered at King's Lynn, Norfolk in the following May.

Rook *Corvus frugilegus*
A numerous, widespread breeding species and a common passage migrant and winter visitor. During the later years of the nineteenth century and the first half of the present century there was a general increase in breeding strength but there has been a reversal of this trend in recent years. A two-year survey of the county undertaken during 1929 and 1930 resulted in a minimum of 35,000 occupied nests estimated in the 720 colonies. Another census in 1944 and 1945 showed an upward tendency to over 45,000 nests in 977 colonies. A considerable decline to 17,600 nests in 731 colonies was recorded in 1970, a pattern followed to 1975, when only 12,500 nests were located in 588 colonies. The causes for these drastic changes are considered to be largely attributable to modernised agricultural techniques. An increased acreage of cereal crops providing an important food source coincided with the earlier increase of the Rook. The decline

which began in the 1960s seems closely associated with the widespread use of toxic seed dressings and probably with increased burning and early ploughing of stubble fields.

Coastal passage migrants have decreased in recent years. Large immigrations often of thousands were noted mainly on the north-east coast until the 1920s. The biggest autumns when many thousands of birds were involved were in 1889, 1890, 1893, 1906, 1913, 1919 and 1921. Birds disperse from the rookeries after the breeding season and birds on the coast may mask the presence of migrants. However, some passage is usually recorded from the end of September to mid-November. Return movements extend from early March to the end of April or early May. Some spring migrants congregate on coastal fields, often with Jackdaws and Hooded Crows, before leaving high to the east and north-east.

The origin of wintering birds is shown by recoveries of birds ringed as nestlings in western Russia, Germany, Denmark and the Netherlands.

Carrion Crow *Corvus corone*

The Carrion Crow, *C.c. corone*, is a common and widespread breeding bird and a coastal passage migrant. It has increased during the present century with the decline of persecution as game preservation is now concentrated on few estates. Outside the breeding season, there are increases on the coast where flocks frequently resort to feed on the open shore but it is not known whether these are local birds from inland or immigrants from outside the county. Communal roosts, sometimes with Rooks, in a number of woods and copses form between autumn and spring.

The huge movements which used to be a notable feature on the coast in October until the early years of the present century now no longer occur. Passage migrants are usually noted in small numbers from the end of September to mid-November with a return movement between mid-March and the first week of May.

The Hooded Crow, *C.c. cornix*, is a scarce passage migrant and winter visitor mainly on the coast but also inland. Until the 1930s, flocks totalling hundreds or occasionally thousands occurred on the coast in autumn. Numbers have declined considerably since then and most records in recent years have referred to single birds or small parties. Occasional immigrants may appear in late September but the main arrivals are between the second week of October and the end of November. Return passage lasts from mid-March to early May with one or two sometimes remaining into June.

One was shot from a nest at Market Stainton, near Horncastle in 1899. In 1954 a nest was located at Crowland Wash, but only one adult was ever seen. Hybridisation with a Carrion Crow could have occurred although the three young birds raised seemed typical of *cornix*. A pair present at Grainthorpe in the summer of 1976 are believed to have made an unsuccessful breeding attempt.

Single birds ringed as nestlings in Norway and Sweden have been recovered in Lincolnshire during their first winters.

Raven *Corvus corax*

Ravens were widespread over much of lowland England until the late eighteenth century but there are few early references to its status in Lincolnshire. A pair is known to have bred on Louth Church in 1693 and it is said to have been common prior to 1750. At the end of the eighteenth century, there was supposed to be a pair still breeding at Broughton, near Scunthorpe. Records of two birds at Croxby Ponds, near Caistor on 1st October 1887 and of one feeding on a dead lamb at Cadney, near Brigg in March 1901 are not fully authenticated. The only recent record is of one present at Donna Nook from 11th to 26th February 1980.

Starling *Sturnus vulgaris*
An abundant breeding bird, passage migrant and winter visitor, well-distributed in all habitats. After the breeding season juveniles form into flocks and large congregations frequent coastal districts.

Between autumn and spring, Starlings form vast communal roosts and some woods contain hundreds of thousands of birds.
Immigration of large numbers begins in late September and many thousands of birds arrive from the continent in October and early November with fewer to the third week of November. Many of these immigrants winter in Lincolnshire but the majority move farther west and south-west. Spring movements are generally on a far smaller scale than in autumn and extend from late February to the end of April.
Ringing recoveries show that autumn immigrants originate from Scandinavian countries, western Russia, Poland, Germany, Netherlands and Belgium although recoveries from the Low Countries probably involve some migrants from farther east. Most recoveries in Lincolnshire are from areas south and east of the Baltic. One bird trapped in the Netherlands in October 1957 was transported and released in Switzerland and subsequently recovered near Grantham in November 1958. Many immigrants evidently continue through the county to winter in other parts of Britain. Recoveries have been in many counties from Lancashire south to the Cotswolds, with a strong concentration in the Midlands. There are also a few recoveries in North Wales and Ireland. A number of birds have been recovered in Norfolk and Suffolk. Some of these were evidently returning to the continent from inland areas in spring while others in subsequent autumns were probably immigrants arriving farther south.
Breeding birds in the county appear to be fairly sedentary with many short-distance and local movements. One bird ringed as a nestling near Sleaford in May 1954 made an unusual journey to the Netherlands, where it was shot two months after ringing. Other movements of local birds show fairly random movements to Midlothian, County Kilkenny, Flintshire, Lancashire, Nottinghamshire, Wiltshire and Hampshire.

Rose-coloured Starling *Sturnus roseus*
A rare vagrant noted on ten occasions. Donovan (1794-1819) recorded that one shot near Grantham prior to 1783 was in the possession of Sir Joseph Banks. Another was recorded by Morris (1851-58) as having occurred in Lincolnshire in July 1818 but no actual locality was given. Four other birds were obtained on the east coast of Britain at the same time. An adult in a Cleethorpes garden from 1st to 3rd August 1909 fed on cherries. One was present at North Cotes on 10th September 1932, and an adult was seen

at Holton-le-Clay, near Grimsby on 29th August 1947. An immature wintered at Skegness from 11th December 1955 to 8th April 1956, during which time it was trapped. Another immature was trapped at Wainfleet on 18th October 1973. A first winter bird was present at Market Deeping from mid-February to 8th March 1983 and an adult was at Rauceby Warren on 21st June 1984. A juvenile was seen at South Witham on 23rd August 1987.

House Sparrow *Passer domesticus*
An abundant resident and a passage migrant on the coast. It breeds commonly in almost all urban and rural areas where it is particularly attracted to all types of buildings offering nesting and roosting sites. It is local, or even absent, from more remote areas of woodland and parts of the coast. It was less plentiful in the early part of the nineteenth century owing to relentless persecution. There was a marked increase during the 1860s attributable to a rise in cereal growing and a discontinuation of widespread destruction by man.

Huge flocks gather in autumn and resort to rural areas where they wander cereal fields, stubble and farmyards. Communal roosts are found in a wide variety of situations, ranging from buildings and haystacks to trees and tall hedgerows. Passage migration on the coast is sometimes quite heavy between mid-September and early November. Spring movements are usually much smaller in late March and April.

Fairly extensive ringing of coastal migrants has produced many recoveries. Most birds have shown merely local movements from inland areas of the county although several others including some in the breeding season have been found up to 65 miles away in Yorkshire, Norfolk, Suffolk, Nottinghamshire and Leicestershire. The most distant recovery is one ringed at Gibraltar Point in autumn 1963 and found 85 miles NNW at Scarborough, Yorkshire in the following March.

Tree Sparrow *Passer montanus*
A numerous resident and a coastal passage migrant. Cordeaux recorded a significant increase during the 1860s which corresponded with a similar increase of the House Sparrow. There was a further spread of Tree Sparrows during the last 25 years and colonies are now well-distributed in many woodlands, parks, gardens, hedgerows, buildings and quarries. In the last five years, however, there has been a marked decline in numbers.

Large flocks gather after the breeding season and visit cornfields and stackyards, often in the company of House Sparrows, finches and buntings. Coastal movements are usually quite marked between late September and early November with a smaller return from mid-March to the end of April.

Ringing recoveries indicate that movements frequently involve greater distances than those of House Sparrows. Autumn migrants on the coast have been recovered in summer, presumably in their breeding areas in Yorkshire and Norfolk. One ringed at Gibraltar Point in October had moved north to Spurn within two weeks and two ringed at Spurn were controlled at Gibraltar Point.

One ringed in October was in Essex in the following February but two others ringed in August were inland in Hertfordshire in January and Wiltshire in November. One ringed in West Yorkshire in March was on the Lincolnshire coast in the following October and another ringed in Surrey in December was recovered at Bourne in May.

Chaffinch *Fringilla coelebs*

An abundant breeding bird, winter visitor and passage migrant. It is widely distributed, nesting in all types of woodland, hedgerows, scrub and gardens. There was a considerable decline in numbers during the 1950s attributed to the use of toxic seed dressings but there has been a good recovery since the mid-1960s. Outside the breeding season many Chaffinch flocks wander the countryside where they are frequently found on stubble and other arable fields.

British breeding birds belong to the race *F.c. gengleri* but there is a strong autumn immigration of birds of the continental race *F.c. coelebs*. Most of these birds pass through the county to other areas but many remain to winter in Lincolnshire. Arrivals begin about mid-September, and large numbers move along the coast and inland until late November. Return movements are pronounced but less heavy between late March and early May.

Six birds ringed in the Netherlands have been recovered in the county in spring and autumn. Migrants ringed in the county between autumn and spring have produced several recoveries. There have been three in Norway, one in Sweden and another in southern Finland. Single birds were found in later winters in the Netherlands, Belgium and Germany with two in Ireland. An adult ringed at Gibraltar Point in July was recovered in Germany in November of the following year. A juvenile ringed in Leicestershire in August 1954 was at Willoughby, near Alford in June 1956.

Brambling *Fringilla montifringilla*

A common winter visitor and passage migrant. Wintering flocks often in the company of Chaffinches and Greenfinches are widespread in many conifer plantations and mixed woodlands, especially those containing beech, but it is also a frequent visitor to arable fields, stubble and stack-yards. Communal roosts sometimes of several hundred birds are usually in conifers, rhododrendons and other evergreens.

Early immigrants arrive in the second half of September followed by larger numbers in October and early November. Birds move quickly inland and many pass through the county to winter in other areas. Small flocks frequently return to the coast in late winter prior to emigration which lasts from about mid-March to early May. A late bird was recorded at Donna Nook on 6th June 1976 and one summered at Limber in 1950.

Birds ringed in the southern parts of Norway, Sweden and Finland have been recovered in the county. One ringed in Belgium in February was in Lincolnshire three years later and another Belgian-ringed bird was trapped at Skegness in November, 12 days after being ringed. Three birds ringed in late March were recovered in Belgium in autumn. One ringed in January was in southern Norway in April and another ringed in April was shot in northern Italy in the following autumn. A bird ringed on the coast in October moved west to Flintshire where it was recovered in February. One ringed in Yorkshire in February 1978 was controlled in the county one year later, and another ringed in Worcestershire in January 1980 was controlled on the coast two months later.

Serin *Serinus serinus*
A rare vagrant recorded on twelve occasions. The first record was of one seen by A.D. Townsend at Gibraltar Point on 16th May 1961. Single birds were recorded at Donna Nook on 4th May 1969, 30th July 1970, 3rd November 1971, 5th September 1973 and 20th October 1974. In 1976 there was a singing male at Cleethorpes Boating Lake from 5th to 7th May and one was trapped at Brumby Common, near Scunthorpe on 12th August. One arrived off the sea at Gibraltar Point on 13th November 1982 and one was present at Saltfleetby on 4th and 5th June 1985. In 1988, one was seen at Donna Nook on 1st May and another at North Cotes on 23rd October.

Greenfinch *Carduelis chloris*
An abundant breeding species, passage migrant and winter visitor. It is widespread in all rural and suburban areas, nesting in woodlands, scrub, hedgerows, parks and mature gardens. Outside the breeding season there are a number of large roosts, especially in evergreens, in many plantations and woods. Passage migrants appear on the coast often in large numbers between the end of September and early December. Later movements occur during hard weather but spring passage is usually fairly light from late March to early May.

Most ringing recoveries involve movements within the county or to neighbouring counties but birds ringed in Lincolnshire in spring and autumn have been recovered in winter in Cheshire, Cardiganshire, Shropshire, Warwickshire, Staffordshire, Hertfordshire, Hampshire, Sussex and Kent. One ringed in Northumberland in winter was found dead, probably in its breeding area, near Lincoln in June and another found dead near Caistor in July had been ringed in Devon in the previous February. One ringed on Heligoland, Germany in November 1959 was found dead on the front of a train running between Lincoln and Grantham in May 1961. A Gibraltar Point bird ringed in December 1971 was controlled in Belgium in March 1975 and another ringed at Willingham Forest, near Market Rasen was controlled in the Netherlands in October 1976 and again in January 1977.

Goldfinch *Carduelis carduelis*
A numerous breeding species and passage migrant. It is widespread throughout the county, nesting in open woodland, parklands, hedgerows, orchards and gardens. The constant exploitation of Goldfinches by bird-catchers was blamed for its scarcity during the nineteenth century, but a gradual increase around the turn of the century followed laws forbidding the practice. This increase has continued to the present day. After the breeding season large flocks of Goldfinches may be seen in many areas, particularly on the coast and on open ground where there is an abundance of thistles and other weeds.

Movements inland but more especially on the coast are often most pronounced in spring when birds are moving in small parties almost daily from mid-April to early June. Post-breeding birds begin to congregate on the coast in late July but the main passage usually extends from early September to mid-November. Birds remaining in winter are in much reduced numbers in many areas.

Many migrants evidently leave Britain in autumn. Four birds ringed in autumn have been recovered in Belgium in October and November, coinciding with the bird-catching season there. Five others have been recovered in south-west France between October and April with 12 in Spain and one in Portugal. Two, ringed on the coast in autumn, were recovered in Essex in October and May and one ringed in Essex in December was controlled in the county in the following May.

Siskin *Carduelis spinus*

A winter visitor and passage migrant in fluctuating numbers. It is usually a fairly common or sometimes common visitor to the main wintering areas in the north-west. There are a few recent breeding records. It seems to have increased during the present century as large flocks were recorded only irregularly during the last century. In recent years flocks of 30 to 50 birds have been noted in several localities and a maximum of 300 was recorded at Twigmoor in early 1971. In some areas small parties exploit peanut feeders in gardens, an adaptive habit also acquired elsewhere in England during the last few years.

Wintering birds are usually present from October to April or early May. Passage birds on the coast are often quite scarce but may be fairly common in some years. Autumn migrants move through between early September and mid-November but spring passage is generally very light from the last week of March to the end of April. There was an unusual influx in 1985 when small parties were seen in several areas from July onwards. In 1973 a male was seen feeding three young birds at Hartsholme Park, Lincoln at the end of May. One or two pairs bred at Snipe Dales in 1985, with another pair in 1986. There have been several other recent summer records.

One ringed at Gibraltar Point in September 1965 was found dead in southern Norway in June 1966. Others ringed in the county in autumn have been controlled later in winter in Shropshire and Surrey and one from Surrey was controlled at Market Rasen in spring, one month after being ringed.

Linnet *Carduelis cannabina*

An abundant and widespread breeding species, passage migrant and winter visitor. It nests in open woodland, young conifer plantations, hedgerows, uncultivated areas, gardens, allotments, sand dunes and salt-marshes. After the breeding season, large flocks form to feed in stubble fields, areas infested by weeds, marshes and samphire beds on the shore. Communal roosts, often with other species of finches, are frequently large in some woods and tall hedges.

Migration on the coast and to a lesser extent inland involves very large numbers. The main autumn movement extends from early September to about the third week of November during which period many birds, probably from the continent, arrive from the east and north-east. Return passage is frequently heavy from late March to mid-May with smaller numbers to early June.

Evidence from ringing recoveries indicate emigration of many birds. There are ten recoveries of birds in coastal areas of France between October and April and nine in central and southern Spain between October and March. Some of these birds were ringed during the breeding season. One ringed in Belgium in October had reached Theddlethorpe by the following May and another ringed in south-west France in October was probably in its breeding area at Ingoldmells in June of the following year. One ringed near Lincoln in March was recovered in southern Norway three months later. A Lancashire juvenile ringed in July 1967 was found dead at Friskney in May 1968 and another ringed in Yorkshire in October 1974 was found dead at Gibraltar Point in the following March.

Twite *Carduelis flavirostris*
A common winter visitor and passage migrant to the coast that may be more numerous in some years. Large flocks are concentrated in the estuary of the Humber and more commonly in the Wash with smaller numbers on the open coast. Birds usually feed on the seashore or on salt-marsh but are also found on adjacent stubble fields and rough pastures.

The first birds occasionally arrive in late September though more normally in early October, with numbers increasing to the end of November. Birds frequently shift from one area to another so that numbers in any one locality may fluctuate markedly. Flocks decline gradually in late winter and many have left the county by March although small numbers occur until mid-April or even later. A few birds are recorded fairly regularly on passage inland and occasionally in winter. Most immigrants belong to the British race *A.f. pipilans* but a number of birds showing characteristics of the Scandinavian race *A.f. flavirostris* have been obtained in the Wash.

Ringing recoveries indicate that probably most of the Twites wintering in Lincolnshire are from the population breeding on the Pennines. Birds ringed in the Wash have been recovered in the breeding season in Cheshire, Derbyshire, Yorkshire and Lancashire and nestlings ringed in Cheshire and Staffordshire and a juvenile from Derbyshire have been controlled in the county. Two birds ringed in October and one in March have been recovered in Belgium in subsequent winters. Two controlled in the Wash in the spring of 1971 had been ringed in the Netherlands in November 1969 and October 1970.

Redpoll *Carduelis flammea*
A very numerous breeding species, passage migrant and winter visitor which greatly increased during the 1960s and 1970s but has shown a recent decline. It is widespread in all areas but local in the Fens, nesting in conifer plantations, heaths, open woods, gardens and uncultivated areas with scrub. Much of this recent increase and spread can be attributed to the extensive planting of forestry. In the late nineteenth century it was a not uncommon breeding bird but was largely restricted to the heaths of the north-west. There was some increase noted towards the turn of the century when it was apparently nesting sparingly in several other areas including the south of the county. By 1918 it was said to be more common as a winter visitor in the Lincoln area and at about the same time it was described as a numerous resident near Scunthorpe. A decline followed in the 1920s and 1930s and the low breeding population was once more chiefly confined to areas in the north-west. The more recent increase began about 1960 and reached a peak

in the mid-1970s.

It is interesting to examine the numbers of Redpolls ringed in recent years compared with the more stable samples of Linnets trapped in the county. The ringing totals are not of course directly comparable as changes of ringing sites and the activity of ringers may produce considerable bias but they serve to indicate the much increased status of the Redpoll. During the 1950s very few Redpolls were being ringed anywhere in the county. In 1967 the number of Redpolls ringed formed approximately 10 per cent of the total combined with Linnets. This had risen to 40 per cent by 1969 and an average of over 50 per cent during the 1970s, but had declined to about 30 per cent by the late 1980s.

Passage migrants occur on the coast usually between late August and early November. A proportion of breeding birds evidently emigrate, although these are replaced by large flocks of winter visitors. Return movements take place from mid-March to the end of May.

Birds breeding in Britain belong to the race *A.f. cabaret*, known as the Lesser Redpoll. The Mealy Redpoll, *A.f. flammea*, which breeds in northern Europe and Asia is a fairly regular winter visitor and passage migrant in variable numbers. Immigrants appear on the coast often only in ones and twos from October to early December. It is usually scarce in winter when it associates with flocks of *cabaret*, particularly in northern areas although in some years it may be fairly common. Most Mealy Redpolls have left by the end of March but occasional records extend to the end of April.

Ringing recoveries involve several in Yorkshire, Cambridgeshire and Norfolk with single birds from Dumfriesshire, Northumberland, Leicestershire and Huntingdonshire, three to Kent and one each to Berkshire, Hampshire and Sussex. Twenty birds ringed chiefly as coastal migrants in autumn have been recovered in the Netherlands, Belgium and France in autumn and winter. One ringed near Scunthorpe in September 1975 was trapped in northern Italy in November 1977. A particularly interesting recovery concerns a bird ringed near the Luxembourg border in West Germany in November 1971, controlled at Bardney in October 1972 and caught again on the Channel coast of France in April 1973.

Arctic Redpoll *Carduelis hornemanni*
A very rare vagrant. Two birds were seen by G.P. Catley and D.A. Robinson at Saltfleetby on 12th October 1975. Another was trapped at Brumby Common, near Scunthorpe on 28th March 1976. One at Saltfleetby was present from 21st February to 11th April 1982 and another was at Gibraltar Point between 15th January and 25th February 1984.

Two-barred Crossbill *Loxia leucoptera*
A very rare vagrant. An adult male shot at South Cockerington, near Louth in September 1889 coincided with several other records in Britain during the same autumn.

Crossbill *Loxia curvirostra*
The Crossbill is mainly an irregular late summer and early autumn immigrant in variable numbers. In most years it is scarce but may be fairly common during irruptions.

Sometimes a few have remained in winter or even into the following summer when birds have bred or attempted to do so on rare occasions.

Invasions which have brought large numbers of Crossbills to Lincolnshire have occurred in 20 years since 1868, the most recent ones being in 1953, 1956, 1958, 1959, 1962, 1963, 1966, 1972 and 1985. Immigrants seldom stay on the coast for any period but quickly spread to inland areas where flocks congregate in woods containing Scots pine, larch and spruce. Flocks are usually quite small but up to 50 birds have occasionally been recorded and exceptionally there were 200 at Limber in early August 1959.

Breeding is thought to have taken place at Hartsholme, near Lincoln in 1910 when birds were seen carrying nest material and males were heard singing throughout the spring. In 1930, paired birds were present at Limber in March and one pair was seen feeding young nearby at the end of June. A pair built a nest at Scawby in March 1959 but failed to rear any young. Another pair was present at Hartsholme from early February 1964 and the female was seen feeding three young birds in late April and early May.

One ringed at Gibraltar Point in August 1962 was found dead in north-east France in October 1963.

Parrot Crossbill *Loxia pytyopsittacus*
A very rare vagrant. A male caught by R.K. Norman, K. Robinson and S. Lorand at Tetney on 13th October 1962 was in an exhausted condition and subsequently died. A male was found dead by P. Prince at Hartsholme gravel pit, Lincoln on 16th January 1963. On 19th January the same observer located a party of six birds of both sexes at the same locality. Nine were present by 26th January and were seen by several other observers. Three to four birds were recorded during February and on 17th March a dead female was found. At least a pair remained until 25th May and during this period the male was heard singing on several occasions. In the early spring a female with an injured wing was captured and kept at a house nearby where it was fed on pine cones. Later in the spring the bird escaped and remained in the area until at least the beginning of 1964. The autumn of 1962 produced an influx of over 70 birds in Britain. In 1982 another small influx occurred. One to two were present at Humberston between 11th and 23rd October and exhausted birds which subsequently died were picked up on 12th October at Grainthorpe and Ingoldmells.

Scarlet Rosefinch *Carpodacus erythrinus*
A very rare vagrant. A female or immature male was seen by S. Lorand at Donna Nook on 21st May 1979. A male occurred at Donna Nook on the same date in 1983, and females or immature males were seen at North Somercotes Warren on 23rd June 1986 and at Donna Nook on 27th May 1987. One was trapped at Gibraltar Point on 18th September 1988.

Bullfinch *Pyrrhula pyrrhula*
A common breeding species and a fairly common passage migrant on the coast. It has increased and spread considerably in all parts of the county since about 1960. It nests

in most areas of open woodland, young forestry plantations, large hedgerows, scrub, parkland and large gardens. It was apparently fairly common and well-distributed during the last century and early part of the present century but declined probably in the 1920s or 1930s.

After the breeding season pairs and family parties wander about hedgerows and woodlands and also visit the coast where the species was rare and irregular 20 years ago. Regular passage of small numbers along the coast extends from late August to early December with a return movement of fewer birds between late March and mid-May. In 1978 several birds showing the characteristics of the northern race *P.p. pyrrhula* were seen in October on South Humberside. Two males were recorded at Killingholme and at least two males and a female at Barrow Haven. British birds belong to the race *P.p. pileata*.

One ringed in Northamptonshire in June 1961 was recovered near Spalding in August 1962 and another recovered in Northamptonshire in November 1964 had been ringed at Cleethorpes in the previous January. One ringed in Yorkshire in October 1965 was on the coast at Theddlethorpe a month later.

Hawfinch *Coccothraustes coccothraustes*

A scarce and local resident occurring mainly in the more extensive areas of deciduous woodland. It is a secretive species and irregular sightings in traditional areas emphasize under-recording of its true status. On the coast it is a rare and irregular visitor. It was evidently spreading into the county in the late nineteenth century having been previously confined to south-east England. A few had been seen in northern central areas in the 1860s but it was not recorded in the north-west until 1886, with annual nesting from 1890 onwards.

Several were recorded in the area around Spalding in the 1895/96 winter, and breeding was noted in the north-east in the following spring. It continued to increase and spread until at least 1914 when it was reported by Blathwayt as nesting in fair numbers in both northern and southern localities. It seems to have declined since then but there is no evidence of any recent change in its status.

There have been 23 coastal records, chiefly of single birds, during the last 30 years. Seven were in spring between April and June with the remainder from late July to January.

American Redstart *Setophaga ruticilla*

A very rare vagrant. One at Gibraltar Point from 7th November to 5th December 1982 was found by R.K. Watson and K.W. Winfield and eventually seen by many other observers. This was the fourth British record of this American wood warbler.

Northern Waterthrush *Seiurus noveboracensis*

One trapped by I. Hartley and K.W. Winfield at Gibraltar Point on 22nd October 1988 was still present next day. It is under consideration by *British Birds*. There have been only four previous British records of this rare vagrant from North America.

Lapland Bunting *Calcarius lapponicus*

A winter visitor and passage migrant on the coast in variable numbers. It is scarce in most years but occasionally it may be fairly common. Inland records are very rare as Lapland Buntings are almost entirely confined to coastal stubbles, marshes, sea banks and the shore where they frequently accompany feeding flocks of larks and finches. Prior to 1953 its appearances were far more uncertain than at present although it was probably overlooked to some extent.

Four were obtained on the north-east coast between 1883 and 1890. Large numbers with a peak of 100 were present at North Cotes in the 1893/94 winter and several were recorded at Holbeach in January 1895. Bird catchers trapped two at Cleethorpes in 1904 and two more in 1913. One was seen at North Cotes in September 1921 and several were obtained at Cleethorpes in the 1923/24 winter.

During the last 30 years it has occurred regularly, particularly on the north-east coast. Most records refer to one or two birds or very small parties, although flocks of 20 to 30 birds have been recorded at several localities in some years. In 1977, roosting birds at Saltfleetby reached a peak of 125 in early November. Exceptional numbers have occurred in the Wash in the last few years with a concentration at Butterwick reaching a maximum of 350 in January 1986.

Early immigrants arrive from mid-September onwards but the majority appear in October and November. In some years very few birds remain after December but in others there are maximum numbers in January followed by a decline in February. Most have usually left by early March and there is litle evidence of regular passage later in the spring although there are one or two isolated records of late birds in April.

Snow Bunting *Plectrophenax nivalis*

A common winter visitor and passage migrant on the coast in variable numbers. In peak years flocks of over 1,000 birds may occur but normally maximum counts produce a few hundred at favoured localities. Flocks usually feed on the sea-shore, marshes, coastal stubble and ploughed fields. Inland records are rare and refer to single birds or small parties but exceptionally there have been records of larger flocks. Small numbers are not infrequently present at Covenham and Toft Newton Reservoirs.

Early birds appear in September but the main immigration is between the last week of October and early December. The highest numbers are generally recorded during December and are often followed by a decline in January and February, most birds having left by early March. Passage birds in March and the first three weeks of April are quite scarce. A male in summer plumage was seen at Donna Nook from 23rd to 29th May 1975 followed by a female on 1st June. An even later male was at Gibraltar Point on 29th June 1950.

One ringed at Spurn, Yorkshire in January 1956 had moved to Gibraltar Point by early March. Two birds ringed at Donna Nook were recovered in Scotland on spring migration. One ringed in November 1967 was found dead in the Outer Hebrides in the following April and the other found dead at Inverness in March 1971 had been ringed in the previous December.

Reed Bunting

Snow Bunting

Yellowhammer *Emberiza citrinella*
An abundant breeding species and a coastal passage migrant in small numbers. It is well-distributed in all types of open country and avoids only the densest woodlands. There was a decline in many areas during the 1950s blamed on the use of toxic chemicals in agriculture and the destruction of many hedgerows. It seems to have made a good recovery since then, particularly in young forestry plantations where the new habitat has compensated for many miles of lost hedges.

Passage on the coast is regular in autumn but seldom involves any significant numbers. The main movements occur between mid-September and early November with later passage when the weather is severe. Arable fields, stubbles and stackyards are frequently visited by flocks in the autumn and winter and during hard weather large numbers may occur. Spring passage is usually very light, mainly from the last week of March to the end of April.

A bird ringed in Essex in late March 1961 was recovered at Donington, near Boston in April 1963. One ringed at Gibraltar Point in March 1980 was controlled in the Netherlands in November 1981.

Cirl Bunting *Emberiza cirlus*
A very rare vagrant recorded on four occasions. One was seen by Cordeaux at Great Coates on 5th January 1889 and another was recorded near Grimsby on 10th December of the same year. One was present at Donna Nook from 29th September to 2nd October 1968 and another was seen at the same locality on 28th October 1977. It was said to have bred locally in the heath district of the north-west during the nineteenth century but there is no reliable evidence to support such claims.

Ortolan Bunting *Emberiza hortulana*
A very rare passage migrant in spring and autumn. All but one of the 30 records were in the north-east of the county. One was seen by Cordeaux at Great Coates on 3rd May 1883. The remaining records, all since 1963, concern 15 at Donna Nook, four at Covenham Reservoir, four at Saltfleetby, three at Tetney and single birds at Saltfleet, Theddlethorpe and Gibraltar Point. Sixteen spring records were between late April and early June. Those in autumn occurred between late August and the third week of September, except for one on 24th October.

Rustic Bunting *Emberiza rustica*
A very rare vagrant. One was seen by J. Whitaker at Chapel St. Leonards on 22nd September 1906. A male at Gibraltar Point on 11th May 1975 was identified by A.O. Aitken and K. Knowles and an immature was trapped at the same locality by R. Lambert and others on 1st October 1978.

Little Bunting *Emberiza pusilla*
A very rare vagrant. An immature male was obtained by E. Gorton at Saltfleet on 5th October 1951. Another was seen at Cowbit Marshes by E.J. Redshaw on 2nd October 1954 and one was recorded by P.R. Boyer at Wyberton, near Boston on 4th December

1980.

Yellow-breasted Bunting *Emberiza aureola*
A male was present for most of the day at Gibraltar Point on 15th May 1977. It was seen by R. Bunten, S.E. Crooks, R. Lambert and other observers. It was only the second spring record of this rare vagrant to Britain.

Reed Bunting *Emberiza schoeniclus*
A numerous breeding species and a common passage migrant on the coast. Despite the contraction of many of its former wetland habitats the species has successfully spread into many drier areas during the last 30 years. It is now well-established in many parts of the county and is particularly common in young forestry plantations, hedgerows, marginal land and scrub as well as in traditional reed beds, ditches and marshes. In some suburban areas it has even become a regular visitor to gardens during the winter.

Coastal movements of regular small parties are recorded between mid-September and the first week of November. Return passage from late March to the end of April is on a much smaller scale.

Ringing recoveries suggest that most movements involve relatively short distances. Birds ringed in Lincolnshire in winter have been found in Huntingdonshire and Cambridgeshire in April. One ringed in November was in Yorkshire in December of the following year, one ringed in October was in Leicestershire in December of the same year and a September-ringed bird from Gibraltar Point was on the Norfolk side of the Wash two years later. One ringed at Barton-on-Humber in September was controlled in Merseyside two months later. One recovered in the county in June had been ringed in Yorkshire in the previous January, and another controlled in April 1978 had been ringed in Kent in December 1976. The only foreign recovery involved a bird ringed at Gibraltar Point in October 1983 and controlled in France in the following December.

Black-headed Bunting *Emberiza melanocephala*
A very rare vagrant. A male was seen by R.K. Norman and D. Harrison at Saltfleetby on 14th September 1974. Another male at Donna Nook from 16th to 25th June 1980 was seen by R. and S. Lorand and C.R. Morrison.

Corn Bunting *Miliaria calandra*
A common and widespread breeding species and a passage migrant on the coast in small numbers. Much of the vast arable landscape of Lincolnshire is ideally suited to this species although population densities vary considerably within the county. Parts of the Fens, coastal and upland areas seem to hold the most territories.

Passage migrants usually in small parties occur regularly on the coast, mainly between early October and mid-November. Winter flocks fluctuate a good deal according to the weather but in prolonged periods of snow and frost there may be hundreds along the coastal marshes and fields, usually in association with Yellowhammers and finches. There is little evidence of any return passage in spring although small parties appear irregularly on the coast between mid-March and early June.

Appendix 1
Species not fully acceptable to the List

Yellow-nosed Albatross *Diomedea chlororhynchos*
An albatross was shot on the Trent at Stockwith, near Gainsborough on 25th November 1836. It was identified as Yellow-nosed but unless the specimen is ever traced its identity cannot be accepted, particularly as there are similarities between this and other species of albatross which were not generally appreciated at that time.

Red Grouse *Lagopus lagopus*
Peacock stated that he had shot Red Grouse at Sandtoft in the north-west and also quoted a record of many birds appearing in the north-west during bad weather about 1835. These records must remain doubtful.

Upland Sandpiper *Bartramia longicauda*
A freshly-killed specimen hanging with Golden Plovers in Leadenhall Market was said to have come from Lincolnshire. It was purchased and identified by J.E. Harting on 27th October 1880. The record probably refers to a genuine Lincolnshire bird but cannot be verified.

Snowy Owl *Nyctea scandiaca*
Peacock recorded one at Bottesford, near Scunthorpe during the winter of 1868/69. Apparently its presence was known to a number of people as he stated that the bird was saved by his father who would not allow anyone to shoot it. He referred to the bird as the great white owl and said that its cry was awful to listen to and audible over long distances on a still night. No further details were given and although the record suggests this species, the lack of a detailed description excludes the possibility of acceptance to the List.

Hawk Owl *Surnia ulula*
One described in an account in *The Field* was said to have been shot in the county in 1864. It was examined in the flesh by J.C. Hawley. No details of the exact locality and date have been traced.

Orphean Warbler *Sylvia hortensis*
A male seen by C.R. Casey at Benington Marsh on 16th October 1988 is under consideration by *British Birds*.

Appendix 2

Species considered to be almost certainly escaped from captivity.

White Pelican *Pelecanus onocrotalus*
One on Read's Island on 16th July 1975 was almost certainly an escape from captivity. It was also seen on the Yorkshire side of the Humber on the same day. This or another individual was also recorded in Essex earlier in the same month.

Greater Flamingo *Phoenicopterus ruber*
There are a number of coastal records of birds, mainly in the Humber and the Wash. It has appeared at all times of the year and some birds have remained on sections of the coast for long periods of up to two years. It is likely that all of these records refer to birds that have escaped from collections.

Wood Duck *Aix sponsa*
An irregular visitor. There have been several records but not all may have been published. Most are probably escapes from wildfowl collections since there is apparently no truly feral population in Britain.

In 1981 a pair was present at Barton-on-Humber in May and a pair with young were seen at Tallington in June.

Egyptian Vulture *Neophron percnopterus*
A fairly tame adult seen at Donna Nook on 12th June 1970 was considered likely to have escaped from captivity.

Red-headed Bunting *Emberiza bruniceps*
There have been several occurrences of adult males of this common cage-bird, mainly on the coast. It is unlikely that any of the records refer to genuine migrants.

Appendix 3

Deletion from the Lincolnshire List

Ivory Gull *Pagophila eburnea*
Smith and Cornwallis (1955) included one record accredited to Cordeaux in their list. We have examined this record and found that although Cordeaux (1899) reported the occurrence the bird was apparently seen only by T. Fisher. Scrutiny of the description of the bird which was present on the shore near Cleethorpes between 29th and 31st March 1883 strongly suggests that the observer was mistaken in his identification and the bird was in fact either a Glaucous or Iceland Gull. An Ivory Gull said to have been shot on the coast about 1860 has not been verified.

Bibliography

The main books consulted were as follows:

ALBIN, E, 1731-38, *A Natural History of Birds,* 3 vols.
BANNERMAN, D.A, 1953-63, *The Birds of the British Isles,* 12 vols.
BIRCH, W. de G, 1911, *The Royal Charters of the City of Lincoln* (Cambridge)
BRITISH ORNITHOLOGISTS' UNION, 1971, *The Status of Birds in Britain and Ireland* (Oxford and Edinburgh)
BROWN, P.E. and DAVIES, M.G, 1949, *Reed Warblers* (East Molesey)
CAMDEN, W, 1586, *Brittania.* English translation by Holland (1610)
CHARLETON, W, 1668, *Onomasticon Zoicon*
COLGRAVE, B, 1956, *Felix's Life of Saint Guthlac* (Cambridge)
CORDEAUX, J, 1872, *Birds of the Humber District*
CORDEAUX, J, 1899, *A List of British Birds Belonging to the Humber District*
CORNWALLIS, R.K, 1970, *Supplement to the Birds of Lincolnshire 1954-68.* Edited and revised by K. Atkin and A.D. Townsend (Lincoln)
DONOVAN, E, 1794-1819, *The Natural History of British Birds*, 10 vols.
DOUIE, D.L. and FARMER, H, 1961, *The Life of St. Hugh of Lincoln*
DRAYTON, M, 1613-22, *Poly-Olbion*
DUGDALE, W, 1772, *The History of Imbanking and Drayning*, 1st edition
GARDINER, L, 1923, *Rare, Vanishing and Lost British Birds*, compiled from notes by W.H. Hudson
GIBBONS, E.J, 1975, *The Flora of Lincolnshire*, (Lincoln)
GURNEY, J.H, 1921, *Early Annals of Ornithology*
HISTORICAL MANUSCRIPT COMMISSION, 1895, *The Manuscripts of Lincoln, Bury St. Edmunds and Great Grimsby Corporation*, 14th report, appendix part VIII, H.M.S.O.
HOLLOM, P.A.D, 1960, *The Popular Handbook of Rarer British Birds*
LACK, P, 1986, *The Atlas of Wintering Birds in Britain and Ireland* (Calton)
LATHAM, J, 1781-1802, *A General Synopsis of Birds*, 6 vols. and 2 supplements
LEWIN, W, 1789-94, *Birds of Great Britain*, 7 vols.
MARTIN, B, 1759, *The Natural History of England*
MILLER, S.H. and SKERTCHLEY, S.B.J, 1878, *The Fenland Past and Present*
MONTAGU, G, 1802-13, *Ornithological Dictionary*, 2 vols. and supplement
MORRIS, F.O, 1851-58, *History of British Birds*, 6 vols.
MOSSOP, J, 1841, *A Synopsis of British Land Birds*
MULLENS, W.H, SWANN, H.K. and JOURDAIN, F.C.R, 1920, *A Geographical Bibliography of British Ornithology*
PADLEY, J.S, 1882, *The Fens and Floods of Mid-Lincolnshire*, (Lincoln)
PAYNE-GALLWAY, R, 1886, *The Book of Duck Decoys*

PENNANT, T, 1768-70, *British Zoology*, 4 vols.
PENNANT, T, 1771, *Tour in Scotland* (Chester)
RAY, J., 1678, *The Ornithology of Francis Willughby*
ROWLEY, G.D, 1875-78, *Ornithological Miscellany*, 3 vols.
SAUNDERS, H, 1889, *Manual of British Birds*
SHARROCK, J.T.R, 1976, *The Atlas of Breeding Birds in Britain and Ireland* (Tring)
SMITH, A.E. and CORNWALLIS, R.K, 1955, *The Birds of Lincolnshire* (Lincoln)
STEVENSON, H, 1870, *The Birds of Norfolk*
STONEHOUSE, W.B, 1839, *The History and Topography of the Isle of Axholme*
THOMPSON, P, 1856, *The History and Antiquities of Boston* (Boston)
TICEHURST, N.F, 1957, *The Mute Swan in England*
TURNER, W, 1544, *Avium Praecipuarum 'Turner on Birds'*, edited by A.H. Evans, 1903 (Cambridge)
VAURIE, C, 1959, 1965, *The Birds of the Palearctic Fauna*, 2 vols.
WALCOTT, J, 1789, *Synopsis of British Birds*, 2 vols.
WENTWORTH-DAY, J, 1954, *History of the Fens*
WHEELER, W.H, 1896, *A History of the Fens of South Lincolnshire* (Boston)
WHITE, G, 1789, *The Natural History and Antiquities of Selbourne*
WITHERBY, H.F, JOURDAIN, F.C.R, TICEHURST, N.F. and TUCKER, B.W, 1938-41, *The Handbook of British Birds,* 5 vols.
YARRELL, W, 1871-85, *A History of British Birds*, 4th edition, 4 vols.

The following unpublished documents were also abstracted:

LINCOLNSHIRE ARCHIVES (Lincoln Castle)
Entries of Lincoln Common Council (1511-41) L1/1/1/1
Entries of Lincoln Common Council (1541-64) L1/1/1/2
Entries of Lincoln Common Council (1565-99) L1/1/1/3
Documents relating to Swans. Cragg 2/5
Photograph of the Fulford Hall Swan Roll. 2 Key 3/16
Lease of Skellingthorpe Decoy (1693). LD/71/12
Lease of Skellingthorpe Decoy (1783). Monson 1/3
Game killed on the Syston Estates (1863-73). Thor XII/2/8
Game killed at Grimsthorpe (1898-1904). 5 Anc 10/25
SPALDING GENTLEMEN'S SOCIETY. Minute books. Vols. 1-6. 1710-58
HAIGH, G.H.C., 1888-1940, 9 vols. of diaries and notes deposited at the British Museum, Tring (Natural History)
STUBBS, F., 1929, *The Wildfowler on the Lincolnshire Coast*

Journals and reports containing information on Lincolnshire birds:

Bird Study, 1954-88
Birds of Lincolnshire and South Humberside, (Report), 1978
British Birds, 1907-88

Cambridge Bird Club Report, 1928-79
Cleethorpes Ringing Group Bird Report, 1959-70
The Field, 1853-1912
Gibraltar Point Bird Observatory and Field Research Station Report, 1949-69
The Ibis, 1858-99
Lincolnshire and South Humberside Ornithological Report, 1977
Lincolnshire Bird Report, 1979-88
Lincolnshire Naturalists' Union Transactions, 1905-88
Lincolnshire Naturalists' Trust Reports and Newsletters, 1949-88
Lincolnshire Notes and Queries, 1888-1934
The Naturalist, 1837-1927
Wash Wader Ringing Group Report, 1964-76
The Zoologist, 1843-1916

The above-mentioned journals contain numerous notes and papers on various aspects of county ornithology. Some of the more important reports and a few other publications are as follows:

ALINGTON, Rev. R.P, 1852, *The Ornithology of Lincolnshire.* The Naturalist, 1852
ATKIN, K, 1970, *The Lincolnshire Wash Breeding Census for 1969.* L.N.U. Transactions, vol. 17, pp 171-75
BLACKWOOD, J.W, 1972, *The Distribution of Nature Reserves in the Natural Regions of Lincolnshire.* L.N.U. Transactions, vol. 17, pp 1-6
BLATHWAYT, Rev. F. L. 1906, *Notes on the Birds which Inhabit Scotton Common,* L.N.U. Transactions, vol. 1, pp 107-13
BLATHWAYT, Rev. F.L, 1908, *Notes on the Birds of a Ballast Pit.* L.N.U. Transactions, vol. 1, pp 222-29
BLATHWAYT, Rev. F.L, 1908, *Lincolnshire Heronries.* The Zoologist, 1908, p 450
BLATHWAYT, Rev. F.L, 1909, *Lincolnshire Gulleries.* The Zoologist, 1909, pp 139-44
BLATHWAYT, Rev. F.L, 1915, *The Birds of Lincolnshire.* L.N.U. Transactions, vol. 3, pp 178-211
BODDY, M, 1983, *Factors Influencing Timing of Autumn Dispersal or Migration of first-year Dunnocks and Whitethroats.* Bird Study, vol. 30, pp 39-46
BOWES, A, LACK, P.C. and FLETCHER, M.R, 1984, *Wintering Gulls in Britain,* January 1983. Bird Study, vol. 31, pp 161-70
BRANSON, N.J.B.A, PONTING, E.D. and MINTON, C.D.T, 1979, *Turnstone Populations on the Wash.* Bird Study, vol. 26, pp 47-54
BROGDEN, T.H.J, 1900, *Birds of Spalding and the South Lincolnshire Fenland, 1886-1896.* The Naturalist, 1900, pp 17-32
CATLEY, G.P, 1982, *The Great Grey Shrike in Lincolnshire/South Humberside, 1960-81.* Lincolnshire Bird Report, 1982, pp 6-12
CATLEY, G.P, 1984, *The Return of the Sparrowhawk in Lincolnshire/South Humberside.* Lincolnshire Bird Report, 1984, pp 4-6
CATLEY, G.P, 1984, *Occurrences of Phalaropes in Lincolnshire/South Humberside,*

1960-84. Lincolnshire Bird Report, 1984, pp 7-10

CATLEY, G.P, 1985, *The Yellow-browed Warbler in Lincolnshire*. Lincolnshire Bird Report, 1985, pp 14-16

CATLEY, G.P, 1987, *The Bluethroat in Lincolnshire and South Humberside, with Special Reference to 1987*. Lincolnshire Bird Report, 1987, pp 11-12

CATLEY G.P, and HURSTHOUSE, D, 1985, *Parrot Crossbills in Britain*. British Birds, vol. 78, pp 482-505

COX, S.A, and MAY, R, 1932, *Bird Notes from the Grimsby District*. L.N.U. Transactions, vol. 8, pp 110-21

COX, S.A, 1939, *Birds of the Brocklesby Lakes*. L.N.U. Transactions, vol. 9, pp 234-44

DAVIES, S, 1981, *Development and Behaviour of Little Tern Chicks*. British Birds, vol. 74, pp 291-98

DAVIS, P.G, 1982, *Nightingales in Britain in 1980*. Bird Study, vol. 29, pp 73-79

DIXON, C, 1889, *Friskney and its Wildfowl*. Leisure Hour, October 1889, pp 669-75

ELTRINGHAM, S.K, 1963, *The British Population of the Mute Swan in 1961*. Bird Study, vol. 10, pp 10-28

GOODALL, A.L. and WILSON, P.J, *1977, National Nightingale Census, 1976*. L.N.U. Transactions, vol. 19, pp 92-93

GOODALL, A.L., 1978, *The Ornithological Section Bunting Survey*. L.N.U. Transactions, vol. 19, pp 146-52

GOODALL, A.L, 1981, *Report on the Grainthorpe Wader Feeding Survey, 1980-81*. Lincolnshire Bird Report, 1981, pp 4-7

GOODALL A.L, 1983, *The 1983 Spring Sanderling Passage Project on the Humber*. Lincolnshire Bird Report, 1983 pp 9-12

GOODALL, A.L. and WILKINSON, R.B, 1985, *Heronries in Lincolnshire and South Humberside, 1960-85*. Lincolnshire Bird Report, 1985, pp 5-8

GRIBBLE, F.C, 1962, *Census of Black-headed Gull Colonies in England and Wales, 1958*. Bird Study, vol. 9, pp 56-71

GRIBBLE, F.C, 1976, *A Census of Black-headed Gull Colonies*. Bird Study, vol. 23, pp 135-45

GRIBBLE, F.C, 1983, *Nightjars in Britain and Ireland in 1981*. Bird Study, vol. 30, pp 165-76

HAIGH, G.H.C, 1914, *The Migration of Birds as Observed in Lincolnshire*. L.N.U. Transactions, vol. 3, pp 81-92

HALLIDAY, J.B, 1981, *The Breeding Birds of the Wash — Survey Results 1978*. L. and S.H.T.N.C. Publication

HARRISON, T.H, and HOLLOM, P.A.D, 1932, *The Great Crested Grebe Enquiry*. British Birds, vol. 26, pp 62-92, 102-3, 142-95

HARTING, J.E, 1872, *British Heronries*. The Zoologist, 1872

HARTING, J.E, 1882, *Cranes at Christmas*. The Field, December 1882

HICKLING, R.A.O, 1965, *The Inland Wintering of Gulls in England, 1963*. Bird Study, vol. 14, pp 104-13

HICKLING, R.A.O, 1977, *Inland Wintering of Gulls in England and Wales, 1973*. Bird Study, vol. 24, pp 79-88

HOLLOM, P.A.D, 1940, *Report on the 1938 Survey of Black-headed Gull Colonies*. British Birds, vol. 33, pp 202-21, 230-44

HORTON, N, BROUGH, T, FLETCHER, M.R, ROCHARD, J.B.A. and STANLEY, P.I., 1984, *The Winter Distribution of Foreign Black-headed Gulls in the British Isles*. Bird Study, vol. 31, pp 171-86

HUDSON, R, 1965, *The Spread of the Collared Dove in Britain and Ireland*. British Birds, vol. 58, pp 105-39

HUDSON, R, 1972, *Collared Doves in Britain and Ireland during 1965-70*. British Birds, vol. 65, pp 139-55

HUDSON, R, 1979, *Nightingales in Britain in 1976*. Bird Study, vol 26, pp 204-12.

HUGHES, S.W.M, BACON, P. and FLEGG, J.J.M, 1979, *The 1975 Census of the Great Crested Grebe in Britain*. Bird Study, vol. 26, pp 213-26

JOHN, A.W.G. and ROSKELL, J, 1985, *Jay Movements in Autumn 1983*. British Birds, vol. 78, pp 611-37

LIMBERT, M, MITCHELL, R.D, and RHODES, R.J, 1986, *Thorne Moors Birds and Man*. Doncaster & District Ornithological Society Publication

LORAND, S, 1980, *The Birds of Donna Nook, Lincolnshire. A Check List of Species recorded during 1965-79*. L. and S.H.T.N.C. Publication

MORGAN, R.A, 1978, *Changes in the Breeding Bird Community at Gibraltar Point, Lincolnshire, between 1965 and 1974*. Bird Study, vol. 25, pp 51-58

MOSER, M.E. and SUMMERS, R.W, 1987, *Wader Populations on the Non-Estuarine Coasts of Britain and Northern Ireland: Results of the 1984-85 Winter Shorebird Count*. Bird Study, vol. 34, pp 71-81

MOULE, J.F, 1963, *The Past and Present Status of the Wryneck in the British Isles*. Bird Study, vol. 10, pp 112-32

MULLENS, W.H, 1919, *The Ruff. An Early Record*. British Birds, vol. 13, pp 13-20

NEEDHAM, A.L. and WILSON, P.J, 1975, *The Mid-Winter Coot Census, 1974*. L.N.U. Transactions, vol. 18, pp 175-78

NEEDHAM, A.L, and WILSON, P.J, 1976, *Report on the Bird Survey of Dole Wood, Thurlby, 1975*. L.N.U. Transactions, vol. 19, pp 31-34

NEEDHAM, A.L, 1976, *Wintering Redwing Survey, 1974/75*. L.N.U. Transactions, vol. 19, pp 26-30

NICHOLSON, E.M. 1929, *Report on the British Birds Census of Heronries, 1928*. British Birds, vol. 22, pp 270-323, 334-72

OGILVIE, M.A, 1981, *The Mute Swan in Britain, 1978*. Bird Study, vol. 28, pp 87-106

OGILVIE, M.A, 1986, *The Mute Swan in Britain, 1983*. Bird Study, vol. 33, pp 121-37

OWEN, J.D.W, 1980, *Nightingales in Lincolnshire and South Humberside in 1980*. Lincolnshire Bird Report, 1980, pp 2-4

OWEN, M. and SALMON, D.G, 1988, *Feral Greylag Geese in Britain and Ireland, 1960-86*. Bird Study, vol. 35, pp 37-46

PARSLOW, J.L.F, 1967-68, *Changes in Status among Breeding Birds in Britain and Ireland*. British Birds, vol. 60, pp 2-47, 97-123, 177-202, 261-85, 396-404, 493-508; vol. 61, pp 49-64

PASHBY, B.S, 1985, *John Cordeaux, Ornithologist*. Spurn Bird Observatory Publication

PEACOCK, M, 1902, 1906, 1908, *The Birds of North-west Lindsey*. The Naturalist, 1902, pp 197-204; 1906, pp 42-47; 1908, pp 272-77, 399-402
PEAKALL, D.B, 1962, *The Past and Present Status of the Red-backed Shrike in Great Britain*. Bird Study, vol. 9, pp 198-216
PILCHER, R.E.M, BEER, J.V. and COOK, W.A, 1974, *Ten Years of Intensive Late-winter Surveys for Waterfowl Corpses on the North-west Shore of the Wash*. Wildfowl, vol. 25, pp 149-54
PRATER, A.J, 1976, *Breeding Population of the Ringed Plover in Britain*. Bird Study, vol. 23, pp 155-61
PRESTT, I, 1965, *An Enquiry into the Recent Breeding Status of Some of the Smaller Birds of Prey and Crows in Britain*. Bird Study, vol. 12, pp 196-221
PRESTT, I. and MILLS, D.H, 1966, *A Census of the Great Crested Grebe in Britain, 1965*. Bird Study, vol. 13, pp 163-203
REDSHAW, E.J, 1978, *The Breeding Birds of Baston Fen Nature Reserve, 1977*. L.N.U. Transactions, vol. 19, pp 152-55
REDSHAW, E.J, 1980, *Rooks and Rookeries*. Lincolnshire Bird Report, 1980, pp 5-8
REDSHAW, E.J, 1982, *Breeding Waders of Wet Meadows, 1982*. Lincolnshire Bird Report, 1982, pp 4-5
REDSHAW, E.J, 1983, *The 1983 Mute Swan Census in Lincolnshire and South Humberside*. Lincolnshire Bird Report, 1983, pp 6-9
REDSHAW, E.J, 1987, *The Survey of Nesting Lapwings in Lincolnshire and South Humberside in 1987*. Lincolnshire Bird Report, 1987, pp 13-15
ROEBUCK, A, 1933, *A Survey of Rooks in the Midlands*. British Birds, vol. 27, pp 4-23
ROEBUCK, A, 1934, *Bird Problems in Lincolnshire*. L.N.U. Transactions, vol. 8, pp 131-44
SAGE, B.L. and VERNON, J.D.R, 1978, *The 1975 National Survey of Rookeries*. Bird Study, vol. 25, pp 64-86
SAGE, B. and WHITTINGTON, P.A, 1985, *The 1980 Sample Survey of Rookeries*. Bird Study, vol. 32, pp 77-81
SHEPHERD, I.G, 1983, *The Nocturnal Gull Roost Census, 1983*. Lincolnshire Bird Report, 1983, pp 4-5
SHEPHERD, I.G, 1986, *Wintering Cormorants in Lincolnshire and South Humberside, 1985-6*. Lincolnshire Bird Report, 1986, pp 4-5
SHEPPARD, R, 1987, *The Status of the Barn Owl in Lincolnshire and South Humberside*. Lincolnshire Bird Report, 1987, pp 4-10
SMITH, K.W, 1983, *The Status and Distribution of Waders Breeding on Wet Lowland Grasslands in England and Wales*. Bird Study, vol. 30, pp 177-92
STAFFORD, J, 1962, *The Nightjar Enquiry, 1957-58*. Bird Study, vol. 9, pp 104-15
STAFFORD, J, 1979, *The National Census of Heronries in England and Wales in 1964*. Bird Study, vol. 26, pp 3-6
TICEHURST, N.F, and JOURDAIN, Rev. F.C.R, 1911, *The Distribution of the Nightingale*. British Birds, vol. 5, pp 2-21
TICEHURST, N.F., 1934, *The Swan Marks of Lincolnshire*. Reports and papers of the

Architectural and Archaeological Societies of Lincoln and Northampton, vol. 42, pp 59-141

TOWNSEND, A.D, 1968, *The Birds of the Bardney Ponds.* L.N.U. Transactions, vol. 17, pp 3-15

UNDERWOOD, L.A. and STOWE, T.J, 1984, *Massive Wreck of Seabirds in Eastern Britain, 1983.* Bird Study, vol. 31, pp 79-88

WATTS, P.N, 1985, *The Ringed Plover and Little Ringed Plover Surveys, 1984.* Lincolnshire Bird Report, 1985, pp 9-13

WHITE, J.H, 1947, *The Rook Survey of Lincolnshire.* L.N.U. Transactions, vol. 11, pp 155-63

WILKINSON, R.B, and ATKIN, K, 1974, *Census of Breeding Black-headed Gulls, Common Terns, Ringed Plovers and Little Ringed Plovers in 1973.* L.N.U. Transactions, vol. 18, pp 141-45

WILKINSON, R.B, 1976, *Great Crested Grebe Survey, 1975.* L.N.U. Transactions, vol. 19, pp 22-25

WILLIAMSON, K, 1965, *A Bird Community of Accreting Sand Dunes and Salt Marsh.* British Birds, vol. 60, pp 145-57

WILSON, P.J. and NEEDHAM, A.L, 1972, *Lincolnshire Winter Survey, 1971* L.N.U. Transactions, vol. 18, pp 30-37

WILSON, P.J. and WILKINSON, R.B, 1972, *Manor Farm, Low Toynton.* L.N.U. Transactions, vol. 18, pp 40-44

WILSON, P.J, and NEEDHAM, A.L, 1976, *Rookery Surveys, 1969-70 and 1975.* L.N.U. Transactions, vol. 19, pp 19-21

Maps showing details of Lincolnshire in former times and illustrating the extent of fenland, duck decoys, etc. may be of interest to the reader. A selective list is as follows:

AKERMAN, J, 1810, *Plan of East Fen before enclosure*

AKERMAN, J, 1810, *Plan of East Fen after enclosure*

ARMSTRONG, A, 1778, *Map of Lincolnshire*

ARROWSMITH, 1800,*Sketch of Wildmore, East and West Fens*

BRYANT, A, 1828, *Map of the County of Lincoln*

CARY, J, 1791, *Map of River Ancholme*

GREENWOOD, C. and J, 1830, *Map of Lincolnshire*

GRUNDY, I, 1774, *Plan of the East Fen*

HOLLOR, W, 1661, *Map of East and West Fens*

JANSSON, J, 1646, *A general plot and description of the fens*

Index

Vernacular English names are printed in Roman type, scientific names in italics. The figures in bold type refer to text pages in the Systematic List;   other figures refer to separate entries.

Index